The Biochemical Bases of Psychoses

The Biochemical

or the Serotonin Hypothesis

John Wiley and Sons, Inc.

Bases of Psychoses

about Mental Diseases

D. W. Woolley

New York London

Library of Congress Catalog Card Number: 62-18357
Printed in the United States of America

Preface

Recent discoveries of the biochemical bases of some mental diseases have made it advisable to set down in one place what they are and how they were made. This is especially so because one hears at many scientific lectures and reads in numerous technical papers that the evidence is confusing and contradictory. Such statements can be made only by those who do not understand this evidence. An effort will be made in this book to show how well it fits together. Partly for this reason, I have departed from the present trend in scientific books and have written the entire book myself, instead of acting as a mere clerk and inviting each of a group of experts to contribute a chapter. Perhaps the unity of the evidence will in this way be made clearer.

I have played a role in the discoveries to be described. This may cause some bias in the way the story is presented, but it may also have the advantage of a first-hand account. It will surely be a source of criticism, especially by those who have not participated or whose part has been that of an accomplice after the fact. I recall that on a former occasion when I had written a book a critic complained querulously that "it was not a random sampling of the literature." The present book is not a random sampling of the literature either. Nevertheless, I have had constantly in mind the obligation to take into account all of the experimental facts of which I was aware and to weigh carefully the numerous hypotheses which have been advanced.

I want particularly to thank Noreen K. Campbell for help in looking up numerous references to the literature and in drawing the illustrations and painstakingly laboring over the mechanics of the manuscript. Many thanks are also due to Mrs. Woolley for help and helpful criticisms and to S. Rostas and L. Mintz for typing the final draft.

D. W. Woolley
The Rockefeller Institute

New York City
November 1961

Contents

chapter 1

Introduction

The prevailing view about the causes of most mental disturbances is that these diseases are to be traced to certain baleful experiences of the earlier life of the sufferer. These experiences, which may have taken place in infancy or even before birth, are believed to have predisposed the person to mental disease, so that the stresses occurring later in life, which would not permanently unbalance ordinary individuals, cause such persons to exhibit the frank mental disease. Such a view was put forward by Sigmund Freud, and by others at the turn of the twentieth century, and it has been elaborated by them and a host of followers into what some have called the Freudian concept of mental diseases. It is a view apparently held widely among psychiatrists and informed laymen, especially in the great cities, although many sensible people have been reluctant to accept such a concept.

The principal point of evidence given for a psychological as opposed to a physical cause of these mental diseases is that sufferers from the diseases in question have never been found to show characteristic anatomical abnormalities, either gross or microscopic. In other words, no characteristic physical change or abnormality has been found in those having these disorders. No examination of any part of the body has revealed any abnormality consistently. Of course, numerous claims of such abnormalities have been made, but always these have been shown to be the result of chance correlations which arose from examination of a limited number of individuals. When large numbers of patients have been studied, these abnormalities have not been found invariably to be characteristic of the disease. The present author was particularly struck by how much this point had influenced thinking while listening to the papers at the Second International Congress of Psychiatry in Zurich in 1957. Repeatedly, with respect to schizophrenia, this failure to find any anatomical sign of the disease was emphasized by the famous professors of psychiatry and put forward by them to support the conclusion that this malady had a psychological rather than a physical basis.

Perhaps the strongest testimony to the importance attached to this point is the distinction made between true mental disease and the so-called organic psychoses. It is recognized that mental derangements may, and frequently do, arise as the result of physical damage to the brain or from the ingestion of certain poisons. The best known of these toxic agents is, of course, ethyl alcohol. The mental effects of physical injury and of chemical poisons are classed separately from the true mental diseases.

The purpose of this book is to present evidence which strongly suggests that several of the most common mental diseases have biochemical bases, in other words, physical rather than psychological causes. These diseases will be pictured as arising as the result of changes in the functioning amounts of a few specific chemical substances in the brain. The abnormality may be in the amounts of certain enzymes which produce and use these chemicals and, thus, may not necessarily be an anatomical abnormality visible by the usual techniques of histology. However, it may be that an anatomical change or abnormality can result in, or be the result of, an alteration in the functioning of one of these chemical substances. For example, it will be suggested that galactosemia, which is characterized not only by mental disorder (idiocy) but also by gross anatomical changes, may have resulted because the enzymic change which produced the abnormal anatomy affects also the biochemical functioning of a specific hormone intimately concerned with mental processes.

For certain common mental diseases with no anatomical abnormalities, much of the evidence will suggest that the hormone serotonin plays a major role in those processes of the brain which have to do with normal mental function and that disturbances in the functioning of serotonin can be reflected in changes in the mental condition of normal individuals. Certain other hormones of the central nervous system seem to be involved as well. These include acetylcholine and the epinephrines. The idea of a physical rather than a psychological basis for common mental diseases has been growing for many years. Recent events have attracted numerous new recruits to this point of view, but even so they are greatly outnumbered by those of the Freudian persuasion.

The present author first saw real evidence for the idea of a physical basis for these mental ills when, in collaboration with Elvehjem, Madden, and Strong, he succeeded in 1937 in identifying the antipellagra vitamin as nicotinamide. When nicotinamide was tried on cases of human pellagra, it brought about rapid and dramatic cures of the disease, including the mental disorder which is a frequent symptom. This mental condition seen in pellagra had never been associated with an anatomical change in the brain, even though there are frank and characteristic signs of anatomical changes found in the peripheral organs of pellagrins. The occurrence of these signs, therefore, beclouded the issue and obscured the fact that the mental disturbance in the disease was not ascribable to a visible lesion of the brain. Here, then, was a naturally occurring mental defect which was curable by a specific physical agent, viz., nicotinamide.

The next step in the author's pilgrimage along this road was the discovery (in collaboration with Shaw) of evidence suggesting that serotonin was causally related to schizophrenia and to epilepsy. This was in 1953 and 1954. The evidence and the deductions from it will be dealt with in several chapters in this book.

The introduction of tranquilizing drugs for the treatment of mental diseases, which began in the mid-1950's, has persuaded many physicians to entertain the possibility of a physical basis of these disorders, even though the drugs now in use leave much to be desired therapeutically. The help which these drugs have provided in the treatment of many mental patients has apparently been sufficient to stimulate a large amount of work as well. In addition, the effectiveness of the drugs has generated enthusiasm for doing something other than trying to reach the psyche from the Freudian standpoint. The finding (subsequent to the enunciation of the serotonin hypothesis) that these drugs actually did influence the functioning of serotonin in the brain must have persuaded many that a right theory might have some tangible practical results. Partly with such a thought in mind this book is being written.

The purpose is not to discredit Freud. Rather it is to turn thoughts about these diseases into other channels for a while. The too-exclusive attention to psychology may be as sterile as the too-exclusive attention to biochemistry. There is much about human nature which cannot be learned from biochemistry. The best which can be hoped for is that this new view of mental diseases will give philosophers a new keyhole through which to peep into some of the most obscure mysteries. Chapters 16 and 17 of this book should serve to show that the author does not believe the therapeutic aspect of mental disease to be solely the preserve of physical scientists.

The author is acutely aware of the criticisms which will be leveled at many of the ideas in this book, and even at some of the facts. He can make no claim to infallibility, and knows that the whole truth is hard to grasp, and even harder to convey. He knows that some will say that either his facts or his interpretations are wrong and will quote authority X or Y or Z to bolster the contention. So much has been written about mental diseases that it is impossible to make any statement about them which cannot be refuted by quotation from some group of authorities. The one certainty is that these diseases exist. They challenge science to understand their causation, and they cry out to medicine for an adequate treatment. The impartial reader will assume, and rightly so, that the author has considered much which has not been given prominence or even mentioned. He is not, however, unaware of many points of view which have been left unmentioned. He has arrived at the position taken in this book, not as the result of a passing enthusiasm, but rather as the result of many years of experimentation, observation, and thought. So far as he is aware, there are no actual facts (in contrast to opinions) which are not accommodated by the concept set forth.

The plan followed in writing this book has been to make it understandable to a wide variety of readers. There is no reason why one must be a biochemist to follow the argument. At the same time it was recognized that considerable detail would be required because of the newness and consequent controversial nature of many of the ideas. If these were not to be documented adequately they might be unduly subject to attack and be discarded by readers under the aegis of hostile critics. Consequently, the main arguments and ideas will be stated simply at the start and supported by detailed evidence later in the book. In this way it is hoped that clarity will be increased without loss of force. The author believes that any reader, regardless of his prior training, will find matters of interest or value even in the more detailed parts.

A book which proposes in its title to deal with the biochemical bases of psychoses might turn out to be just a conventional textbook of biochemistry. It might describe the nature of the chemical substances and the enzymic processes which occur in nerve tissue. Many of these substances and processes occur in other tissues as well as the nerves. Although there can be no doubt that the fundamental biochemical reactions which provide energy and build up tissues are somehow related to mental processes, and might thus be said to be the biochemical bases of mental diseases, they are not all directly at fault in a diseased mind. Consequently, it is not planned to present a monograph on neurochemistry. Rather, it is planned to describe those biochemical substances and processes for which there is direct and tangible evidence that they are intimately related to psychoses. The more fundamental biochemistry of the brain has been dealt with at length in other books and needs no repetition here. This book is concerned directly with showing that there are biochemical bases to several mental diseases and to show what these bases are.

chapter 2

Abstract of the concepts

The purpose of this chapter is to state briefly what will be described more fully in the remainder of the book. In this way it is hoped that the main concepts can be presented clearly and rapidly. The statements made will be supported with only a minimum of evidence, and no references to the literature will be given. The succeeding chapters will marshal the evidence much more completely and will give references to published papers. Most of the deductions from the evidence will likewise be dealt with in greater detail in succeeding chapters. It is hoped that for those readers who are not biochemists, but who want to know the character of biochemistry as it gropes into mental disorders, this simplified summarizing chapter will be helpful.

Definitions and classifications. Orthodox psychiatry classifies mental diseases into three categories: organic psychoses, toxic psychoses, and functional psychoses.

Organic psychoses are those mental diseases in connection with which one can find some characteristic change in the anatomy of the central nervous system. Examples are the visible changes which occur in the brains of patients with senile psychoses and the changes both anatomical and serological which are found in the brains of patients with syphilitic paresis. In other words, organic psychoses are those in which one finds characteristic visible deterioration of the brain. They have a physical cause, or at least can be assumed to owe their symptomatology to a visible cause.

Toxic psychoses also have a demonstrable cause—the entry of a toxic chemical substance into the body. Examples are the delirium of alcoholism, the psychosis caused by ingestion of sodium bromide or of food infested with ergot. These psychoses usually disappear if the poisonous substance is removed.

The functional psychoses are those which have not been attributed to a physical cause. These include, among other conditions, schizophrenia, manic depressive psychosis, and involutional melancholia. Because no anatomical lesions or chemical toxins have been invoked to explain the symptomatology of these conditions, they are said to arise from psychological trauma, and numerous hypotheses have sprung up to account for them. One purpose of this book is to suggest that these functional psychoses have a physical and chemical origin.

The symptomatology associated with the three subdivisions of mental disease is not characteristic for each category. A psychosis induced by sodium bromide cannot be distinguished from schizophrenia until one does a chemical analysis for bromide in the tissues or until one knows that the patient is taking bromide. It is true that some toxic psychoses are distinguished by extreme manifestations of fear, or by other psychiatric changes, or that the catatonic stupor of some schizophrenics, or the paranoid delusions of others may seem to set them apart. However, one can find these same symptoms in some toxic psychoses. Some psychiatrists will maintain that auditory hallucinations (the hearing of voices) or visual hallucinations are diagnostic for schizophrenia, but it is well known that these same symptoms can be found in organic or toxic psychoses. Consequently, it is plain that symptomatology is not sufficient to distinguish the various categories of mental disease even though symptomatology is the principal evidence on which the categories are built. It must not be forgotten, however, that a knowledge of the past history of the patient (that he has taken bromides, or alcohol, or has a positive Wassermann test) figures prominently in the decision as to whether his psychosis is organic, toxic, or functional.

The confines of a given mental disease are not easy to define to the satisfaction of all. Fashions are constantly changing in this matter. Thus, according to Menninger, who admits to having subdivided schizophrenia some two decades ago into more than a score of separate diseases, the present trend seems to be to call most forms of this disorder one single disease. Many of his colleagues, however, continue to subdivide it into many diseases, based on the prominence, or lack, of one or another given symptom. The diagnosis of a single patient's disease may vary from country to country, or even from city to city. Meduna has pointed out that what would be considered to be schizophrenia in Vienna would not necessarily be so called in Chicago. In the face of such lack of agreement, it is probably to be expected that some scholars tend to turn away from subtle distinctions, and feel it better to make the borders of definition somewhat ill-defined until understanding of the disease or diseases is far more advanced than at present.

The situation is not very different from that which prevailed in medicine a hundred years ago, before the advent of the germ theory of infectious diseases. In those days it was the fashion of medical scholarship to define, subdivide, and classify fevers. Numerous separate entities thus arose only to be discarded when the causes of many were traced to specific infectious bacteria and viruses. If the chemical cause of the so-called functional psychoses can be established, the classification scheme will receive less attention. It will not be surprising to find that what has in the past been considered to be a variety of separate diseases may be only minor variations of a single mental disease.

For this reason the present author will not use the complicated schemes of classification which have already begun to crumble from their own weight. Rather, an effort will be made to speak of symptoms such as depression, agitation, excitement, hallucinations, anxiety, and loss of contact with reality, rather than to use names assigned to supposedly distinct diseases. Nevertheless, one cannot completely avoid the use of some of these names. Hebephrenia is still a short and convenient name for the silliness and inappropriate simpering behavior of some young adult schizophrenic patients. Schizophrenia likewise is a descriptive short name covering a large class of mental patients whose thoughts, actions, and emotions seem out of gear. Manic depressive psychosis is a useful term for the alternating excitement and depression of an extroverted mental patient who exhibits these violent swings from one extreme to the other of thought and behavior. Such names will be used in this book for their descriptive value in assembling together, in one word or phrase, a group of symptoms rather than as names for discrete diseases.

Introductory remarks about the biochemistry of the central nervous system. The brain contains a large number of individual chemical substances which have been identified and undoubtedly a large number which are still unknown. Most of the known chemical substances have also been found in other parts of the body and are not unique to the central nervous system. Similarly, a large number of enzymic reactions have been studied in the brain, but these reactions also are not found to occur there uniquely. They take place in other organs as well. Quantitative differences may exist, and may even be quite large. Substances such as the gangliosides or enzymic reactions such as the decarboxylation of glutamic acid may be much more prominent in the central nervous system than in most other tissues, but they do exist in other tissues, even those not related to the central nervous system.

Because of these facts, the study of the over-all biochemistry of the brain does not seem to offer a clear pathway to the understanding of mental processes. It is necessary to know about this over-all biochemistry, but it is not sufficient to know only this. There are additional aspects which must be understood. Nevertheless, the study of the kinds of chemical substances which occur in the brain and of the enzymic reactions which take place there is most necessary. Such study is the groundwork for any understanding of the actions of the brain, because these substances and enzymes are the machines by means of which the actions take place. If, however, some of these machines occur in other parts of the body, we may expect some advantage from studying them there rather than in the brain itself. Some of the complicated interactions which take place in the brain, thus obscuring the nature of a unit-process under study, may be absent in some other tissue so that the particular process can be seen there more easily. Furthermore, in some other tissue the particular process may be much more prominent quantitatively than it is in the brain. In such cases, the use of the other tissue to lead to the first rudiments of understanding of the process in the brain may be advantageous. Actually, this has proven to be the case. The hormone serotonin was discovered first not in the brain, but in blood serum, and its actions were traced first by the use of smooth muscles. Only then was it possible to study directly its effects in the central nervous system.

The numerous chemical substances and biochemical reactions in the central nervous system are thus fundamentally concerned with mental and neurological processes, but these by themselves cannot give an understanding of such processes. The organization of these substances and reactions and their interrelationships must be understood. To do this it is perhaps wise to begin with a description of those chemical compounds and reactions which can be demonstrated to play a direct role in mental processes rather than to start with descriptions of biochemical reactions which nourish all kinds of cells in the body.

Serotonin. Serotonin (sometimes called 5-hydroxytryptamine) is the substance for which there is now the most evidence of direct involvement in mental processes. It is a molecule of rather simple structure (see Figure 1). It was discovered because it causes various smooth muscles to contract and because of its unusual staining properties. Thus, the muscles in the walls of blood vessels are made to contract when they come in contact with serotonin. When this takes place in a living animal the result is a rise in blood pressure. The smooth muscles in other organs also contract in its presence so that it can, for example, cause defecation by action on the intestinal muscles. By using the contraction of blood vessels as an assay, Rapport, Green, and Page first isolated a pure compound from serum which they named serotonin.

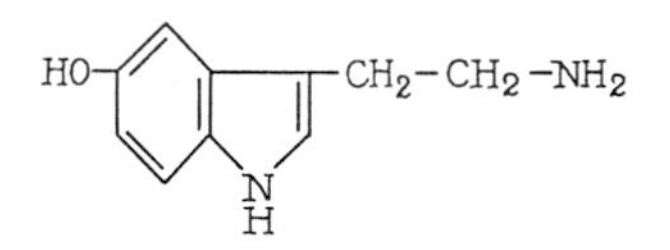

Serotonin

FIG. 1.

Quite independently, Erspamer had been attempting to isolate a substance from gastric and intestinal mucosa which he had called enteramine. He had recognized it as being particularly abundant in these mucosae, and had followed it by its ability to make tissues containing it stain readily with silver ions. He also knew that the substance in question caused certain smooth muscles, such as those of intestines or of uteri, to contract, and was thus able to distinguish it from epinephrine. Enteramine was soon shown to be identical with serotonin when the latter became available in pure form by synthesis in 1952.

In mammals, most of the serotonin occurs in the gastric and intestinal mucosa. In lower animals, and even in some higher ones, much of it may be in the skin. Spleen also seems to contain a considerable amount. In the blood it is found almost exclusively in the platelets, from which it is liberated at the site of a wound. The constriction of small blood vessels which it causes when so liberated presumably has a role to play in the staunching of the flow of blood, although some dispute this. Serotonin is found in certain parts of the brain, notably the hypothalamus, and the pineal gland. The enzymes which synthesize it from 5-hydroxytryptophan are also found in some parts of the brain, and, of course, in certain peripheral tissues. The enzymes which destroy it likewise can be found in the brain and in other organs such as lungs, intestines, and livers.

The reason why serotonin causes smooth muscles to contract is not known. However, considerable evidence has recently been found to suggest that the reason is that the hormone provides a cyclic mechanism by means of which calcium ions are carried into the muscle cells. The action of the hormone consequently seems to be on the membranes of susceptible cells. These membranes are likewise the places at which some of the electrical changes are found. Briefly, this work on the action of serotonin envisions the muscle cell as being enclosed within a permeability barrier, the cell membrane. This membrane seems to be composed of lipid [a] in which the water-soluble nutrients for the cell are not soluble. The barrier is a submicroscopic film, visible only with the electron microscope, and approximately 70 Ångstroms thick. Its lipoidal character was deduced from the fact that it stains with osmium tetroxide, whereas after extraction of the tissue sections with fat solvents, it no longer stains with this reagent.

The machinery within the cell which does the actual contracting consists of fibrils of actomyosin which shorten when they combine with calcium ions plus adenosine triphosphate. In the resting muscle the component which is lacking is the calcium ions. These may pass into the cell from the surrounding fluid if they can find their way through the lipoidal membrane, in which they are not soluble.

One way for calcium ions to get inside the cell is the following. When serotonin comes into contact with the membrane of a susceptible cell it finds within this membrane (because it is susceptible to serotonin) a specific lipid which combines with the serotonin. The complex thus formed picks up calcium ions as a salt or chelate, and it does so because the compound of calcium, serotonin, and the lipid is fat soluble. Inside the membrane, this complex encounters an enzyme which cleaves some grouping from it. The calcium ions are now no longer able to remain in combination and are consequently discharged into the aqueous medium inside of the cell. They are then available to combine with the actomyosin and adenosine triphosphate which causes contraction of the cell. The lipid which is in the membrane and which combines with the serotonin to carry the calcium ions, along with the enzyme which destroys the complex, is called the serotonin receptor. The evidence to support such a concept will be found in Chapter 4.

Although this concept of the mechanism of action of serotonin is not yet firmly established, most of those who study the action of hormones agree that their effects are brought about by combination with specific receptors. It is the exact nature of the receptor chemically, and what change comes about as a result of combination of the hormone with it, which are in debate. If the reason why serotonin causes smooth muscles to contract is its intervention in the way just described for the transport of calcium ions, then the reason for its

[a] Much controversy rages about the nature of a cell membrane. Some say that it is made of protein, and some say of lipoprotein. Elaborate hypotheses which maintain that it is a sort of sandwich of lipid and protein have also gained recent popularity.

effects on nerve and brain cells also may be this same transport of calcium ions. Inside the muscle cell the calcium ions activate the actomyosin system with resultant contraction. Inside the brain cells the calcium ions could activate some system which likewise requires calcium ions, but for signal transmission, not for mechanical contraction. What this system is in brain cells is not known, but there are some likely candidates.

Neurophysiologically, the chief property of serotonin is that it causes inhibition of transmission of some nerve impulses. For example, it can cause inhibition of the passage of nerve impulses in the optic system. It can also inhibit the passage of nerve impulses from one side of the brain to the other through the corpus callosum. Furthermore, it can cause inhibition of the transmission of pain impulses from various parts of the body. These inhibitions are not the only neurophysiological properties of serotonin, but in the work thus far undertaken they have been prominent ones. Epinephrine and norepinephrine also can cause such inhibitions but these hormones are less active than serotonin in the systems examined up to the present time.

Other significant hormones of the central nervous system. Although serotonin is the substance in the brain for which there is most evidence to connect it directly with mental processes, other substances occur there also for which there is evidence of similar connection. Some of these substances can be shown to influence the action of serotonin as well as to have activities of their own. They include norepinephrine, epinephrine, acetylcholine, and histamine. Their chemical structures are shown in Figure 2. All of these have been found in certain parts of the brain or central nervous tissue, as well as in various organs of the peripheral tissues. The enzymes which make them and those which destroy them are also found in the central nervous system, as

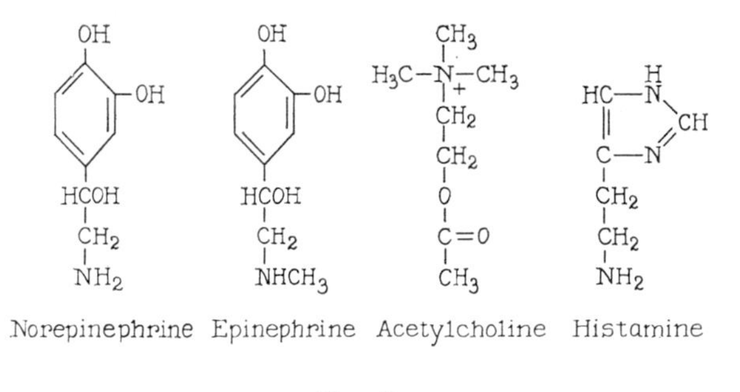

FIG. 2.

well as in peripheral organs such as adrenal glands, intestines, kidneys, and livers. Each of these hormones will cause certain kinds of smooth muscles to contract. Some such as acetylcholine or histamine will cause various glands to secrete their special products.

In addition to the four compounds just mentioned there are others, the relationship of which to our subject is not yet clear, but which are known to occur in nerve tissue and to exert actions on suitable test systems. However, none of these has yet been shown to participate directly in mental processes. These include γ-aminobutyric acid, melatonin, dopamine, and bradykinin. There are probably more yet to be discovered.

Antimetabolites. Because the first, and perhaps the strongest evidence for the participation of serotonin in mental processes was found through the use of antimetabolites, we should understand something about them. An antimetabolite is a chemical substance which resembles in chemical structure an essential metabolite, and which is able to bring about in some living thing the specific signs of deficiency of the related metabolite. The essential metabolites are compounds such as those we have just been discussing (serotonin, norepinephrine, acetylcholine, etc.). They are hormones or vitamins or other chemical substances which occur naturally in living creatures and which are necessary to these for specific normal life processes. Antimetabolites are not merely chemical compounds analogous in structure to one of these hormones; neither are they any substances which destroy the biological activity of a hormone or vitamin. Antimetabolites are structural analogs of the metabolites which have in addition the property of causing specifically a deficiency of the metabolite in question.

Each essential metabolite performs its special functions in living things by acting as a substrate for some special enzyme or receptor. These enzymes and receptors contain active centers which are parts of the molecule made so that they will combine in a reversible fashion with the substrate and hold it in such a position as to activate it. When so activated, it reacts with a new molecule or undergoes some decomposition within itself. The antimetabolite is a molecule shaped sufficiently like the metabolite (substrate) so that it also can combine with the active center of the enzyme or receptor. The reason for the need of structural similarity of the antimetabolite to the related metabolite is thus clear. It must fit the active site which ordinarily combines with the related essential metabolite. The result of the combination of the antimetabolite with the active center for the metabolite is to occupy the space needed by the essential metabolite, and thus to exclude it from its normal function. A specific deficiency of that metabolite thus occurs.

The situation can be visualized by use of the lock-and-key analogy of enzyme action. The substrate fits the enzyme just as a key fits its lock. The turning of the key opens some metabolic door, and this allows succeeding doors to be approached in the metabolic chain of events. The antimetabolite is shaped enough like the real key to be inserted into the keyhole, but, because of its slight difference from the real key, is cannot turn the lock. It also occupies the keyhole so that the real key cannot be readily inserted. The result is that the door is not opened.

Sometimes the structural analog is shaped enough like the real metabolite that it, like a slightly damaged key, can be inserted into the lock and turned. In this case the analog is no antimetabolite for that particular reaction, but instead does exactly what the real metabolite does. Sometimes the analog fits the lock so poorly that it can be turned only with difficulty. If this is the case, the metabolic events (the opening of the doors) are slowed down with consequent damage to the whole system.

An antimetabolite displaces its essential metabolite from tissues. It does this because it occupies the specific site which ordinarily holds its essential metabolite. It is this displacement which causes the specific deficiency. The displacement can usually be found by chemical analysis for the essential metabolite in the tissues affected by the antimetabolite. The content of the essential metabolite is reduced. For example, when an animal is treated with an antimetabolite of serotonin, this hormone is displaced from susceptible tissues. When analyzed for serotonin, these tissues are found to contain less than those of untreated animals.

Participation of serotonin in mental processes and its relationship to mental disease. The first evidence for the participation of serotonin in mental diseases was that of Woolley and Shaw, obtained by the use of antimetabolites and published in 1954. It is still the most direct evidence, although a body of supporting data of various kinds has been added to it. The original evidence was that a number of drugs which caused, in normal men, some of the signs of schizophrenia were structural analogs of serotonin. They acted as antimetabolites of it in isolated smooth muscles. The first of such compounds were some synthetic analogs of serotonin which had been studied for possible use in the treatment of high blood pressure and some natural alkaloids such as certain of the ergot alkaloids, harmine, and yohimbine. The synthetic analogs of serotonin first used for this purpose were 2-methyl-3-ethyl-5-nitroindole and medmain or 2-methyl-3-ethyl-5-dimethyl aminoindole. The nitroindole caused profound mental depression in sane human beings on whom it was being tested for therapeutic effects in high blood pressure. Medmain was not tested on human beings because in mice it called forth convulsive fits quite reminiscent of grand mal seizures of epilepsy.

The naturally occurring alkaloids which were found to be antimetabolites of serotonin and which caused psychic changes were the ergot alkaloids, the harmala alkaloids, and yohimbine. The ergot alkaloids include such potent substances as lysergic acid diethylamide (LSD) and ergotoxine. Woolley and Shaw recognized the ergot alkaloids and yohimbine to be structural analogs of serotonin and showed that they acted as competitive antagonists of this hormone in smooth muscles. These drugs were thus proved to be antimetabolites of it. Gaddum also showed the antagonism between serotonin and LSD in smooth muscles, and many subsequent investigators added a flood of additional data.

The ergot alkaloids and yohimbine had been known for many years to antagonize the actions of epinephrine. The new demonstrations of the relationship of these drugs to serotonin added a fascinating aspect to the understanding of their biological effects. Yohimbine had long been known as an aphrodisiac, and the mental aberration of ergot poisoning had also been recognized for a long time. The unusually high potency of LSD in causing visual hallucinations and changes in personality of normal individuals who ingested very small amounts of it had focused attention on it, especially since the changes caused by LSD resembled in several respects the signs of schizophrenia. The harmala alkaloids, such as harmine, had apparently not been tested in normal men with the aim of producing mental changes, but had been tested in dogs, which were thus made mad. They would bark at unseen objects and attempt to pass through non-existent doors. After the enunciation of the serotonin hypothesis, harmine was tested in normal human beings and found to induce auditory hallucinations and other psychic disturbances, although not visual hallucinations.

The fact that all of these rather dissimilar chemical compounds would call forth mental symptoms resembling some of those seen in schizophrenia or in certain other mental diseases suggested to Woolley and Shaw that they did so because each of them was interfering with the functioning of serotonin. If this were so, then the natural mental diseases might be the result of a disturbance in the functioning of serotonin in the brain. This would be brought about, not by ingestion of any hallucinogenic drug, but merely by a metabolic failure to produce the proper amount of the hormone there, much as diabetes results from a metabolic failure to form enough functioning insulin in the pancreas.

The discovery (subsequent to the appearance of the serotonin hypothesis) of a variety of psychosis-inducing chemical agents, each of which was clearly linked to serotonin, has added support to the hypothesis. Some of these agents have been found in natural plant sources and others have been made synthetically in the laboratory. Thus, ibogaine, an alkaloid from an African plant long used in religious ceremonies for induction of changes in the mental state, has been isolated, and its chemical structure has been shown to be related to that of serotonin. Bufotenine, which is merely N,N-dimethylserotonin has been isolated from a Caribbean bean (Cahobe) also used in aboriginal rites for its effect on the mind. Pure bufotenine has been shown to induce some sort of vague mental change in normal humans, although its effects are not as dramatic as are those of LSD, and a larger dose is required. Finally, psilocybin, the hallucinogenic agent of the Psilocybe mushrooms of Mexico has been isolated in pure form, and its structure has been shown to be that of bufotenine with the hydroxyl group moved to the 4-position, and converted to a phosphate ester. Several synthetic analogs of serotonin also have been produced and tested as therapeutic agents in non-psychotic disorders, only to find that they induced mental disturbances similar to those frequently seen in patients with schizophrenia. A fuller account of many of these examples will be found in Chapter 6. It must not be thought that all of these discoveries were unexpected. Several laboratories appreciated the possibilities of the serotonin hypothesis about mental diseases and were able to predict and to produce numerous structural relatives of serotonin which were able to cause mental changes.

As the studies of these hallucinogenic drugs were intensified, it became plain that many of their effects on the mind were related to their ability to act like serotonin in some tissues rather than as antagonists to it. The visual and auditory hallucinations and other forms of excitement seemed to be correlated with the possession of a serotonin-like action on some tissues, even though on others they might act as antagonists to serotonin, and thus like true antimetabolites of it. Psychotic depression rather than excitement seems to result from those compounds which act primarily as antagonists; the excitement is found with those having serotonin-like action. Nevertheless, this point has not been entirely clarified. It has been supported by some independent evidence. Thus, for example, the increase in serotonin content of the brains of a few schizophrenic subjects, which was induced by administration of the serotonin-precursor 5-hydroxytryptophan, has resulted in a worsening of their disease condition. Similarly, the giving of bufotenine, which is a close relative of serotonin and which has many of the same pharmacological properties as the hormone, also caused schizophrenic patients to become worse. Such findings are compatible with the idea that an excess of serotonin in the brain results in the excited state of hallucinations and the schizophrenic personality. However, until such experiments are done on a larger scale, one must accept them with some caution.

The idea that depression can result from a deficiency of serotonin in the brain gathers support from much clinical work which has been done with drugs which inhibit the enzyme monoamine oxidase. These inhibitors increase brain serotonin and relieve simple mental depressions. They include Marsilid (iproniazid) and nialamide which have been found in extensive clinical trials to improve the psychiatric condition of people suffering from simple depression. These monoamine oxidase inhibitors usually have been found to make worse the condition of schizophrenia. Amine oxidase is the principal enzyme in the body which destroys serotonin, and the use of its inhibitors can be shown to result in an increase of serotonin content of the brain. However, the inhibition of this enzyme also brings about increases in the content of epinephrine and norepinephrine in the tissues, as well as that of other amines which may well be of psychiatric importance. Some of the drugs also inhibit other enzymes. Interpretation of the mental effects consequently is not clear. The results of the use of inhibitors of monoamine oxidase therefore are compatible with the interpretation given (that is, that mental depression can arise from a lack of cerebral serotonin), but do not prove it.

The tranquilizing drugs reserpine and chlorpromazine gave unexpected support to the serotonin hypothesis about schizophrenia. These drugs were discovered quite empirically, they sedate or calm or tranquilize excited animals and men, and were introduced into the treatment of mental diseases in the early 1950s. The conclusion is widespread that these drugs do not cure schizophrenia. Rather, they seem to calm the excited patient, and make him easier to handle so that adjustment into the life of the community may become possible.

Shortly after the enunciation of the serotonin hypothesis the chemical structure of reserpine became known, and it was clear that it was a derivative of yohimbine, which as we have just seen, had been shown to be an antimetabolite of serotonin. It was next found that reserpine brings about a displacement of serotonin from its positions in the brain, intestines and other tissues. This is the sort of behavior which had been shown to be characteristic for an antimetabolite, and the conclusion became widespread that its tranquilizing action—that is, its property of depressing[b] both animals and men—was probably the result of its displacement of serotonin, or in other words, of its antiserotonin effect. Reserpine is not a reversible antagonist of serotonin as yohimbine is, and for this reason its character as an antimetabolite was obscured, and a considerable divergence and confusion of interpretation arose.

Chlorpromazine is not a structural analog of serotonin, and is not an antimetabolite of it. It does not, as does reserpine, displace the hormone from its receptors in tissues. Nevertheless, it proved to be a potent antagonist of the action of serotonin on susceptible tissues. In some way not yet understood it blocks the hormonal action of serotonin, and of norepinephrine and histamine on smooth muscles, and presumably other tissues. The finding that the two foremost drugs for the treatment of psychotic excitement were agents able to interfere in the biological activity of serotonin naturally gave additional support to the serotonin hypothesis of the causation of schizophrenia. However, the similar involvement of these very same drugs with the action of norepinephrine and of chlorpromazine with histamine, gave rise to obscurity once more, as we shall see presently.

To sum up the evidence for the relationship of serotonin to schizophrenia, several kinds of experience all point to the hypothesis that an abnormality of the functioning of this hormone in the central nervous system is probably related to the cause of the disease. There is reason to postulate that depressions can arise from a deficiency of serotonin, and psychotic excitement from an excess of it. This might lead one to suspect that the control mechanism for regulation of the amount of it in the various parts of the brain had gone astray. The problem of deciding just what the defect in serotonin metabolism is in schizophrenia seems to be a most important one in dealing with the disease, because the attempts at "rational" chemotherapy depend on the correct resolution of this point.

It is important to note that all the evidence cited for the relationship of serotonin to schizophrenia (or more directly to hallucinations, personality change in the direction of schizophrenia, agitated behavior, and catatonia) is direct evidence obtained through experiments on

[b] Reserpine given to nonpsychotic patients for prolonged periods may occasionally lead to profound psychotic depression, a fact which came to light during the prolonged use of reserpine for the control of high blood pressure.

human beings. There has been no extrapolation from neurophysiological effects in laboratory animals, or even from behavioral tests with laboratory animals. Many experiments of this latter kind have been done, and these in the main support the idea of a relationship of serotonin levels in the brain to mental state and behavior. Such experiments, however, always suffer from the defect that one must argue from them to the situation in human diseases, a thing which many are unwilling to do for mental diseases. The principal reasons for entertaining the serotonin hypothesis have been the findings in human beings who have received chemical substances which demonstrably affect serotonin in the brain. Normal men have been made to develop a transient condition resembling that of schizophrenia. Schizophrenics have been made worse for brief periods by increasing brain serotonin and somewhat better (or at least more manageable) by decreasing it. Simple depressions have been controlled by drugs which increase serotonin and certain other hormones in the brain.

Relationship of acetylcholine, norepinephrine, epinephrine, and histamine to mental processes, and their interrelationships with serotonin and with each other. Evidence exists which suggests that acetylcholine, norepinephrine, epinephrine, and histamine are concerned in reactions in the brain which maintain normal mental processes. Thus, certain drugs which cause normal persons to develop visual hallucinations and changes in mood and affect can be shown to be antagonists to the action of acetylcholine. Others can be shown to be antagonists to the action of norepinephrine, or of epinephrine or histamine. Some of the tranquilizing drugs which are used to calm agitated mental patients have been found to displace norepinephrine from its position in the brain, just as one would expect an antimetabolite of norepinephrine to do. For example, reserpine displaces norepinephrine as well as serotonin from brain. It is a structural analog of both hormones. The sedating effects of reserpine on normal animals can be overcome by an increase in the norepinephrine and epinephrine content of the brain by administration of dihydroxyphenylalanine. Increases of the serotonin content of the brain by means of 5-hydroxytrytophan also overcome some of the tranquilizing effects of reserpine, but to a lesser degree than do increases in cerebral norepinephrine. For this reason a school of thought has arisen which maintains that it is norepinephrine and not serotonin which is the substance of importance in schizophrenia.

Careful consideration of all the data indicates that each of these several hormones is of importance to those reactions of the brain which together constitute normal mental functioning. It is not just serotonin, and not just norepinephrine, and not just acetylcholine or histamine. Interference with the actions of any one of these compounds by antimetabolites of them, or by other means will cause hallucinations or depressions or bizarre behavior or other signs of mental disease.

The question now arises as to why this should be so. As yet, knowledge is rudimentary, and understanding even more so. Some facts have nevertheless been established. Thus, for example, it has been shown that in a given single tissue norepinephrine, which causes no response by itself, strongly interferes with the action of serotonin. On other types of tissues these two hormones may act in unison, each by itself causing a response. Further exploration of the antagonism of these two hormones on an isolated smooth muscle has indicated that norepinephrine acts as an antimetabolite of serotonin.

Norepinephrine is the precursor from which the body makes epinephrine. In a given organ it might be possible that a restriction of the supply of norepinephrine could result in a failure to make enough epinephrine.

Within the autonomic nervous system, which controls most of the glands of the body, one sees that the parasympathetic fibers often are opposed in their function to the sympathetic ones. Acetylcholine is the principal chemical mediator for the parasympathetics; and the epinephrines, and possibly serotonin, are known mediators of the sympathetics. Histamine also seems to play a role in the action of some of the sensory nerves. Because of the physiological opposition of many sympathetic and parasympathetic effects it is probably not surprising to find that in many kinds of animals, and in several organ systems, acetylcholine and serotonin have opposing actions. Nevertheless, one can also find other tissues on which they act in unison. Thus, the heart of clams is slowed by acetylcholine, but the amplitude of the beat is increased by serotonin. The result is that acetylcholine decreases the blood output, whereas serotonin increases it. This is an example of their opposing actions. The fact that either hormone will cause smooth muscle such as that of the isolated uterus to contract is an example of their similarities of action.

The net result of all of such demonstrations is to show that, although each of these hormones seems to have a separate receptor and a distinct function, their actions are by no means unrelated. The interrelationships may well account for many phenomena which have been confusing in the past. One should therefore not be surprised to find that chemical substances which interfere with the functions of serotonin may cause visual hallucinations, and so also may others which interfere with acetylcholine or with norepinephrine. This will be especially understandable if it should be definitely proven that each of these hormones provides a separate means for the transport of calcium ions through cell membranes. Their activities would be different because the receptors are different, but they would all add up to the same final biochemical result—the entry of calcium ions.

The genetic aspect. Much has been written about whether mental diseases such as schizophrenia are hereditary (genetic in origin) or environmental. Followers of the Freudian school have placed great emphasis on environment because they picture the environment as being the source of the disease. Others have produced statistical data to support the belief that the genetic makeup of an individual predisposes him to the mental disease, and that all environment can do is to provide the stress which precipitates it. It is certainly true that there are many people who have been raised in environments which, according to Freudian belief, should have resulted in their being schizophrenic or otherwise deranged, and yet they have been well. This would be a point against the believers in environment as the sole cause of mental disease. And yet it is not easy to be sure that merely because schizophrenia tends to run in families it must have a genetic cause. If a mother is schizophrenic, or just schizoid, she may well transmit by precept and example to her children the habits of thought and behavior which will start them on the road to schizophrenia without any great genetic predisposition. Consequently, the familial frequency of schizophrenia does not of itself prove the hereditary nature of the disease.

The bulk of the evidence does seem to suggest that the genetic makeup of an individual, which he has inherited from his parents, makes him more susceptible to a frank attack of schizophrenia. When we come to some other mental diseases such as galactosemia and phenylketonuria the evidence for genetic determinance is quite clear. These mental deteriorations which begin early in childhood and almost always end very early in imbecility are the result of inheritance of the lack of a single enzyme. Much more will be said in the succeeding sections about phenylketonuria and galactosemia, but to illustrate the point about genetics the following facts are needed. Phenylketonuria is caused by the inherited inability to hydroxylate phenylalanine (lack of phenylalanine hydroxylase). Galactosemia results from the inherited lack of the enzyme which converts galactose to uridine diphosphate galactose. By knowing the amounts of these enzymes in the parents it is possible to predict accurately what percentage of the children may be expected to have these mental diseases. By knowing the specific enzymic difficulty it is possible to detect by biochemical means the affected children at birth before they develop a mental failure. It is then possible to prevent the mental failure by specific dietary measures which protect the enzyme-deficient individual from the effects of his inherited defect. These results have come about through the biochemical understanding of genetics.

The biochemical understanding of genetics tells us that the ability to form and use an enzyme is inherited from the parents. If two individuals mate, each of which is a heterozygous carrier of the recessive gene which controls the ability to make the enzyme phenylalanine hydroxylase, one out of four of the offspring will lack the ability to make this enzyme. In other respects this individual will be normal. The lack of the enzyme, however, will set in motion a chain of events which will end in the development of idiocy. The first link in this chain is the accumulation of a large excess of phenylalanine in all of the tissues. This accumulation of phenylalanine does not take place in normal individuals, because they have inherited the ability to make the specific enzyme which metabolizes phenylalanine.

It would be strange indeed if there were not a hereditary predisposition to schizophrenia, or galactosemia, or phenylketonuria. So many diseases of all sorts have been shown to have genetic aspects. Even infections such as tuberculosis seem to be governed by a hereditary predisposition which decides whether the entry of tubercle bacilli will result in tuberculosis or not.

In those mental derangements where the genetic cause has been proved (such as phenylketonuria and galactosemia), the lack of the enzyme involved is complete. Heterozygotes (carriers) who have less than the normal amount of enzyme, but who still have some of it are apparently not mentally defective. The total lack of the enzyme brings about mental failure very early in life. We might say that these are the extreme cases of inherited mental diseases. There may also be less extreme situations. These would be conditions in which a partial deficiency of some specific enzyme is inherited. During childhood and early maturity there might be thus enough enzyme to meet the needs for normal functioning. As emotional pressures multiply with increasing age the partially deficient enzyme system may not be able to supply the needs for the increased load. A mental failure then sets in. Such a failure might correspond to the onset of the so-called functional psychoses (schizophrenia, manic depressive psychosis, melancholia) which develop primarily in adults. The inherited biochemical defect would thus be partial instead of total as it is in the more extreme situations which begin in infancy.

Let us suppose for a moment that schizophrenia, or any other mental disease of unknown etiology, is the result of an excess of serotonin in the brain. This could arise in a variety of ways. There could be too much 5-hydroxytryptophan decarboxylase in the hypothalamus. There could be too much of the enzyme which forms 5-hydroxytryptophan, or there could be too little of the enzymes which destroy the hormone. Any one of these defects would cause an excess of serotonin in the brain.

Because it is now well established that the ability to synthesize any given enzyme is inherited from the parents, it is easy to visualize a genetic defect which would predispose an individual to schizophrenia by increasing or decreasing one of the enzymes in the brain which deals with serotonin. Measurements have not yet been made to determine whether such enzymic defects do in fact occur in patients suffering from schizophrenia. The technical and sociological problem of being able to get those parts of the brain which would be required for the analyses has made this direct test impossible. Fresh hypothalami cannot be taken from patients and from normal people for comparison of their enzyme contents.

The genetic predisposition to a disease such as schizophrenia, if it could be proved beyond reasonable doubt, would have some direct practical application. In galactosemia, which has a proven genetic background, the lack of the specific enzyme can be detected in the blood even though the mental disorder seems to reside in the brain. It thus becomes possible to make the enzymic measurements in the blood, which is accessible. In infants, where the complete lack of the specific enzyme can be demonstrated by blood analysis, prophylactic measures can be started before the mental failure becomes established. The imbecility can thus be avoided. If it were possible to make such enzymic analyses for the probable onset of schizophrenia, similar prophylactic measures might be worked out for avoidance of the disease.

One does not always know that the genetic defect will be found in all tissues, because it may be restricted to the brain, but if it is general throughout the body the practical advantage just discussed is obtained. There are some indirect means of determination of certain enzymes which do not require excision of tissue. The enzyme can be determined *in situ* without undue harm to the individual by measuring products it forms. It is important now to begin to measure these enzymes in various patients with mental disease and to compare the results to those found in normal people. Because of the evidence, obtained by other means, that serotonin has something important to do with schizophrenia, the enzymes concerned with it should be the ones to be measured. To measure enzymes at random, that is to say, to measure phosphatases or those concerned with the Krebs cycle would seem to be less promising.

Galactosemia. Although galactosemia and phenylketonuria were mentioned in the preceding section as illustrations of the genetic aspects of some mental diseases it is now necessary to say something more. Certain infants are born with a defect in the metabolism of galactose. In normals this sugar can be converted into glucose by way of uridine diphosphate galactose. An enzyme concerned in this transformation of galactose to glucose is uridine diphosphate galactose transferase, or more simply the transferase. This enzyme is lacking in infants with galactosemia. As a result, the galactose which they get from hydrolysis of lactose in the milk they ingest is not metabolized, and it, as well as galactose phosphate, builds up in their blood. If these infants are fed galactose-containing foods (such as milk), they develop an idiocy which remains for life. Very recently, through the work of Kalckar and his students, these biochemical defects have been discovered. The genetic aspect of the disease has also been demonstrated. The lack of the transferase is inherited as a recessive gene. Infants born of parents who carry this gene can now be tested for the presence of this enzyme in their blood at the time of birth, and if it is lacking, they can be fed with galactose-free food. When this is done, the galactosemia does not develop, and neither does the mental defect.

Why should unmetabolized galactose incite a mental disease? The reason why is still unclear. One possibility is that the excess (unmetabolized) galactose phosphate interferes in the formation of galactose-containing lipids. It may be that these lipids, such as cerebron sulfate and gangliosides, which occur most abundantly in the brain and other nerve tissue, are not formed properly. This remains to be established.

Why should a defect of the galactose-containing lipids lead to mental derangement? The lipids in question—cerebron sulfate and gangliosides—have quite recently been found to have activity as the serotonin receptor. These substances may be part of the special lipids in the membrane of cells which pick up serotonin and calcium ions and thus allow passage of calcium ions into the cells through the lipoidal barrier. One thus begins to see a working hypothesis which, if substantiated, would link idiocy of untreated galactosemia with the functioning of serotonin.

Phenylpyruvic oligophrenia (phenylketonuria). There is a kind of mental deficiency among children which is characterized by idiocy and by the excretion of phenylpyruvic acid in the urine. This is called phenylpyruvic oligophrenia (phenylketonuria). The phenylpyruvic acid is a degradation product of the amino acid phenylalanine, and the disease is marked by a failure to metabolize this amino acid normally. Considerable quantities of it are then found in the blood and phenylpyruvic acid is found in the urine.

The precise reason why this failure of phenylalanine metabolism leads to mental deficiency is not known, but there are some possibilities which are currently under study. Thus, phenylalanine is the precursor of norepinephrine and epinephrine. By oxidation of phenylalanine to dihydroxyphenylalanine (dopa), decarboxylation, and hydroxylation of the side chain, one arrives at norepinephrine. Methylation of norepinephrine at the amino group gives epinephrine. Phenylalanine is of course used for other purposes in the body such as for protein synthesis and as a precursor of tyrosine. It is conceivable that the mental deficiency might arise from an excessive amount of the epinephrines which might be made from the excess phenylalanine in the tissues.

This, however, is not the explanation because the conversion of phenylalanine to the epinephrines requires hydroxylation, and it is the failure of this hydroxylation which is known to be the cause of the disease. Another possibility which has some experimental work to support it is that the excess phenylalanine creates a lack rather than an excess of the epinephrines in the following way. It has been demonstrated that phenylalanine and especially phenylpyruvic and phenyllactic acids can inhibit the enzyme which makes both serotonin and the epinephrines. This enzyme is the decarboxylase which carries out the penultimate step in the formation of norepinephrine and which also carries out the final step in the synthesis of serotonin—the decarboxylation of 5-hydroxytryptophan. Inhibition of this enzyme by excess phenylalanine (an inhibition which has been demonstrated experimentally) could thus result in a failure to make enough serotonin or enough of the epinephrines. The deficiencies of serotonin and of epinephrine have actually been demonstrated in tissues of phenylketonuric idiots.

We have seen earlier in this chapter some of the other interrelationships of norepinephrine and serotonin. These include the ability of norepinephrine to act as an antimetabolite of serotonin in certain tissues. These relationships may well play a role in the phenylpyruvic oligophrenia.

The fact that the excessive amounts of phenylalanine really are the cause of the mental retardation has been established by restricting the intake of this essential amino acid in the food of phenylketonuric infants. When this is done, the development of the idiocy (the oligophrenia) is prevented.

The next step in the understanding of the pathogenesis of this disease may come from manipulation of serotonin and the epinephrines. If some way of prevention of the development of the disorder could be found as the result of changing specifically the epinephrine, or serotonin concentrations in the brains of these infants it might be possible to distinguish which (if either) of these hormones is responsible for the development of the disease. This could be attempted with pharmacological agents which are now being developed. These agents specifically overcome the deficiency of serotonin. Others specifically increase the epinephrines. It might, thus, be possible to establish whether serotonin or the epinephrines or neither is the prime cause of the mental failure.

The discoveries about phenylketonuria have great importance for the philosophical problem about the origins of mental diseases, especially the so-called functional psychoses. Phenylketonurics are not abnormal physically. Careful histological examination of their tissues has failed to show any anatomical abnormality which is characteristically associated with the disease. They do tend to be of blonde complexion, but so do many people who are sane. They also tend to suffer from epilepsy, but do not invariably have this neurological disorder. The lack of any characteristic physical defect would thus set them apart from the organic psychoses. Similarly, they cannot be placed with the classical toxic psychoses because the phenylalanine they eat, though toxic to them, is not toxic to normal people. They have, therefore, been classed with the functional psychoses.[c] Their disease would thus be considered to arise from baleful psychological disturbances. Actually, however, we know now that this is not the case. Their disease arises from the genetic inheritance of the lack of a single enzyme—phenylalanine hydroxylase. This enzymic defect allows phenylalanine to accumulate in their tissues. If this accumula-

[c] Actually, many phenylketonuric children have been committed to mental hospitals with a diagnosis of childhood schizophrenia. The true nature of their disease was only established by chemical tests for phenylpyruvic acid in their urines.

tion is prevented by dietary control, they do not develop the mental failure. Now that we know what to look for (that is, phenylalanine and phenylpyruvic acid), we can find a physical or biochemical defect. This defect was invisible to the methods of classical histology. It may be the same way with other so-called functional psychoses.

Phenylketonuria is a more striking case than galactosemia for throwing light on the philosophical problem. In galactosemia, there are prominent physical signs in addition to the mental failure. The affected infants have characteristically enlarged livers, and experience severe gastric disturbances. In phenylketonuria, such physical signs are lacking just as they are in schizophrenia or melancholia.

Other inherited severe mental deficiencies. There are additional diseases which appear in infancy as the result of inheritance of a metabolic defect from the parents. These diseases result in the development of idiocy early in life just as in the cases of phenylketonuria and galactosemia. These include Niemann-Pick disease, gargoylism, Tay-Sachs disease, Gaucher's disease, and Hartnup's disease. Except for Hartnup's disease, all of these are characterized not only by mental failure early in life, but also by very marked physical signs. In Tay-Sachs disease blindness and convulsions usually occur, and in gargoylism the body is deformed. All of these diseases (except Hartnup's) involve disturbances in the metabolism of the complex lipids. As we have just seen it is these lipids which are under scrutiny as constituents of receptors for serotonin and related hormones, and it may be that the disturbance in complex lipid metabolism is connected to the mental failure through relationship to these hormones. Hartnup's disease is not a disturbance of lipid metabolism and does not cause complete mental failure in infancy. Rather, this seems to be an inherited error in the metabolism of nicotinic acid and tryptophan. The mental deterioration sets in later in life and consists of a slow decline in intelligence quotient along with the development of neurological difficulties less awesome than those of the Tay-Sachs or Gaucher's diseases. All of these conditions are quite rare, fortunately, and, with some, although only a small number of cases have been studied, they do show the variety of inherited mental defects which are possible.

Some relationships of nicotinic acid to mental and neurological changes. In the disease called pellagra, which is the result of dietary lack of nicotinic acid in man, there is in addition to the dermatitis and other physical signs, a mental disorder. Before the discovery that nicotinic acid would prevent or cure the disease, pellagrins who showed this mental disorder were committed to mental hospitals. With the discovery of the curative properties of nicotinic acid in 1937, it became possible to restore these patients to society and to take steps on a nationwide scale to prevent the occurrence of pellagra. These have been rather effective. The occurrence of the mental disorder as a result of nicotinic acid deficiency is, however, the point to be emphasized here.

A number of plausible postulates can be made as to why the deficiency causes the mental disorder. Thus, nicotinic acid is converted in the body into the coenzymes diphosphopyridine nucleotide (DPN) and triphosphopyridine nucleotide (TPN). These coenzymes are essential for the normal oxidation of glucose by means of which energy is obtained for the many cellular processes. The coenzymes play an essential role in a considerable number of other oxidative reactions as well. Thus, for example, the hydroxylations of which we have frequently spoken in this chapter depend on TPN. The formation of 5-hydroxytryptophan from tryptophan, and of DOPA from phenylalanine are examples. Even if we leave out these special oxidations and consider only the metabolism of glucose, we see that the brain, like other tissues, gets much of its energy from the oxidation of this sugar or of lactic acid derived from it, and these oxidations depend on DPN. It is, therefore, not difficult to understand that the functions of the brain might be impaired as a result of a lack of nicotinic acid. The problem is to find out the exact reactions which are the ones responsible directly for the mental disorder. It cannot be merely the failure of glucose metabolism because such a failure can be induced in other ways (as in thiamine deficiency) without production of the same mental disturbance as seen in pellagra. It must be that the lack of nicotinic acid, and its derived coenzymes, affects primarily some one or a few special reactions, or that some special structure of the brain is more susceptible to this deficiency than are others.

Two antimetabolites of nicotinic acid have given some interesting clues about the parts of the brain dependent on nicotinic acid for keeping up their end of normal mental processes. The two antimetabolites are 3-acetylpyridine, and 6-aminonicotinamide. Both are very close structural analogs of nicotinic acid, and both can be shown to induce nicotinic acid deficiency in animals. Both bring about a histological lesion of the hippocampus, and apparently of no other region of the brain. The use of either antimetabolite is attended by a neurological change which can be noted by abnormal behavior, and this neurological defect can be traced to the hippocampal lesions. 3-Acetylpyridine has not been used in human beings, but 6-aminonicotinamide was used in trials against cancers before its neurotoxicity was appreciated. It brought about psychiatric disorders.

Chemotherapy of mental diseases. This section will deal with strategy and only incidentally with tactics. Consequently, there will be no listings of drugs which have been used in attempts to treat schizophrenia, hysteria, depressions, or any other category of mental disease, nor will there be a critique of the respective merits of these drugs.

In the past, almost all of the attempts to treat mental diseases with chemical agents have depended on a chance observation. Some part of a strange plant or some synthetic organic chemical was found quite by accident to change the behavior of animals and men in a way such as to suggest that such substances might be of value in the treatment of this or that mental disease. Medical history contains many examples, but in recent times reserpine and chlorpromazine were discovered in this way. The next step is to modify the chemical structure of such a drug in the hope of making it more useful. The various phenothiazine derivatives now in use for the treatment of schizophrenia were derived from chlorpromazine in this way. It is quite certain that this strategy of reliance on chance, and the large-scale testing of chemical compounds in screening programs will continue, and will probably lead to the introduction of useful drugs. So long as the causation of a mental disease is unknown such an empirical strategy is the only one feasible.

When the cause of a disease becomes known in biochemical terms a new strategy of chemotherapy can be considered. Let us suppose that schizophrenia has a relationship to serotonin as outlined earlier in this chapter. Let us suppose that the excited phase, which manifests itself as agitation, hallucinations, etc., is the result of an excess of serotonin in certain parts of the brain. Several possibilities for attempts at treatment present themselves. An antimetabolite of serotonin could be designed so that it would penetrate readily into the brain. It should be designed so that it would lack serotonin-like action but have only antiserotonin effects. Such an antimetabolite could be used to nullify the effects of the excess serotonin which is causing the mental symptoms. Another way to attack the problem would be to devise drugs which would inhibit the synthesis of serotonin. For example, an inhibitor of 5-hydroxytryptophan decarboxylase could be produced and tested. In all such efforts it would be necessary to take advantage of existing knowledge, and to gain new information about how to get the drug to the desired site of action.

Let us suppose further that depressions are the result of a deficiency of serotonin in some parts of the brain. One might logically attempt to make chemotherapeutic agents which would act like serotonin, and which would reach the desired site in the brain. One might alternatively devise agents which would accelerate the production of serotonin in the brain, or diminish its destruction by those enzymes which attack it. Some limited success therapeutically has already been achieved by following this strategy. This has been the use of inhibitors of monoamine oxidase. This enzyme is one of those which destroys serotonin and the epinephrines. Inhibitors of it increase the concentration of these substances in the brain and other tissues. They have been used in the treatment of certain kinds of depression with considerable success.

The practical problems encountered in following a rational strategy of this sort are considerable. Problems of transport of the drug to the brain, and of prolonging the action there, as well as of protection of other organs from the effects of the drug must be met. This is, however, not impossible to do. The possibilities of success seem much greater with the directed strategy than they do with the one which relies on a chance observation of an effective drug. The ultimate and only test of a successful chemotherapeutic agent is to find that it controls the disease. If the drug has been found by following the serotonin hypothesis (or the norepinephrine hypothesis, or the acetylcholine hypothesis), and if it can be shown beyond reasonable doubt that its therapeutic effect is the result of its relation to the hypothesis, then the strongest evidence possible is at hand for the correctness of the hypothesis. In such a way it may be possible to establish the etiology of some of these diseases, and at the same time to obtain a measure of control over them. Theory as well as practice needs chemotherapeutic success.

Prevention. It would be a mistake to think only about treatment of mental diseases and not also about prevention, just as it would be for infectious diseases. In combatting typhoid fever, one has a means of treatment once the infection has been established and diagnosed. One can hold it in check with sulfaguanidine or chloramphenicol. One also has some prophylactic measures when the danger of infection is acute. The population can be vaccinated, and the drinking water can be boiled. Nevertheless, the only really satisfactory method of dealing with the disease from a public health standpoint is prevention by cleaning up the water and food supplies. It would seem that the same might apply to various mental diseases.

In mental diseases such as galactosemia and phenylketonuria, prevention has proved to be rather effective. In an infant in whom biochemical tests for the missing enzyme have detected the genetic susceptibility to the disease (one might almost say the inevitability of it) the mental change is avoided by removal of galactose or phenylalanine from the food. This corresponds to boiling the drinking water during a typhoid epidemic.

In a disease such as galactosemia there is a quality of inevitability which is hard to recognize in, let us say, schizophrenia. If the infant lacks the UDPGal transferase it will develop the mental derangement. In schizophrenia one does not know what the biochemical abnormality is. All that is at hand is evidence which says that the disease is the result of a disturbance of the serotonin metabolism of the brain. There is also suggestive, but not conclusive evidence of a genetic predisposition to the disease, but there is not any evidence of its inevitability. The environmental influences such as the training of the child, and the emotional stresses which arise throughout life seem to be some of the deciding factors as to whether the genetic predisposition will be converted into frank disease.

The immediate aim of chemotherapy must be to develop ways of controlling the frank disease once it has appeared. What is needed are the equivalent counterparts of sulfaguanidine and chloramphenicol used in typhoid fever. However, to depend on these for an over-all solution of the problem of schizophrenia from a public health point of view would seem to be short-sighted. Any thoughtful observer of society must have been struck by the inadequacies of training of a large number of people. Their technicological training may have been adequate, but their adjustment to life seems insufficient. This is probably not surprising when one reflects on the large amount of misinformation, borne up by some psychological or sociological theory, which has been directed at them. A great deal has been learned during the past 3000 years about adequate ways to adjust to many of the complex situations of life. History and philosophy have taken note of the answers. It is unfortunate that they have not been more widely understood. If and when they are, we will have reached the real solution of the problem as it concerns most individuals. In the language of the typhoid-fever analogy, we will then have cleaned up the water and food supplies. However, one discouraging thing which history also tells us is that utopias are never attained. It may be so with this one, especially since it seems so hard to get agreement even among intelligent people as to just what it is that history and philosophy are trying to say to us, and educators are so bent on something new that they have not time to listen. There thus seems to be every reason to suspect that chemotherapeutic agents will continue to be needed.

chapter 3

Antimetabolites

The evidence which first suggested that serotonin had a direct relationship to mental diseases was found through the use of antimetabolites. This evidence is still the principal reason for belief in such a relationship. Consequently, it is necessary to know what an antimetabolite is, and particularly, how it functions if an understanding of the whole concept about mental diseases is to be had. Considerable confusion has arisen because some who subsequently have written much about the concept, or who have criticized it, have apparently not understood the basic facts about antimetabolites.

This chapter is not going to be an exhaustive treatise on antimetabolites. Rather, it is intended as a description of some of the principles, especially those which are needed to understand the evidence on the relationship of serotonin and certain other hormones to mental diseases. A more complete description of antimetabolites, and the principles which govern their biological actions can be found in a monograph entitled "A Study of Antimetabolites" (1).

Definition. An antimetabolite is a chemical compound which resembles in its chemical structure one of the essential metabolites, and which specifically interferes with the biological functioning of that essential metabolite. The essential metabolites are substances which are uniquely needed for some process in the living body. Examples of essential metabolites are the various vitamins, the hormones, the special amino acids, and other substances which an organism requires for normal functioning. Because many processes must go on in order to maintain life, and because each of these processes depends on one or more specific chemical substances, there are many essential metabolites. Sometimes one essential metabolite is used by an organism for more than one process but always the number of processes activated by one essential metabolite is small in comparison to the entire metabolic machinery. Each separate essential metabolite is required for the processes which it activates. Other essential metabolites usually cannot take its place. A few exceptions to this last statement are known and, as we shall see subsequently, may be important, but in general the rule of specificity in the biological actions of essential metabolites holds.

An antimetabolite is a structural analog of an essential metabolite, and is one which is able to interfere with the biological functioning of that metabolite. Both parts of the definition are important. Mere structural analogy is not enough to make a compound an antimetabolite of some hormone or vitamin, because many such structural analogs are known which have no biological action. Furthermore, mere ability to antagonize the biological action of a hormone or vitamin does not make a compound an antimetabolite. Many chemical substances are known which interfere with some biological action initiated by an essential metabolite, but these are not necessarily antimetabolites. Thus, although diisopropylfluorophosphate and several other nerve gases profoundly affect the biological systems which use acetylcholine, these poisons are not antimetabolites of acetylcholine. They are not structural relatives of the hormone, and their mechanism of action is different from that of antimetabolites of acetylcholine.

What an antimetabolite does is to create a specific deficiency of its related essential metabolite in living processes. It does this by beginning to undergo the same chemical reaction as that which the essential metabolite uses in the fulfillment of its biological role. The antimetabolite, however, can only partially fulfill the role of the metabolite and either stops the whole process, or impedes it. To understand this mechanism of action of antimetabolites it is necessary to know about the mechanism of enzyme action, and about hormonal receptors. These will be described after consideration of some actual examples of antimetabolites.

Examples of antimetabolites. To understand more clearly what an antimetabolite is, and what it does, let us consider briefly two historically important examples. These are sulfanilamide and pyrithiamine. The chemical structures of these and their related essential metabolites are shown in Figures 1 and 2.

Sulfanilamide is a therapeutic agent used in the treatment of some bacterial infections. Its chemotherapeutic properties were discovered by Tréfouël, Tréfouël, Nitti, and Bovet (2) who modified the Prontosil of Domagk (3). Sulfanilamide inhibits the growth of certain kinds of bacteria cultured either *in vitro* or *in vivo*. Woods (4) discovered that a constituent of yeast extract which would overcome the bacteriostatic action of sulfanilamide was *p*-aminobenzoic acid, which he postulated to be an essential metabolite. This postulate was soon confirmed when it was found that the vitamin folic acid was a derivative of *p*-aminobenzoic acid, and that folic acid was synthesized by the bacteria from *p*-aminobenzoic acid. Sulfanilamide was shown to inhibit this synthesis (5). Woods demonstrated further that the antagonism between sulfanilamide and *p*-aminobenzoic acid was of the competitive kind. The poisonous action of sulfanilamide on bacteria thus turned out to be due to a blockage of the synthesis of folic acid. The blockage was caused by an antimetabolite which created a deficiency of *p*-aminobenzoic acid in the synthesis of folic acid.

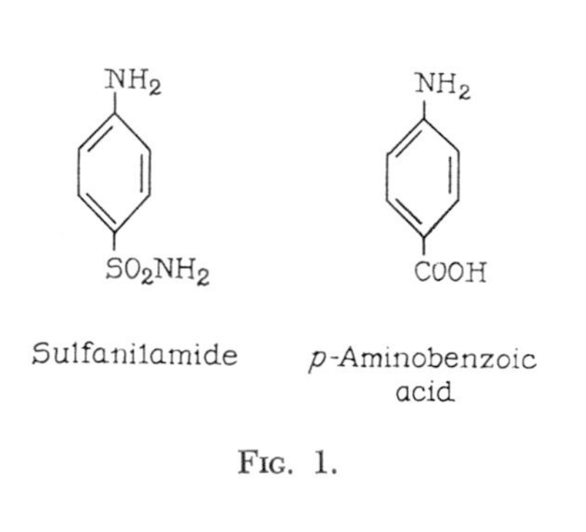

FIG. 1.

The chemical structure of pyrithiamine is very similar to that of the vitamin thiamine (see Figure 2). When pyrithiamine, in doses of about 0.3 mg per day, is given to adequately nourished mice, they begin to lose weight and to show the typical signs of thiamine deficiency (6). These are rather characteristic and involve the development of neurological signs such as opisthotonos, and convulsions. Death ensues unless thiamine is administered. The development of the deficiency syndrome can be prevented as well as cured by administration of extra thiamine. The antagonism between pyrithiamine and thiamine is of the competitive kind, in that the minimal lethal dose of the analog is directly dependent on the thiamine intake. When the thiamine intake is 2 μg per day, the dose of pyrithiamine required is 25 μg; when thiamine is 20 μg, pyrithiamine is 250 μg; and when thiamine is 200 μg, pyrithiamine is 2500. The work with pyrithiamine was initiated with

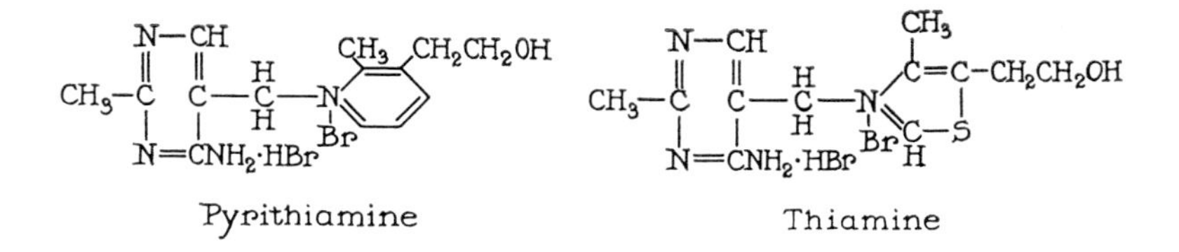

FIG. 2.

the idea in mind of producing an antimetabolite of thiamine. It was one of the earliest examples of the induction of typical signs of vitamin deficiency in higher animals with such compounds. Because the signs of thiamine deficiency in higher animals are well known and characteristic, the induction of these signs by pyrithiamine and their cure by extra vitamin left little doubt that the drug acted by creation of a specific deficiency.

The effects of pyrithiamine can be seen in an enzyme system as well as in living animals. It inhibits the enzyme which synthesizes cocarboxylase from thiamine and adenosine triphosphate. It does so in competition with thiamine (7), so that the inhibition can be relieved merely by an increase in the thiamine concentration in the system.

A large number of antimetabolites directed at many kinds of essential metabolites are now known. The monograph mentioned (1) discusses several hundred, and many more have appeared since its publication. There are antimetabolites for each one of the water-soluble vitamins, for several fat-soluble vitamins, for several hormones, for many amino acids and other important compounds in living organisms.

Mechanism of enzyme action. The widely accepted mechanism to explain the catalytic role of an enzyme in promoting a reaction is summarized by the equations:

$$\text{Enzyme} + \text{Substrate} \rightleftharpoons \text{Enzyme-Substrate complex} \qquad \text{(a)}$$

$$\text{Enzyme-Substrate complex} \rightleftharpoons \text{Enzyme} + \text{Products} \qquad \text{(b)}$$

The enzyme combines in a reversible fashion with its specific substrate to form an unstable complex which readily dissociates into the materials from which it was formed. All that is necessary to bring about this dissociation is to reduce the concentration of E or S. The dissociation then takes place and a new position of equilibrium is established in accordance with the law of mass action for reversible reactions.

The ES complex is unstable because some bonds of the substrate have been activated as a result of union with the enzyme. The substrate molecule in the complex thus is induced to undergo a reaction, and to form products. These products are now different from the substrate molecules, and have a reduced affinity for the enzyme. The result is that they are parted from the enzyme, and the enzyme is left free to repeat the process with new substrate molecules. In a short time by means of this process all of the substrate may be converted into products.

The enzyme is believed to unite with a specific substrate because one part of its molecule has a chemical structure which attracts and binds the substrate but does not attract and bind many other substances. The special substrate fits into this active site of the enzyme molecule as a key fits into its lock. The precise size, shape, and conformation of the substrate are thus deciding factors which determine whether or not the enzyme will combine with it and act on it.

Relatively little is known about the exact chemical structure of enzymes. They are proteins composed of chains of amino acids in peptide linkage but the exact sequence of these amino acids is known only for one enzyme—ribonuclease (8). The precise structure of the active site has not been established for any enzyme. Efforts to do so have been numerous in recent years, and considerable information has been accumulated, especially about some of the esterases. Thus it is known that in several esterases the active site contains the amino acid sequence glycylaspartylserylglycine. The serine is the acceptor of the acyl part of the substrate as hydrolysis proceeds. There is also considerable evidence to show that a particular histidine residue is somehow part of the active site of several esterases. It seems reasonable to expect that the complete chemical structure and the reason for the catalytic function of the active site will be discovered soon for some enzymes.

For most enzymes there is more than one substrate required. Thus, in hydrolytic enzymes the second substrate is water. The need for two or more substrates is seen most clearly in the case of those enzymes which catalyze synthesis of a large molecule from two smaller, and dissimilar ones. In many of the cases of this kind studied up to the present time, adenosine triphosphate has been one of the substrates which is used to contribute phosphate groups to a second substrate with the resultant production of a phosphorylated product. Thus, thiamine and adenosine triphosphate give rise to thiamine pyrophosphate (cocarboxylase) and adenylic acid in the presence of a suitable enzyme.

Mechanism of action of antimetabolites. The antimetabolite is a structural analog of an essential metabolite and is consequently shaped much like it. The analog can thus fit the active site of the enzyme which uses the essential metabolite as a substrate. This is the reason for the importance of the structural analogy between antimetabolite and essential metabolite. The analog thus combines with the active site of the particular enzyme, but because it is not an exact fit the enzyme may not be able to use it in the normal fashion. The analog is like an ill-fitting key which can be thrust into the keyhole, but cannot be used to turn the lock. Furthermore, the keyhole is now occupied by it so that the proper key (the essential metabolite) cannot be inserted. The result is to create a deficiency of the real key, the essential metabolite. This mechanical analogy is useful in visualization of the basic idea, but must not be carried too far.

Many cases are known in which the analog fits the active site of the enzyme well enough that it can take the place of the essential metabolite, and undergo the metabolic reaction which the essential metabolite ordinarily would undergo. Several consequences then ensue. The analog may be able to function biologically as well as the essential metabolite for all subsequent reactions. We then say that the analog has prometabolite activity. The analog may not be as efficient as the essential metabolite, in which case one says that it has this or that percentage of activity, as when tryptamine is said to show 10 per cent of the activity of serotonin in the blood pressure test. However, a few analogs are known which are more active than the essential metabolite to which they are related. Thus, for example, lysergic acid diethylamide (LSD) is three times more active than serotonin in the blood pressure test (9). In these cases, the analog is no antimetabolite because it acts like the metabolite instead of antagonistically.

If the essential metabolite is used in an organism for more than one reaction, then it may turn out that a given antimetabolite of it may act as an antimetabolite in one or more of these reactions, but may act like the metabolite in another one of the reactions. This seems to be the case with LSD. In various smooth muscles such as those of the rat uterus LSD is an antagonist to the action of serotonin. In the clam heart, or in the test involving increases in blood pressure of the dog, LSD acts like serotonin, and its effects on these tissues are antagonized by certain other antimetabolites of serotonin (9). In a living animal in which the hormone is being used for more than one function the effects of an antimetabolite thus can be complicated. A large and growing number of examples of this sort of behavior of an analog are known. For example, some analogs of the vitamins have been shown to act like the essential metabolite in some reactions, and as antagonists of it in others within the same individual. Analogs of pyridoxine, riboflavin, choline and biotin are known which have both pro- and antivitamin activities, depending on the particular reaction under study. The reason why this should be is clearly understandable in terms of the mechanism of action outlined above. Some enzymes are more exacting than others in the fit demanded before action takes place.

Sometimes an antimetabolite exerts its effect, not so much at one particular enzymic step, but, rather, along a sequence of reactions. The analog may actually replace the essential metabolite in one step of the sequence and be converted into an unnatural product which then disturbs one or more of the subsequent reactions in the sequence. Thus, in the formation of nucleic acids, a sequence of reactions may start with a purine base which is converted to the nucleotide which is then incorporated along with other nucleotides into a large chain or polynucleotide. There may also be alternate routes for several of these steps. For example, the nucleotide may be made from the purine base and 5-phosphoribose pyrophosphate, or it may be made from the imidazole ribotide precursor of the purines. An antimetabolite of the purine may then undergo the same reactions as does the real purine. That is, the analog may be converted to a ribotide, which in turn may be incorporated into the polynucleotide chain. The final product, however, may be unsuitable as a substitute for the real or natural nucleic acid, and be unable to fulfill the required biological function.

N=C—OH
HO—C C—Br
N—CH

5-Bromouracil

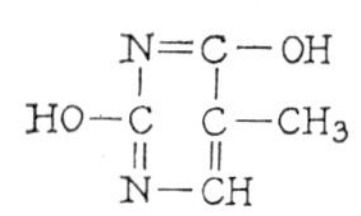

Thymine

Fig. 3.

This sort of effect has been much studied with analogs of the purines, pyrimidines, and amino acids. Thus, an analog of the purine base guanine, namely 8-azaguanine, is incorporated into the nucleic acid of the tobacco mosaic virus, but the virus so formed is incapable of carrying out an infection of the host plant in the normal way. The analog of the pyrimidine uracil, known as 2-thiouracil, is incorporated into the nucleic acid of tobacco mosaic virus with somewhat similar results (10 and 11). The thymine analog, known as 5-bromouracil (see Figure 3), is incorporated into the desoxynucleic acids of the bacterium *Escherichia coli* or of *Bacillus subtilis*, but the nucleic acid so formed is not able to function adequately in the cell division processes of the organism (12, 13, and 14). One result is the formation of filaments rather than normal cells. The phenylalanine analog known as *p*-fluorophenylalanine is incorporated into the proteins of animals or of bacteria treated with it (15 and 16) and although some of these abnormal proteins are apparently able to function in the normal way, others are not able to do so. The number of examples of this phenomenon is large, and growing.

All of this work shows clearly that even though an analog of an essential metabolite may be able to function in place of the natural metabolite, it may be built into an unnatural molecule which fails to function, or may even inhibit normal function at a later step in a long sequence of metabolic events. Again we see that enzymes differ in the exactness of the fit they require in their substrates.

Hormonal receptors and their reactions with antimetabolites. Most investigators believe that a hormone exerts its specific physiological action by combination with a special receptor. This receptor is believed to exist in those tissues on which the hormone exerts an effect. Such tissues are often called the target organs to distinguish them sharply from those which produce or transport the hormone. The physiological effect is believed to be the result of combination of the hormone with the receptor, but beyond this vague picture very little is known. For no hormone can chemical reactions be written which are adequate to explain the physiological actions.

It is possible that the combination of the hormone with its receptor is analogous to the first step of an enzymic reaction, that is, that it may correspond to the formation of the enzyme-substrate complex. There is as yet little evidence that the second step of the enzymic process then ensues, because no products of the reaction of hormone and receptor can be demonstrated as can be done in enzyme reactions. Instead, one finds that, by dilution (that is, by washing off the hormone which has been applied to a receptor system), the combination is reversed, and the hormone can be recovered. The receptor too seems to be intact after the response, and is able to undergo reaction with the hormone again. Because the chemical nature of any hormonal receptor is entirely unknown, and because the chemical reactions responsible directly for the effects of a hormone on a target organ are also unknown it may well be that when the mechanisms of action of hormones are finally understood in terms of chemical reactions, the simple view just outlined of combination in reversible fashion with a receptor will need to be expanded into a sequence of dependent chemical reactions.

It may seem strange to some that so little is known about the mechanism of action of hormones. The impression is prevalent that a great deal is known. Thus insulin increases the entry of glucose into muscle cells, thyroxine increases the basal metabolic rate, and serotonin causes smooth muscles to contract. All sorts of physiological details are known about these effects, but almost nothing is understood about the chemistry of these physiological events which the hormones call forth. To understand in chemical terms the mechanism of action of any hormone would be a great intellectual achievement. With the water-soluble vitamins such as thiamine or folic acid, and with many of the amino acids and other important essential metabolites one has a clear picture of mechanism of action. It involves each of these metabolites being used as a specific substrate for a special enzyme which converts it into a product which again acts as a substrate for another special enzyme. With this picture of mechanism, one can readily understand much about the actions of antimetabolites of these essential metabolites, as we have seen earlier in this chapter. A large body of experimental evidence has been found which supports these ideas, and they are found to offer a satisfactory picture of many physiological phenomena. With the hormones and their antimetabolites, the understanding is not so clear because of the vagueness of knowledge about the chemistry of hormonal action.

Many antimetabolites of hormones are known. Their chemical structures are well established, and their physiological effects are well documented. Many of them are used as drugs in the practice of medicine.

The mechanism of action of an antimetabolite of a hormone is pictured in terms of the receptor hypothesis. The antimetabolite, because of its structural resemblance to the hormone, is believed to combine with the receptor and thus to exclude the hormone from such combination. Just as in the case of antimetabolites acting in an enzymic reaction the antimetabolite of the hormone competes with that hormone for combination with the specific receptor. The action is thus believed to be the same in essence as it is in the enzymic processes. In support of such a picture of events some experimental evidence can be found. One can show that an antimetabolite of acetylcholine does in fact compete with the hormone for action on a susceptible cell or tissue. One can show that it does not interfere with the actions of other hormones on the tissues. Furthermore, one can find that the antimetabolite displaces the hormone from the tissue and the displaced hormone can be demonstrated to be in the surrounding medium. What is lacking is the ability to isolate the actual chemical substances involved (such as the receptors) and the precise chemical reactions which are responsible for the hormonal action. Most agree that the mechanism of action of a hormone involves combination with a receptor. What is not clear is why this combination brings about the physiological effect of the hormone. When and if it becomes possible to clarify this it may also be possible to substantiate the mode of action of antimetabolites of hormones, and to do so in the absence of living cells. Always up to the present it has been necessary to use such cells to find the effects of the hormone.[a]

[a] With a few hormones such as thyroxine and epinephrine it has been found possible to cause stimulation of the action of some enzyme system in the absence

Quite recently some progress has been made towards demonstration of antimetabolite action of hormone analogs in a cell-free system. Ehrenpreis (17 and 18) has extracted a soluble substance containing protein and lipid from a target organ, and has found it to combine with a hormone which can then be displaced by an antimetabolite. The hormone was acetylcholine, the target organ was the electric organ of the electric eel, and the antimetabolite used was either tubocurarine or cocaine. How the combination of the hormone with the extracted substance was to explain the physiological effects of acetylcholine however, was not made clear.

The chemical events set in motion by combination of a hormone with its receptor may be complex. Consequently the precise point of action may not be the same for each one of a group of antimetabolites. We have already examined this problem with respect to a sequence of enzymic reactions. Let us now examine it for the case of a hormone. Recent findings have indicated (as described in Chapters 2 and 4) that serotonin exerts its effects on cells because it provides a mechanism for the transport of calcium ions through the cell membrane (19 and 20). The hormone finds in the membrane of susceptible cells a substance, believed to be a lipid, with which it combines reversibly. Such substances have been extracted from cells (20). They might be considered to be part of the serotonin receptor. The compound which is formed with the hormone then can combine with calcium ions and render them soluble in lipoidal materials (21). It has been postulated that the fat-soluble compound is now attacked by an enzyme just inside the membrane. This enzyme removes some group from the lipoidal receptor substance so that the complex of calcium, serotonin and receptor now lacks the forces to hold together. The calcium and the serotonin are then liberated, unchanged but inside the cell.

If this mechanism is correct there are several points at which an antimetabolite of serotonin could exert its effect. The analog could unite with the lipoidal receptor substance and exclude serotonin from combination. The complex of antimetabolite and receptor substance could fail to pick up the calcium which the normal complex ordinarily does. Finally, the complex of analog plus receptor plus calcium, which is the substrate for the special enzyme just inside the membrane, could prove to be an unnatural one which competes with the corresponding serotonin complex for this enzyme. Any one of these effects,

of whole cells. Usually, however, the amounts of hormone required for such a demonstration have been much larger than those which are found to act on living cells. There are other reasons as well to make one question whether these demonstrations constitute a solution to the problem.

or a combination of them could decide the potency of a given analog of serotonin as an antimetabolite.

The fact that a potent antimetabolite of serotonin can stop the calcium-transporting system which serotonin seems to activate, but not other calcium-transport systems, has been demonstrated in smooth muscles (22). For this purpose the isolated rat uterus was used. This tissue contracts when serotonin is applied to it. It also contracts when large concentrations of calcium ions are applied (19). Apparently, if the calcium concentration outside the cells is high enough, enough gets through the membrane by leakage to set off a contraction of the actomyosin-adenosine triphosphate system. If the tissue is treated with an antimetabolite of serotonin such as 1-benzyl-2-methyl-5-methoxytryptamine, serotonin will no longer cause contraction. The analog has blocked the serotonin system for calcium transport. Nevertheless, high concentrations of calcium ions in the external fluid will still induce contraction. The leakage of the membrane still allows enough to enter even though the serotonin system is closed down by the antimetabolite. Data to illustrate this point are shown in Table 1.

Reversibility. The combination between an essential metabolite and its enzyme or receptor is reversible. As mentioned earlier the amount of combination for any single enzyme or receptor is determined by the law of mass action. If the enzyme concentration is held constant

TABLE 1. *Comparative effects of an antiserotonin on uterine contractions caused by serotonin and by calcium ions*

Serotonin, μg per ml	$CaCl_2$, μg per ml	Antimetabolite,* μg per ml	Contraction, cm
0.01	20 †	0	4.1
0	20	0	0.0
0	220	0	4.3
0.01	20	1	1.0
0	220	1	4.5

* The antimetabolite was 1-benzyl-2-methyl-5-methoxytryptamine.

† This was the amount of $CaCl_2$ present in the saline solution in the bath.

(as it is in a short time experiment in a living animal) the amount of substrate which combines to form the complex is determined by the concentration of substrate. If substrate is increased, more complex will be formed, and vice versa. This is a corollary of the equilibrium constant of this reversible reaction. When the second step of the enzymic reaction takes place (the formation of products) the concentration of ES complex decreases, but for any given instant the equilibrium situation is as described.

Most antimetabolites likewise form a reversible complex with the enzyme or receptor in question. Here, too, the amount of union with the enzyme depends on the concentration of the antimetabolite, and, of course, on its chemical nature. For a given antimetabolite and a given enzyme, the amount of union depends on the concentration of the antimetabolite.

If both substrate (essential metabolite) and antimetabolite are present together, the two analogs will compete for union with the enzyme. Let us suppose that the affinities of both substances for the enzyme are equal. If equal concentrations of the two are present along with the enzyme, then the same amounts of metabolite and antimetabolite will combine with the enzyme. The combined antimetabolite will not be converted to products (if we take only the simplest case in which abnormal products are not formed) but the combined metabolite will be converted to products. The reaction will be inhibited because half of the enzyme has been taken out of action by combination with the antimetabolite.

Now suppose that the concentration of antimetabolite is increased tenfold, but that all other factors remain the same. Ninety per cent of the enzyme will then be combined with the antimetabolite, and only about 10 per cent with the substrate (essential metabolite). The result will be a 90 per cent inhibition of the enzymic action on the substrate. Similarly, if the antimetabolite concentration had been increased a hundredfold, the inhibition would have been about 99 per cent. If now the concentration of antimetabolite were to be kept at the tenfold level mentioned above, but the concentration of essential metabolite were also to be increased tenfold, the ratio between the two would be the same as in the original situation, and only about 50 per cent inhibition of the enzyme would result despite the fact that the same amount of enzyme was operating in the presence of a tenfold increase in inhibitor concentration. If the concentration of essential metabolite were to be increased still further, say to a hundredfold the original concentration, then the enzyme would be only slightly inhibited even though the inhibitor concentration was still tenfold the original concentration.

These relationships hold true because of the reversible reaction between substrate and enzyme and between antimetabolite and enzyme. The two analogs compete for the active site of the enzyme. The thing which decides the outcome is the relative concentrations of the two substances and not the absolute concentration of either. If substrate is combined, and the concentration of antimetabolite is increased, then some substrate is displaced from union, and its place is taken by antimetabolite. Similarly, if antimetabolite is combined with the enzyme, and the concentration of substrate is raised sufficiently, then substrate molecules will displace antimetabolite molecules from union with the enzyme, and the inhibition will be relieved. This is what is meant by reversible inhibition of a reaction. It is found with a large number of antimetabolites, but not with all. Thus, it can be seen between *p*-aminobenzoic acid and sulfanilamide in the inhibition of bacterial growth, or between thiamine and pyrithiamine in the induction of thiamine deficiency of mice or of microorganisms, or between serotonin and 2,5-dimethylserotonin in the contraction of various smooth muscles. There are numerous other examples.

Some investigators have taken the existence of competitive (that is, reversible) antagonism as the *sine qua non* of an antimetabolite. They have maintained that unless such competitive antagonism can be demonstrated there is no reason to justify the conclusion that one is working with an antimetabolite phenomenon at all. To the present author, such a view seems untenable. For example, whether or not a given compound can be shown to act as a competitive antagonist to its related essential metabolite sometimes depends on the organism in which the testing is done. Thus, for example, 4-aminofolic acid (aminopterin) is a competitive antagonist to the vitamin folic acid in the growth of certain lactic acid bacteria, but is a non-competitive inhibitor of growth of some closely allied species.

To conclude that in these allied species the toxic action of the analog had nothing to do with folic acid would seem unjustifiable, especially in view of the fact that the reason for the inhibition of growth in both kinds of organisms can be shown to be the result of the induction of folic acid deficiency as demonstrated by the failure to carry out those biochemical reactions which involve the use of folic acid. Reversible, competitive antagonism between analog and essential metabolite makes the relationship of the two compounds much clearer, and greatly adds to the evidence that the analog is actually an antimetabolite of the essential metabolite, but it is not the only evidence to be considered. Much excited discussion of this point is to be found in the literature.

There are all gradations of reversibility or antagonism. One extreme is represented by complete failure of the metabolite to overcome the effects of the antimetabolite. The other extreme is competitive antagonism. In competitive antagonism, between an antimetabolite and its essential metabolite, the toxicity of the antimetabolite is not a fixed quantity. It depends on the amount of essential metabolite which is present at the same time. There are however many cases of non-competitive antagonism. In these the biological effect of the antimetabolite is not dependent on the concentration of essential metabolite. When no amount of the related essential metabolite will overcome the effects of the analog, the latter is said to be an irreversible antagonist. In some cases, however, the effects of the antimetabolite can be overcome over a limited range of concentration, but with each increase in the amount of antimetabolite, the increase required in the essential metabolite is much greater, so that soon a point is reached at which no practicable amount of essential metabolite will overcome the biological effects of the analog. This is the case of non-competitive antagonism.

An example of an antimetabolite which shows non-competitive antagonism is oxythiamine acting as an antagonist to thiamine in chickens. This compound induces the signs of thiamine deficiency in these animals, and its effects can be overcome with excess thiamine in the food provided that the amount of oxythiamine used has not been too large (23 and 24). Another such case is that of dicoumarol. This compound is a distant structural relative of vitamin K and calls forth the signs of vitamin K deficiency in animals. Its clinical usefulness rests on this property. It inhibits the formation of blood clots. Its effects can be overcome by vitamin K, provided that minimally effective doses of the analog have been used. Nevertheless, these effects cannot be overcome if very large amounts of the analog have been given. This type of behavior is in contrast to the situation with a competitively reversible antimetabolite such as pyrithiamine. This antimetabolite of thiamine, as was explained earlier in this chapter, calls forth in animals the signs of deficiency of thiamine, and these signs can be either prevented or cured with thiamine regardless of how much pyrithiamine has been given. It is only necessary to give a correspondingly larger amount of thiamine.

Some of the reasons for non-competitive antagonism or for completely irreversible antagonism can be understood by consideration of the basic mechanism of action of antimetabolites. For example, if the reaction between the enzyme or receptor and the antimetabolite is not freely reversible, the antimetabolite may be attached firmly to the enzyme and held there so that the related essential metabolite cannot displace it, regardless of the amount applied. Such firm attachment is likely to take place if the antimetabolite contains groups which are chemically reactive with parts of the enzyme or receptor. These may then form covalent bonds with groups on the enzyme with resultant permanent loss of the enzymic activity. Such reaction with the enzyme is not the only reason for irreversibility, however. Some cases seem to be associated with difficulty of penetration into cells. An example of this sort was mentioned above in connection with antimetabolites of folic acid, and there are several others of similar nature.

Irreversibility is often a desirable property in an antimetabolite which is to be used therapeutically as a drug. If the drug in its actions on tissues is antagonized by the essential metabolite which is also present in the tissues, a larger dose will be required. The competitively-reversible drug is counteracted by the essential metabolite produced in the tissues, whereas the non-competitive or completely irreversible one is not. Clearly, then, if the antagonism of drug and metabolite is competitive then the situation from a practical standpoint is worse than if the antagonism is non-competitive or irreversible. It is true that the demonstration that a given drug acts as an antimetabolite is always weaker if the antagonism to the essential metabolite is non-competitive or irreversible. We might say that irreversibility is good for practice but bad for theory of drug action. It is a factor which designers of new therapeutic agents keep much in mind.

Displacement of essential metabolites by their antimetabolites. From the theory about the mechanism of action of antimetabolites one can see that the antimetabolite acts by taking the place of the essential metabolite, and creates a deficiency of it. Consequently, if one were to analyze appropriate tissues of an animal treated with an antimetabolite the expectation would be that the amount of the related essential metabolite would be found much reduced. This is indeed what is found. Thus, in animals given pyrithiamine, an antimetabolite of the vitamin thiamine, the amount of this vitamin excreted in the urine immediately thereafter is sharply increased (25 and 26), and analysis of the tissues shows that the thiamine content is subnormal. In like fashion, if one gives an antimetabolite of serotonin, the excretion of serotonin and its degradation products increases in the urine, and the serotonin content of the tissues decreases. This has been demonstrated with reserpine (27) and with 1-benzyl-2-methyl-5-

TABLE 2. *Serotonin content of rabbit blood and of rabbit blood platelets before and after administration of the antimetabolite BAS*

	μg per 10^8 Platelets	μg per ml Blood
Before treatment	2.7	9.4
One hour after BAS	3.1	8.2
After 2 days of BAS	1.0	5.0

Values shown were the averages from four rabbits.

methoxytryptamine (BAS) (28). Data to illustrate this point are shown in Table 2. The serotonin content of blood platelets of rabbits was determined before and after the administration of BAS (15 mg per kg body weight). The serotonin was displaced by the antimetabolite.

The finding of this property of reserpine caused much excitement and much making of conflicting hypotheses until it was realized that it was the expected behavior of an antimetabolite. Even today the understanding of this property of antimetabolites seems to be limited.

Inhibition index. An inhibition index is a number which expresses the potency of an antimetabolite. It is determined by measurement of the amount of antimetabolite needed to overcome the biological action of a given amount of essential metabolite. The inhibition index is then the quotient obtained by dividing the concentration of antimetabolite by the concentration of essential metabolite. The index thus represents the amount of antimetabolite required to antagonize the action of a unit weight of essential metabolite. The higher the index, the lower is the potency of the antimetabolite.

For nearly all antimetabolites, the index is greater than 1 and may be as large as 10,000 even in therapeutically useful drugs. This means that many molecules of antimetabolite are needed to displace one molecule of essential metabolite. It means that the affinity of the enzyme or receptor for the essential metabolite usually is much greater than it is for the antimetabolite, a situation one would expect if the active site of the enzyme is designed to make the best possible fit with the natural substrate. The unnatural analog, the antimetabolite, makes a less perfect fit and hence is bound less well. The inhibition index of sulfanilamide in hemolytic streptococci is 5000, and of pyrithiamine in mice is 12. However, the index is not always greater than 1. Thus, for carbon monoxide acting as an antimetabolite of oxygen for union with hemoglobin the index is 0.005. For yohimbine acting as an antimetabolite of serotonin in sections of carotid artery the index is 1.

The magnitude of the inhibition index varies with the organism and with the tissue under study. Thus, medmain, when it acts against serotonin in sheep arterial sections, shows an index of 0.4, but in rat uterus the index is 20 (29). These differences reflect the divergence in affinity of the antimetabolite for the serotonin receptors in the two kinds of muscle.

An inhibition index only has meaning if the antagonism between metabolite and antimetabolite is of the competitively reversible kind. If irreversible or even non-competitive antagonism exists, the index is meaningless. The amount of inhibition required is not proportional to the amount of essential metabolite present. In fact, the constancy of the inhibition index of any antimetabolite over a range of concentrations of its essential metabolite is the best criterion of competitive antagonism.

Natural occurrence of antimetabolites. Antimetabolites are not just the products of organic chemists and pharmacologists. A considerable number of them have been found in living organisms, and there is reason to believe that these organisms use them to control various aspects of their physiology. Several of the antibiotic agents formed by microorganisms presumably to aid in their struggle for existence with other microorganisms have been shown to be structural analogs of various essential metabolites, and to antagonize the biological actions of these metabolites. Cycloserine, also called oxamycin (see Figure 4) has been shown to be a structural analog of and a competitive antagonist to D-alanine (30 and 31). It harms bacteria by interference with the enzymic synthesis of their cell walls from D-alanine. Chloramphenicol has been shown to act as an antagonist to the structurally similar metabolite phenylalanine (32). The antibiotic agent from *Chromobacterium iodinum* is a structural analog of and a competitor to vitamin K (33) and the phytopathogenic toxin of *Pseudomonas tabaci* is an antimetabolite of methionine (34).

In physiological processes within one individual, similar phenomena of natural occurrence of antimetabolites can be found. For example, estrone and testosterone are both close structural analogs and competitors in the physiological determination of sexual characteristics. Serotonin and norepinephrine which occur in the same individual have some structural resemblance, and in some tissues such as smooth muscles of uterus, norepinephrine antagonizes the action of serotonin. In some other biological systems, however, they act in concert just as bonafide antimetabolites are known to do (see section on mechanism above). The interrelationship of serotonin and norepinephrine seems to be of much importance to the understanding of mental processes and will be dealt with at length in Chapter 9.

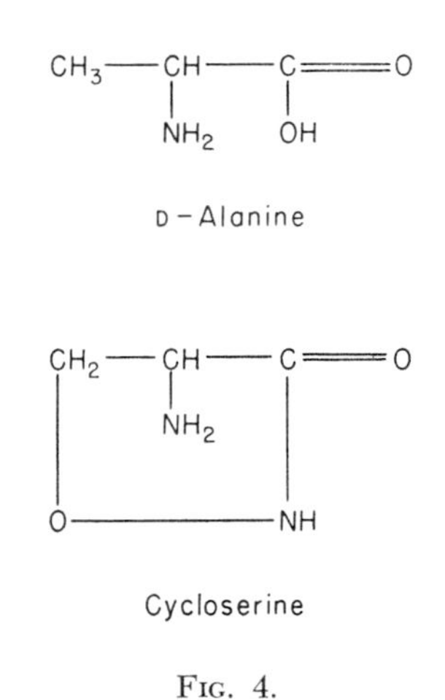

FIG. 4.

A considerable number of structural analogs of serotonin have been found in living things. Thus, a variety of alkaloids from plants have a close structural resemblance to this hormone. Many of these have been shown to act as antimetabolites of it. This has been the case with yohimbine, the ergot alkaloids, and the harmala alkaloids. Some of the naturally occurring analogs of serotonin also have been shown to act like the hormone rather than as antagonists to it on various animal tissues. This is the case with bufotenine. All of these cases will be described in more detail in Chapter 6.

The natural occurrence and physiological functioning of antimetabolites is a well-established phenomenon.

What constitutes structural analogy? Because structural analogy is one of the hallmarks of an antimetabolite we must ask: what is the criterion of analogy and when is one chemical structure sufficiently like another to justify the conclusion that the two are analogs? There are no precise answers to these questions. There have been numerous differences of opinion among investigators. All agree that the two chemical structures should look alike, and the more alike they look the better, but just how much they must resemble each other in order to pass the test of being a metabolite-antimetabolite pair finds no agreement. No one doubts that pyrithiamine is an analog of thiamine, or that sulfanilamide is an analog of *p*-aminobenzoic acid but from there on out the disagreements begin to increase.

Some of the following considerations may be helpful. Let us consider the structures shown in Figure 5. Sulfanilamide is clearly an

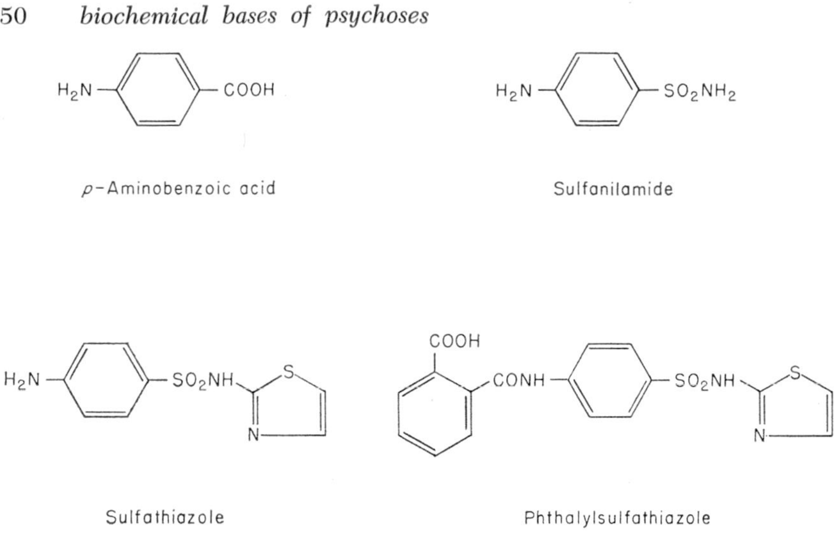

FIG. 5.

analog of *p*-aminobenzoic acid, and most investigators agree that sulfathiazole is also. This conclusion came easily because sulfathiazole was developed as a therapeutically more active congener of sulfanilamide, and since its pharmacological properties resembled those of the parent drug, most people were willing to agree to the idea that it was just the same sort of drug. If sulfanilamide had not come first, then there would have been more objection to the statement that sulfathiazole was analogous in structure to *p*-aminobenzoic acid. What are we then to say about phthalylsulfathiazole? If we compare the structures of *p*-aminobenzoic acid and of phthalylsulfathiazole we see that there are many differences. We know that the basic pharmacological action of the phthalyl compound is the same as that of sulfanilamide. Both drugs are antagonists of *p*-aminobenzoic acid. In the phthalyl compound desirable properties have been added to sulfanilamide by suitable chemical changes. The ionization constant has been changed by the addition of the thiazole ring so that maximal bacteriostatic activity will be exhibited at the pH of the animal body. With sulfanilamide, maximal bacteriostatic effect is not seen unless the pH is about 9. Furthermore, the phthalyl grouping has been added to change the distribution of the drug in the animal body. Sulfanilamide is taken up readily from the intestinal tract into the blood stream. Phthalylsulfathiazole is concentrated more in the intestinal tract so that it can be used against infections there which sulfanilamide or sulfathiazole affect only little.

If we knew only phthalylsulfathiazole, and not the other sulfa drugs, many investigators would consider most unjustifiable the idea that it was a structural analog of *p*-aminobenzoic acid and an antimetabolite of it. Even when the antagonism of the action of the drug by *p*-aminobenzoic acid had been demonstrated there would be many who would hesitate to say that it was an antimetabolite of *p*-aminobenzoic acid because the structural resemblance would be considered to be too remote. However, because of the accident of history that gave us sulfanilamide before the more complicated drugs, there is little hesitancy in accepting phthalylsulfathiazole as an antimetabolite of *p*-aminobenzoic acid.

Consider now the series of structures shown in Figure 6. These compounds all occur in nature, and to complicate matters, were not discovered in chronological sequence. They were observed merely as so many different substances with distinctive pharmacological properties. Only recently has their relationship been found. Harmine is clearly a structural analog of serotonin since it can be pictured as resulting from only slight structural alteration of the hormone. Yohimbine is a much more complex structure, but it can be seen to be just a more complex harmine to which two more rings have been

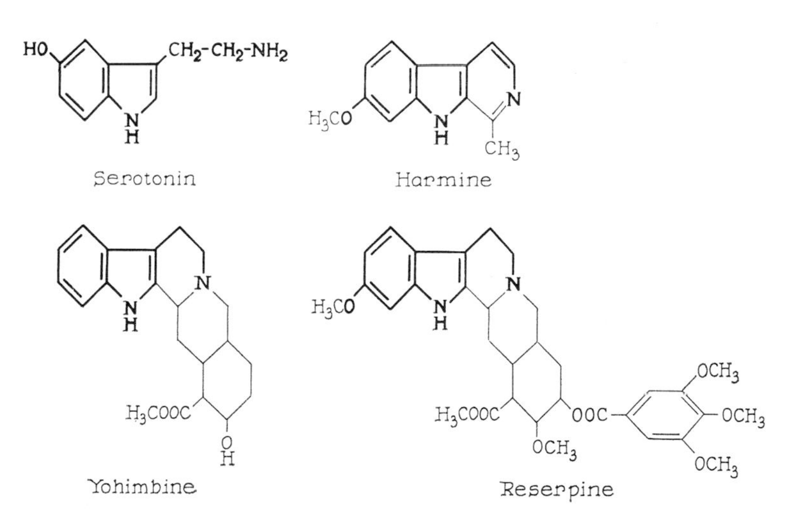

FIG. 6.

added and a methoxyl group removed. Reserpine is still more complicated but is clearly a derivative of yohimbine. Thus, although reserpine shows a rather remote structural resemblance to serotonin, we see that there are a series of compounds which tend to fill in the gaps between, and make a graded series of structural changes. Each of the compounds shown in Figure 6 has been shown to act as an antimetabolite of serotonin when tested on smooth muscles. When harmine and yohimbine were found so to act, several of the chemical structures intermediate between these two were synthesized, and these also were shown to be antagonists of serotonin in smooth muscles (35). The series of similarly acting compounds was made even more gradual than that shown in the figure. Some of the gaps were filled in.

The antagonism of each of the drugs up to and including yohimbine was shown to be of the competitively reversible kind. With reserpine, however, no competitive antagonism to serotonin can be found in smooth muscles such as the isolated uterus. Reserpine reduces the sensitivity of this muscle to serotonin (36) but the effect is not dramatic, and is not reversible. Reserpine does, however, show other properties expected of an antimetabolite of serotonin. It displaces the hormone from the tissues which contain it. There is thus a long series of drugs each member of which has some structural analogy to serotonin. The resemblance becomes more and more remote as the series is ascended, but even in the last member a functional relationship to the hormone is to be found.

The pharmacological properties of these drugs are not identical. Each structural change which is introduced modifies the character of the drug. Just as in the example discussed for the sulfonamide drugs, the progressive structural changes alter the details of pharmacological actions such as the distribution of each member in various organs of the body, the affinity for various tissues, the ease of destruction and excretion, and other properties which contribute to biological action. For example, we might attribute the fact that reserpine action is not readily reversible by serotonin to a non-reversible attachment of it to the serotonin receptor. Experiments with radioactive reserpine have in fact shown that it is firmly attached to brain tissue.

To form the right answer to questions about structural analogy requires both knowledge and judgement. If the resemblance is remote, the right answer is always in doubt. However, if the suspected antimetabolite induces in living things signs attributable to lack of the essential metabolite there is reason to suspect that the pharmacological action of the analog is related to the functioning of the metabolite. These signs may be biochemical as well as anatomical or behavioral.

Use of antimetabolites to learn about the causation of idiopathic diseases. If a normal animal is given an antimetabolite of thiamine such as pyrithiamine, it exhibits all the characteristic signs of thiamine deficiency. These signs are known from prior studies of animals fed diets deficient in this vitamin. However, if these signs of deficiency were not known, the induction of a train of pharmacological changes by pyrithiamine would tell us what the signs of thiamine deficiency are. All we would need to know is that the pyrithiamine induces the signs of thiamine deficiency. We would then be able to recognize opisthotonos and other characteristic neurological changes as signs of deficiency of thiamine.

Suppose that we have given a pharmaceutical agent to a normal animal and that it has called forth in that individual a group of signs and symptoms which we can recognize to be those of a disease for which the etiology had previously not been understood. If we knew that the compound which called these forth was an antimetabolite of let us say serotonin, then we would be led to suspect that a disturbance of the functioning of serotonin was responsible for the disease of unknown etiology. It was in this way that the relationship of serotonin to schizophrenia was first found. Chapter 6 will deal in detail with this discovery.

The danger in this use of antimetabolites is the assumption that all of the pharmacological signs called forth by the antimetabolite are an expression of interference with the action of the related essential metabolite. This is not necessarily true, because chemical compounds of all kinds have many effects on living things, and for a variety of reasons. Consequently, a particular pharmacological property of an antimetabolite may be the result of some action it has which is unrelated to its ability to call forth the signs of deficiency of a structurally similar essential metabolite. Fortunately, however, ways exist for gaining independent evidence as to whether or not the disease in question is actually concerned with the essential metabolite mentioned. Thus, for example, it must be possible to call forth the symptoms in question with a variety of antimetabolites of the one essential metabolite in question. It is unlikely that a group of compounds which differ in many ways among themselves but which have in common the ability to antagonize the action of a single metabolite would all have in addition some other capability to which the symptoms were really due. Furthermore, other ways exist which are independent of antimetabolite theory and which can be used to gain additional evidence about etiology of disease. What the use of antimetabolites gives is the first clue.

Use of antimetabolites in the treatment of disease. Many diseases are known which result from disturbances in the metabolism of one or another hormone. Thus Grave's disease is the expression of too much thyroxine, and the carcinoid syndrome is the result of an excess of serotonin in the peripheral tissues. In like fashion excessive production of acetylcholine, estrogens, histamine, epinephrine, insulin, and growth hormone has implicated each of them as causative in some disease.

Because an antimetabolite of a hormone is able to overcome the biological action of that hormone the idea of treating such diseases with such antimetabolites has arisen. It should be possible to negate the effects of the hormone which is in excess by administration of a suitable antimetabolite of it. This idea was first put forward in 1946 (37 and 38), and illustrated with a demonstration in laboratory animals with antimetabolites of thyroxine. The clinical successes with antimetabolites of histamine, acetylcholine, and serotonin have shown that the basic concept is sound. However, only in the case of antimetabolites of serotonin has the work been started with the idea of making such an antimetabolite. With the antagonists of acetylcholine, for example, and of histamine, the drugs of clinical usefulness were first found by chance, and only later were pointed out to be antimetabolites.

Designing of antimetabolites. If the chemical structure of an essential metabolite is known it is now possible to foretell the structures of antimetabolites of it. In this way it is possible to predict the chemical structures of the first members of new series of drugs. This first member of the series then can be modified in the ways familiar to classical pharmacology in order to improve the potency or to give additional desirable properties.

General rules which tell the kinds of structural alterations most likely to succeed in the changing of an essential metabolite into a potent antimetabolite can be found in either one of the references (1) and (39). These include the exchange of a carboxyl group in the metabolite for a sulfonamide or phenyl ketone group, or other acidic groups, the replacement of a C atom in a ring system by a N or O or S atom, the replacement of H atoms by alkyl groups or halogen atoms, and the replacement of hydroxyl groups by amino groups or hydrogen atoms.

Once such a change has been made, and an antimetabolite has been found to result, it is usually necessary to make additional modifications to enhance the potency. A variety of useful rules are available to guide these operations also. There are, for example, ways of rendering a compound firmly attachable to tissues, as by introduction of benzyl groups. There are ways of diminishing the rate of destruction by enzymes which the antimetabolite will encounter in the animal body. An example of this is the conversion of a primary amino group to a tertiary amine so that monoamine oxidase will fail to destroy the drug. Some of these additions may make the difference between a useful therapeutic agent and a laboratory curiosity. They should not be ignored. For the present discussion, however, the important point to bear in mind is that the structures of antimetabolites can be predicted with fair accuracy as can also many of their pharmacological properties. These predictions arise from a knowledge of the chemistry and physiology of the related essential metabolite.

Antagonistic compounds which are not antimetabolites. All chemical compounds which interfere with the action of a given essential metabolite are not antimetabolites of it. Sometimes a chemical compound merely reacts chemically with an essential metabolite and destroys it. Such is the case with certain fatty peroxides, which destroy vitamin A *in vivo* and can thus induce deficiency of this vitamin when given to an animal. There are also chemical compounds which react with and destroy the active centers of certain enzymes. These frequently show considerable specificity. Examples of this are the so-called nerve gases such as diisopropylfluorophosphate which may select esterases from among all the other enzymes, and render only those inactive. Such compounds are not antimetabolites even though they are specific poisons for certain kinds of enzymes.

There are also compounds such as chlorpromazine which may be related structurally in a vague sort of way to some essential metabolite, as chlorpromazine is to histamine, but which interfere with the activity not only of histamine, but also of serotonin and epinephrine and acetylcholine. Although some slight structural relationship might be pictured between chlorpromazine and serotonin, there is clearly none between it and acetylcholine. For such reasons the mere demonstration of ability of a pharmacological agent to interfere with the action of an essential metabolite does not make that agent an antimetabolite. Antimetabolites are a special kind of blocking agent, but they are not the only kind.

chapter 4

Serotonin

Serotonin was so named because it was first isolated from blood serum. It had been recognized there because it gave increased tone to blood vessels through which the serum passed; that is, it constricted these vessels. Its full chemical name is 3-(β-aminoethyl)-5-hydroxyindole or 3-(5-hydroxyindolyl)-ethylamine. Because it is a derivative of tryptamine, it is frequently called 5-hydroxytryptamine in a effort to give it a name shorter than its full chemical one, but yet of a more chemical sound than serotonin. It was also called enteramine before it was known that that substance was identical with serotonin. The chemical structure is shown in Figure 1 which also gives the numbering system for the atoms.

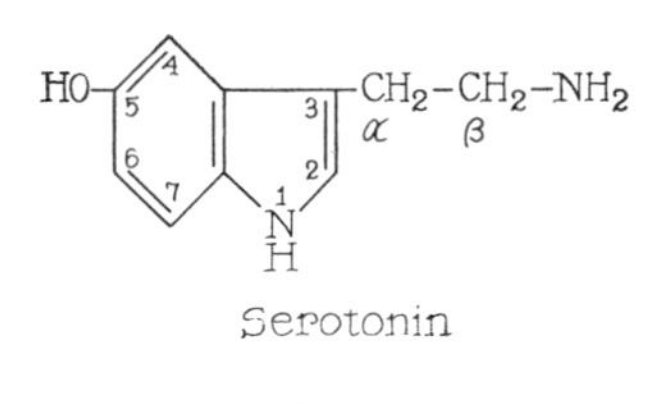

FIG. 1.

Discovery. Serotonin was first isolated in pure condition in 1949 by Rapport, Green, and Page (40). Its chemical structure was deduced that same year by Rapport (41), but it was not until late in 1951 that the structure was confirmed by chemical synthesis (42). It had been known for a long time that blood serum, in contrast to blood plasma, contains a vasoconstrictor which will bring about a rise in blood pressure when the serum is perfused into a living animal. Page and his collaborators wished to isolate this vasoconstrictor as an adjunct to their work on angiotonin in relation to high blood pressure (essential hypertension). They chose as test object for the assay the excised ear of a rabbit. When a saline solution is perfused through the vascular tree of such an ear, it flows through at a determinable rate. If some vasoconstrictor is added to the solution the blood vessels constrict, and the fluid flows through more slowly. Many investigators had had trouble with this assay, and Page undertook to use it partly to show that it was practicable.

Through the aid of this test to guide the chemical separations, a crystalline active substance was isolated from beef blood serum. The empirical formula of this compound was $C_{14}H_{23}O_7N_5S$. The problem of its chemical constitution was greatly simplified when Rapport showed that the crystals were in fact a salt of the active agent with creatinine sulfate. This reduced the unknown part of the molecule to $C_{10}H_{12}ON_2$. Because of the rather unusual absorption spectrum of the substance, and because it gave a positive color test with Ehrlich's reagent for indoles, Rapport postulated the structure to be that given above. It was a correct deduction, as was proved by total synthesis chemically. The availability of enough material, which was made possible by these syntheses, was of great importance in the study of the biological significance of serotonin. If it had been necessary to use only material isolated from animal tissues the great scarcity of pure substance would have prevented most of the important discoveries about the biological importance of serotonin.

In 1940 Erspamer (43) had become interested in the substance responsible for the characteristic staining reactions of certain cells of the gastrointestinal mucosa. These are the argentaffin cells, so named because of the affinity they show towards silver ions. They readily stain black with such ions. These are also called enterochromaffin cells. Erspamer attempted to isolate the substance responsible for the staining reactions of these cells. He also showed that concentrates of the material, obtained by extraction of the mucosa with acetone had pharmacological activity in that they caused smooth muscles, especially those of the uterus of a rat in estrus, to contract. By such pharmacological tests he could distinguish the substance as being different from epinephrine. From the color tests which his preparations gave he postulated that the active agent might be an indole. When synthetic serotonin became available in 1952, Asero and Erspamer (44) quickly showed that it was identical with the mucosal substance, which Erspamer had earlier named enteramine. Erspamer also succeeded in isolating the pure enteramine as a picrate from the salivary glands of the octopus, where it occurs in large amounts.

The discovery of serotonin had been missed several times in the past. One interesting example of this was some work done on carcinoid tumors of the intestinal tract. In 1937 extracts of such a human carcinoid had been made, and tested for ability to cause contraction of smooth muscles. Although the extract showed this ability, it was erroneously attributed to epinephrine. The active substance of the extract is now known to be serotonin. Others too (45) had mistaken serotonin for epinephrine, largely through the notion (now discredited) that the ergot alkaloids were specific antagonists of epinephrine. Actually they have proved to be directed against both serotonin and epinephrine.

Chemistry. Serotonin is chemically a rather reactive compound. It is consequently somewhat unstable. It is an indole and therefore subject to ready reaction with aldehydes at the 2-position. The indole ring system is likewise attacked by strong acids, by light and by oxygen. Because it is in addition an hydroxyindole, and thus a substituted *p*-aminophenol it has an extra susceptibility to oxidation. Not only is it a phenol; it is a primary aliphatic amine. It is thus amphoteric, and behaves as both base and acid. The phenolic group is however only very weakly acidic, so that only above pH 10 does this group begin to form salts and to ionize. The undissociated free base exists at pH 10. At physiological pH (for example, 7.4) the amino group is completely present as an ionized salt.

The indole portion allows serotonin to be detected by those reagents which give colors with indoles. Thus *p*-dimethylaminobenzaldehyde plus concentrated hydrochloric acid (Ehrlich's reagent) generates a blue color. The aliphatic amino group is responsible for the formation of a blue color with ninhydrin. The sensitivity of this color test can be greatly increased in the presence of acetic acid. Another useful color reaction is carried out by treatment with nitrous acid, mineral acid, and α-nitroso-β-naphthol, which gives a red color not given by unhydroxylated indoles (46).

The oxidation of serotonin can take place at several points in the molecule. Thus, the primary amino group may be oxidized to an aldehyde and eventually to an acid. This however is an oxidation which is found more frequently in enzyme-catalyzed reactions than with the usual chemical oxidants. Atmospheric oxygen as well as other oxidizing agents attack the double bond between positions 2 and 3 of the indole ring. The first point of attack in this reaction seems to be the N atom in the indole ring to form an N-oxide, from which the oxygen atom then migrates to form a cyclic oxide between positions 2 and 3. This unstable structure then cleaves, thus destroying the pyrrole part of the indole ring, and giving a substituted N-formyl aniline. The indole ring can be protected from this kind of oxidative attack by substitution of an alkyl group on the indole nitrogen at position 1, thus preventing the oxide formation. The benzene portion of the indole ring is also subject to oxidation because of the occurrence of the hydroxyl group there. Thus, there is some evidence for the formation of 5, 6-dihydroxyindoles both *in vitro* and *in vivo*. The unstable nature of this product has made complete elucidation of its structure impractical.

The chemical synthesis of serotonin has been accomplished in a variety of ways. The first synthesis started with 5-benzyloxyindole, which was converted to benzyloxygramine, which was then converted to 3-(cyanomethyl)-5-benzyloxyindole. This compound was reduced to 3-(β-aminoethyl)-5-benzyloxyindole, and the benzyl ether group was finally removed by hydrogenation (42). A particularly useful method starts with 5-benzyloxyindole which is condensed with oxalylchloride to give the acid chloride of 5-benzyloxyindole-3-α-ketoacetic acid. This was converted to the amide by reaction with ammonia, then both amide and keto groups were reduced with lithium aluminum hydride. Removal of the benzyl ether by hydrogenation then gave serotonin (47).

Serotonin usually comes on the market as a salt with creatinine sulfate. This is the salt which crystallizes most readily. It is soluble in water to give an acidic solution. The free base of serotonin is also quite soluble in water, and cannot be extracted readily from aqueous solution into organic solvents such as ether or benzene or chloroform. The free base is extractable, although not completely so, by *n*-butanol from aqueous solution at pH 10. Because of the instability of this hormone, solutions of it must be made fresh daily and stored away from sunlight and elevated temperatures. Because of its phenolic character it tends to be much more unstable as the pH is raised above 7 to 8.

Quantitative measurement in tissues. Three kinds of analytical methods are available for the measurement of the amount of serotonin in extracts of tissues. There are physical (spectrofluorometric) methods, chemical (colorimetric) methods, and pharmacological ones. Before an analysis is performed the fresh tissue must be extracted in such a way as to get all of the serotonin, and to prevent destruction of it by the enzymes such as monoamine oxidase which are liberated when cells are disrupted.

Two methods of making extracts are in common use. One is to grind the fresh tissue in cold acetone (3 volumes), filter, and remove the acetone from the filtrate by evaporation under reduced pressure. The other way is to grind the fresh tissue in 10 volumes of cold 0.2 N hydrochloric acid, or in a cold aqueous solution of some other inhibitor of serotonin-destroying enzymes. Iproniazid (0.01 molar) which inhibits monoamine oxidase is frequently used. Fractionation of the extract must then be carried out to remove the serotonin from interfering substances. This is essential if the physical or chemical methods are to be used, but may not be required for the pharmacological assays. The purification of the extract is sometimes done by chromatography but more usually by solvent partition. If either method of fractionation (solvent partition or chromatography) is used, a serious problem of partial destruction of serotonin during the manipulations must be solved. Serotonin in very dilute solution is readily destroyed by exposure to air or to alkali.

The amounts of serotonin necessary for each of the three kinds of analytical method are shown in Table 1. These values have been taken from the author's own experiences. The colorimetric method requires the most, and is so insensitive that it cannot be used for analysis of most tissues. The spectrofluorometric method needs only about one tenth of the amount required by the colorimetric process, but it is still rather insensitive when one remembers the concentration of serotonin in all but the richest sources. The pharmacological methods are the only ones which are sensitive enough to use for assay of many tissues. They have been avoided by many investigators in the mistaken belief that they are not as specific as are the physical or chemical methods. Actually they can be quite specific, especially if the responses

TABLE 1. *Quantities of serotonin needed for precise measurement by various analytical methods. (The quantities shown are those needed for ordinary manipulations. If special apparatus and technique adapted for small volumes are employed, the amounts required can be reduced by as much as tenfold)*

Method	Total Serotonin Required, μg
Colorimetric (nitrosonaphthol)	10
Spectrofluorometric	0.5–2.0
Pharmacological (rat uterus)	0.05–0.1
Pharmacological (rat stomach)	0.001–0.002
Pharmacological (clam heart)	0.01–0.1

are proved by showing that an antimetabolite of serotonin abolishes them, whereas antimetabolites of acetylcholine do not. The pharmacological methods avoid much of the loss of serotonin which frequently occurs during the fractionation procedures essential in the other methods. It must be emphasized that each of the kinds of method has its place in the analysis of tissues. When it is possible to confirm the findings with one method by use of a second one the results are most meaningful. This is said with full knowledge of the somewhat extravagant claims urged by proponents of this or that type of measurement. They all have limitations.

The spectrofluorometric method takes advantage of the fact that, when serotonin-containing solutions are illuminated with ultraviolet light of 2950 Å, a fluorescence is produced for which the maximal intensity of emission is 3320 Å (48). Specificity is achieved by proper selection of the wavelength of light for activation and of the emitted fluorescent light to be measured. This method is very rapid. It does, however, require purification of the tissue extract. This is accomplished by adjustment of the extract to pH 10, extraction of the unionized serotonin into butanol, and re-extraction of the serotonin into water by addition of acid and heptane. Many interfering substances are thus eliminated. The analysis requires use of a highly specialized and expensive spectrofluorophotometer, but it is the most sensitive of the physical and chemical methods.

The colorimetric method takes advantage of the fact that serotonin yields a red color when it is treated in aqueous solution with nitrous and sulfuric acids, followed by α-nitroso-β-naphthol. This color can be extracted and determined in conventional apparatus for colorimetry (48) and the method therefore does not require expensive special instruments. The specificity depends on the fact that most compounds do not give the red color with the reagents, and most which do can be eliminated by a solvent fractionation before the color is developed. The same solvent fractionation described for the spectrofluorometric method is used.

Three pharmacological methods for quantitative assay are now in common use, the rat stomach method of Vane (49), the rat uterus method of Erspamer (50, 51) as modified by Gaddum and Hameed (52), and by Woolley (19), and the clam heart method of Erspamer and Ghiretti (53) as modified by Welsh (54). Each depends on the fact that the isolated tissue mentioned contracts when small amounts of serotonin are added to the bath in which it is suspended. The amount of the contraction can be measured quantitatively and compared to that given by graded amounts of a tissue extract. Because acetylcholine also may cause a contraction if it is present in relatively large amounts, an antagonist of acetylcholine such as atropine is usually added to all solutions to avoid interference. The rat stomach method is the one which will measure the smallest amounts of serotonin (see Table 1).

In all of the pharmacological methods, the importance of the concentration of calcium ions in the saline solutions used has not been sufficiently emphasized. It is particularly true of the rat uterus method (19), but also applies to the rat stomach assay. Calcium ions, if they are present in large enough concentration, will cause contraction of the tissues. The concentration required is great enough (0.2 mg per ml) that it is not a usual source of interference in the estimation of serotonin in extracts of tissues. Rather it is that the concentration of this ion in the saline solution used in the bath must be kept low enough to avoid spontaneous contractions. For rat uterus this concentration is 20 mg of $CaCl_2$ per liter.

In the experience of this author the rat stomach method is the best one to use if one is dealing with tissues of very low serotonin content. This is true even where there is enough serotonin to use the rat uterus or clam heart. A decided advantage of a properly chosen pharmacological method is that it can be used on an aqueous extract of tissue without purification of the serotonin from the extract. This advantage looms very large when the concentration of serotonin is very small, because it is then that the loss of the hormone from contact with air becomes a major problem. If extractions with solvents or evaporations under reduced pressure are applied to such dilute solutions, the losses can be as much as 90 per cent. For tissues very rich in serotonin, the colorimetric method or the spectrofluorometric one have proved satisfactory. They are especially useful, however, in enzyme experiments for determination of the amounts of serotonin produced or destroyed. They have also been useful in the assay of tissues from animals previously treated with antimetabolites of serotonin which interfere with the biological methods. The rat uterus method has proved most useful in the measurement of the effects of antimetabolites of serotonin. The clam heart method has been useful for demonstration of serotonin-like actions of analogs of the hormone, but has not proved to have sufficient precision for quantitative analysis of tissue for serotonin content. This fact has not been recognized by some investigators who use this method for assay of tissue extracts, but it can readily be appreciated from examination of a dose-response curve. The slope of such a curve is low enough that an appreciable change in concentration of serotonin can be seen to cause only an insignificant change in the response of the heart.

Occurrence in living things. Serotonin has been found in many kinds of animals, both vertebrates and invertebrates. It has also been found in a few plants, notably the fruit of the banana (55) and pineapple (56) and the spines of the leaves of cowhage. However, many plants seem not to contain it (57). In the animal kingdom it has been found in sea anemones, the venom of wasps and scorpions, the skins of amphibians, the salivary glands of the octopus, the intestinal mucosa of mice, rabbits, dogs, and human beings, and in the brains of various mammals, including man. This is only a partial list. The studies of Erspamer in particular (58, 59) have shown the variety of living things in which it is found.

Within an individual mammal (or invertebrate for that matter) serotonin is not found in all tissues. The largest concentration is in the mucosa of the gastrointestinal tract, and consequently this organ contains the largest store of it in the body. In fact, it is made there in the argentaffin (enterochromaffin) cells. The concentration of serotonin is also high in the spleen, in the platelets of the blood, and in certain parts of the brain. Thus the pineal glands of humans have been found to contain as much as 22 gamma per gram wet weight (60). The brain stem is, however, the place in the central nervous system which contains most of the sum total. The concentration may be smaller than in the pineal gland, but the amount of tissue is larger. The cortex also contains some. The cerebrospinal fluid has none, except in some diseased conditions (61).

Serotonin was first detected in nerve tissue by Florey and Florey (62), who found it in the stellate ganglia of clams. It was first detected in brains of mammals by Twarog and Page (63) and by Amin, Crawford, and Gaddum (64). The distribution in the brain of a dog is shown by the data in Table 2, which has been reprinted from a paper by Amin et al. (65). Some species of mammals contain higher concentrations than those shown for the dog (409, 410).

The occurrence of serotonin in a given structure of the body does not necessarily mean that it has been formed there, even though the amount present may be large. Thus, the platelets of the blood may contain, per mg of tissue, almost as much as intestinal mucosa, but all of the evidence points to the fact that platelets do not synthesize serotonin as the mucosa does. The platelets merely pick up the serotonin with which they come into contact. They have a fascinating ability to concentrate it inside themselves against a large concentration gradient.

However, the brain does synthesize the hormone. The enzymes which form it, such as the 5-hydroxytryptophan decarboxylase, are found in most of those parts of the brain which contain appreciable amounts of serotonin.

TABLE 2. *Serotonin content of parts of the central nervous system of the dog*

Tissue	Serotonin, μg per kg
Telencephalon	
Cerebrum: White matter	0
Grey matter	29
Area 4 (motor)	21
Area 17 (visual)	0
Areas 51 (olfactory) and 28	16
Corpus callosum	0
Caudate nucleus	0
Olfactory bulb	48
Hippocampus	45
Diencephalon	
Thalamus: Whole	18
Medial	67
Lateral	0 ?
Hypothalamus: Whole	280
Anterior	220
Posterior	225
Mesencephalon	
Whole	205
Peduncles	0 ?
Colliculi	130
The remainder	330
Mid-brain without peduncles, colliculi, or aqueduct	190
Central grey matter	280
Cerebellum	0
Medulla oblongata	
Whole	33
Floor of 4th ventricle	98
The rest of the medulla	71
Area postrema	215
The rest of the floor	125

It is important to note that the serotonin carried in the blood is pharmacologically inactive. It will not cause smooth muscles to contract or nerves to respond because it is sequestered inside the platelets. When wounding takes place, and the blood-clotting mechanism is set in motion, the first step is the breakdown of the platelets. The serotonin inside them thus is released so that it can exert a pharmacological action. This is the reason why plasma is not a vasoconstrictor, although serum is.

Natural occurrence of derivatives of serotonin; bufotenine and melatonin. Many structural analogs of serotonin have been found in living things, usually in plants. Some of these such as bufotenine are only slightly different from serotonin, but an almost continuous series exists, each succeeding member of which differs more and more in structure from the hormone. Most of these analogs will be discussed in Chapter 6, because these are the hallucinogenic plant alkaloids. Two very close structural relatives of serotonin will be mentioned now, however, because they resemble the hormone so closely. These are bufotenine and melatonin, the structures of which are shown in Figure 2.

Bufotenine was first discovered in the skin of toads long before serotonin was known. More recently it has been isolated from a higher fungus *Amanita mappa* (66), from the cahobe beans of the Caribbean coast (67), and from human urine (68). All investigators are not in agreement about its occurrence in normal urine, and some think that only the monomethylserotonin, not the dimethyl derivative, occurs there (69). An enzyme system capable of forming bufotenine from serotonin has recently been found in mammalian tissues, so that it would not be surprising to find bufotenine in mammals. Bufotenine has many pharmacological properties similar to those of serotonin. Thus, it causes various smooth muscles to contract. It does, however, show both qualitative and quantitative differences. In general, bufotenine affects nerves more than serotonin does.

Melatonin was first isolated from the pineal gland of the brain in 1958 by Lerner and his collaborators (70), and was shown to be the

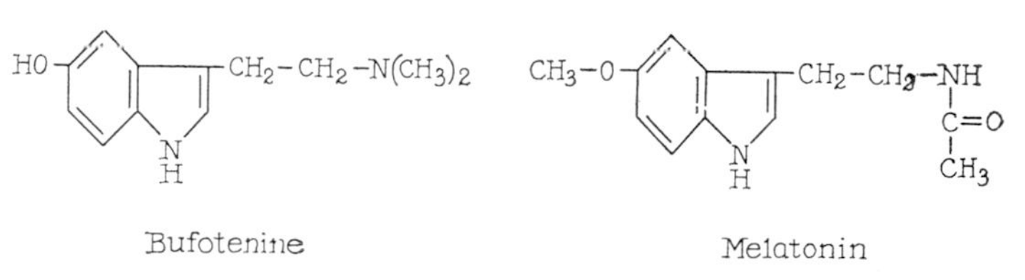

FIG. 2.

methyl ether of N-acetylserotonin in 1959 (71). It has been detected in peripheral nerves (72) as well as in the pineal, but not in other tissues. Unlike serotonin, melatonin does not cause smooth muscles to contract. Melatonin was discovered because of its great potency in antagonizing the action of the melanophore-stimulating hormone. Pieces of frog skin are caused to darken when this hormone is applied to them, and this darkening is prevented by melatonin. Serotonin also is active in this test, but is 5000 times less potent than melatonin.

Some special function for melatonin in the nervous system is a current and enticing speculation. Its exclusive occurrence in nerve tissue and its relationship to serotonin have been the principal reasons. There is also the fact that from the time of Descartes to the present, postulates have been advanced that the pineal body has some control over animal behavior and emotions. Although this notion has been almost totally unsupported by experimental evidence, it persists and gives added attraction to any special component of the pineal body. Up to the present time there has been no experimental demonstration that melatonin actually does have a specialized function in nerves, but it has been known for such a short time.

It is possible, although not proved, that melatonin is a derivative of serotonin modified in such a way as to make it capable of ready passage into nerve cells. In contrast to serotonin, it is a lipid-soluble substance not open to attack by several enzymes which destroy serotonin. Once inside the cells, and past the permeability barrier, it could then be converted enzymically back to serotonin or its methyl ether, which might be the actual active agents. The importance of such properties can be appreciated better after discussion of the blood-brain barrier to the passage of serotonin.

Formation. The biochemical formation of serotonin begins with the amino acid tryptophan, as Udenfriend and his collaborators have shown (73). Tryptophan is oxidized (hydroxylated) by an enzyme system which uses as one of its coenzymes TPN (triphosphopyridine nucleotide). The product is 5-hydroxytryptophan. This intermediate is then attacked by the enzyme 5-hydroxytryptophan decarboxylase, which forms serotonin and carbon dioxide. Like other decarboxylases which attack amino acids this one employs pyridoxal phosphate as coenzyme. Serotonin does not come from the hydroxylation of tryptamine.

The hydroxylating enzyme which forms hydroxytryptophan has not been purified much. It is a rather unstable system, and is found in the particulate (insoluble) matter when cells are disrupted. This makes purification difficult. The decarboxylase has, however, been considerably purified. A controversy about this enzyme arose because some said that it was a specific enzyme which attacked only 5-hydroxytryptophan. Others said it was the same as the dopa decarboxylase which forms dihydroxyphenylethylamine (dopamine) and hence norepinephrine from dopa. It has finally been agreed that the same enzyme is probably responsible for both of these decarboxylations (74).

5-Hydroxytryptophan is generally not found in tissues. Only in the case of one atypical patient suffering from a carcinoid tumor has this amino acid been identified in mammalian tissues. Whatever 5-hydroxytryptophan is formed under normal conditions apparently is immediately attacked by the decarboxylase and converted to serotonin. The decarboxylase is found in many organs of a mammal. If 5-hydroxytryptophan is injected into the animal this enzyme reacts with it and converts it to serotonin. The result is to increase the serotonin content of many of the tissues (75). When serotonin itself is injected, its life span is short because it is rather rapidly destroyed by the enzymes adapted for this purpose. On the other hand, when 5-hydroxytryptophan is injected it passes into the cells of many organs and is there converted into serotonin at a slow rate and in a place where it is not so accessible to the destroying enzymes. The net result is to get serotonin into tissues (for example, the brain) where it ordinarily does not go from the blood, and to prolong the pharmacological effects of the hormone. This will be an important point in some of the later chapters. Thus, the serotonin content of the brain can be greatly increased by injection of 5-hydroxytryptophan peripherally (76 and 77), but not by similar injection of serotonin (78).

The decarboxylating enzyme is not distributed equally through all parts of the brain. In general, the enzyme is found in those structures which contain the serotonin.

Storage and sequestration. Much of the serotonin in animal tissues is kept away from the actual structures which respond to it. This fact can be well illustrated by consideration of the situation in blood. Almost all of the serotonin there is found in the platelets. Only a very small amount is in solution in the plasma. In fact, it can be debated whether under normal circumstances there is any serotonin in the plasma.

The serotonin inside the platelets is pharmacologically inactive. If undamaged platelets (which contain relatively large amounts of serotonin) are applied to a smooth muscle no contraction takes place. The serotonin is contained within the platelets, but before it can cause a muscle to contract it must be set free into solution. This can be done readily merely by dilution of the platelet suspension with distilled water. The osmotic shock ruptures the membrane of the platelets and allows the serotonin within to diffuse out.

One may picture the serotonin inside the platelets as being sequestered and thus removed from the sphere of biological action. It is not necessary to think of it as being chemically bound inside of these cells. This is said despite the fact that there has been much discussion about bound serotonin in tissues. For example, Born et al. (79) have found that inside platelets there is just the right amount of adenosinetriphosphate to form a salt with the serotonin there. Because such a salt ionizes readily in aqueous solution the serotonin is still pharmacologically active just as it is in other salts such as the one with creatinine sulfate. The salts also are diffusible through cellophane membranes. Probably the serotonin as it exists inside the platelet is biologically active regardless of whether it exists as a salt with adenosinetriphosphate. It is simply that it cannot get out until the membrane of the platelet is ruptured. Once this has taken place, the serotonin ion which now comes out is capable of reaching and affecting other cells. It is as if the serotonin in the blood is being carried around in little impervious bags. While it is inside the bags it exerts no biological action, but when it is liberated by disruption of the bags it is free to do so.

In other tissues serotonin also can be found sequestered in little particles. Thus, for example, Blaschko (80) has demonstrated that small particles liberated by disruption of adrenal cells, and separated by differential centrifugation, contain serotonin. The particles themselves exert no serotonin effects but immediately after they are ruptured the serotonin effect is measurable. Similarly, he has shown that epinephrine and norepinephrine are contained in other particles in the cells where they are held biologically inert (81).

Blood platelets show a remarkable ability to concentrate serotonin. When these particles are suspended in blood serum to which serotonin is added they readily pick up the hormone and store it inside themselves. Because the concentration of serotonin inside the platelets is very much greater than that outside it is plain that a powerful pumping mechanism for this purpose is present. It has been demonstrated, as one might expect, that energy in the form of adenosinetriphosphate is needed to operate this pump (79). It has also been demonstrated that certain metallic ions are required for its operation (82). To the present author it seems quite probable that the pumping mechanism is simply the calcium transport system but without the return mechanism which, in muscle cells, carries the calcium back out of the cell.

This calcium transport system seems to constitute the fundamental biochemical mechanism of action of serotonin which will be described in the last part of this chapter.

Enzymic destruction and metabolic transformations. Once a charge of serotonin has been sent to a susceptible tissue, and the tissue has responded, it is most important that the serotonin then be destroyed, otherwise it would continue to cause the tissue to respond. If an additional response is needed, more serotonin is sent out. Speed in disposing of the hormone is important in the actions of nerves and muscles, and for this reason the body probably finds it inadequate to depend on blood or other fluids to carry the hormone away. This would be too slow.

The body has several enzyme systems for destruction of serotonin. These are monoamine oxidase which oxidizes the primary amino group, a system (probably phenolsulfatase) which converts the phenolic group into a sulfate ester, a methylating system which converts the phenolic group into a methyl ether (although this does not completely inactivate the hormone pharmacologically) and probably an oxidase which adds one more hydroxyl group to the 6 position of the indole ring. In addition, there is some reason to believe that there is also an oxidase system which cleaves the indole ring between positions 2 and 3.

The most-studied enzymic destruction is that involving monoamine oxidase. In dogs this one accounts for approximately half of a test dose of injected serotonin. The first product formed from serotonin by action of this enzyme is probably 5-hydroxyindole acetaldehyde. This unstable aldehyde is then converted to 5-hydroxyindoleacetic acid by a further oxidation not catalyzed by this same enzyme. The 5-hydroxyindoleacetic acid which is found in the urine of non-herbivorous mammals arises in this way. In herbivores, however, this compound is not excreted, even after injection of large amounts of serotonin. In other mammals the injection or ingestion of serotonin results in a sharp increase in the urinary excretion of 5-hydroxyindoleacetic acid, although not enough to account for all of the administered serotonin (83, 84, 85).

The determination of urinary excretion of 5-hydroxyindoleacetic acid has been much used to study the probable amounts of serotonin which are being formed within the body. The quantitative measurement of it is relatively easy since it employs the same reagents as are used in the colorimetric measurement of serotonin (85). An estimate can thus be made as to whether unusually large amounts of serotonin are being formed inside a given individual, or are being taken in with the food. Thus, normal humans excrete 2 to 5 mg of this acid in 24 hours. If large quantities of bananas are eaten (which contain much serotonin) this excretion may be increased tenfold. If an individual develops the carcinoid syndrome, a cancer of the argentaffin cells of the intestinal mucosa (the cells responsible for synthesis of most of the serotonin in the body) the excretion of 5-hydroxyindoleacetic acid usually increases to about 25 mg per day, and may go as high as 400 mg per day.

Serotonin was first found to be a substrate for monoamine oxidase by Blaschko and Hellman (86). Prior to this work it had been widely held that this enzyme was present in tissues primarily to destroy epinephrine. Blaschko and Hellman showed that serotonin was a much better substrate for the enzyme. Both epinephrine and norepinephrine, especially the latter, are attacked by the enzyme with consequent loss of pharmacological activity. The enzymic activity occurs in many tissues of the body. Liver, intestine, lung, serum, smooth muscle, and brain each contain it. Some doubt exists as to whether the enzyme from all tissues is the same. The bulk of the evidence suggests that it is not. In most organs the enzyme is not in solution in the cytoplasm, but is found in the mitochondria when cells are broken and fractionated by centrifugation. An occasional tissue is found in which the enzyme is soluble (87). Our own experience with the so-called soluble monoamine oxidase of guinea pig liver has been disappointing.

The soluble monoamine oxidase of blood serum recently has been shown to be a different type of oxidase from that generally called monoamine oxidase. It has been identified with a blue, copper-containing protein previously known in blood plasma and called ceruloplasmin (270). Ceruloplasmin oxidizes serotonin by attack of the benzenoid part of the indole ring. Other phenolic compounds such as epinephrine and norepinephrine also can be oxidized by it.

The fact that monoamine oxidase of several tissues is inhibited by various indole derivatives is not without interest. If this enzyme were designed to combine with indolic compounds such as serotonin, then its enzymic center should be shaped to accommodate indoles, and it may be for such a reason that indoleacetic acid and LSD inhibit it. It must be remembered, however, that preparations of monoamine oxidase oxidize a variety of amines, although usually at a slower rate than is shown with serotonin.

The other ways in which serotonin is destroyed enzymically have not yet been studied in great detail. An enzyme system in liver has been demonstrated which attaches a glucuronic acid residue to the phenolic hydroxyl of the hormone, and this glucuronide is excreted in the urine. An enzyme system which attaches a sulfate as an ester at the phenolic group also has been detected (104). Methylation has been found to take place at two different points in the molecule, either at the hydroxyl group, or at the amino group (68). The products of each of these reactions have been isolated and identified. In addition, there is some evidence to suggest that tissues can oxidize serotonin to a 5,6-dihydroxy compound, and can cleave the indole ring between positions 2 and 3. The products of these changes have not been extensively characterized. The evidence for 6-hydroxylation is perhaps best with melatonin (88). The best known case for cleavage of the indole ring between positions 2 and 3 is the formation of kynurenine from tryptophan. There is some evidence that an analogous cleavage of serotonin and of indoleacetic acid takes place in living organisms (105).

Although some of the products of these various degradations are biologically inactive, this is not true for all of them. The methylated products, whether O-methyl or N-methyl still have activity in some test systems, and may even have the ability to affect some tissues more powerfully than does serotonin. Melatonin, the O-methyl-N-acetylserotonin is able to antagonize the action of the melanophore-stimulating hormone in vastly smaller concentration than is serotonin. Bufotenine, the N,N-dimethylserotonin, is able to inhibit nerve transmission in the Janiculate nucleus, although serotonin is not able to do so. Bufotenine can induce psychotic episodes in man which are not caused by serotonin. For such reasons one should probably regard some of these metabolic transformation products not as enzymic inactivation products, but as steps in conversion of the hormone into forms which can act on specialized tissues.

Pharmacological properties. The most prominent pharmacological property of serotonin is that it causes many kinds of smooth muscle to contract. A kymographic tracing of such a contraction as seen with the isolated rat uterus is shown in Figure 3. Most striated muscles, in contrast to smooth muscles, do not contract when serotonin is applied to them. The susceptible smooth muscles are found in many organs such as uterus, stomach, intestine (especially ileum and cecum), nictitating membrane of the eye, blood vessels, and bladder.

Many of the effects which follow the injection of serotonin into living animals are the result of contractions of various smooth muscles. Intravenous injection of it into a dog results in a rise in blood pressure. In some individuals a sharp fall in pressure immediately precedes the rise. In this respect serotonin does not differ from epinephrine because

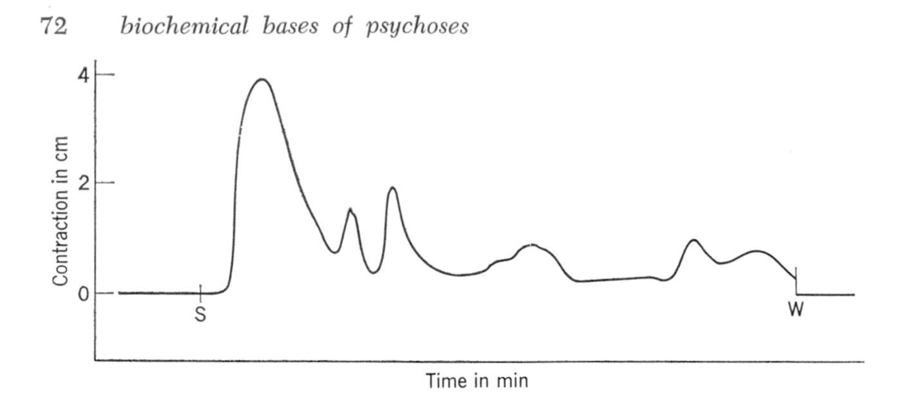

FIG. 3. *Contractions of an isolated rat uterus caused by application of serotonin. At the point marked S, 0.1 μg serotonin was added to the 10-ml bath of Ringer's solution in which the isolated tissue was suspended. At W, the serotonin was washed away.*

intravenous injection of this substance too brings about a fall in pressure which is immediately followed by a sharp rise. With serotonin the rise is usually not as great as with epinephrine, and the whole series of changes takes a little more time than is the case with epinephrine. Figure 4 will show typical responses to serotonin (89).

If the buffer nerves are cut surgically, or blocked with atropine or other antiacetylcholine drugs, the transient fall in blood pressure is abolished, and one sees only the rise, which may be then considerably

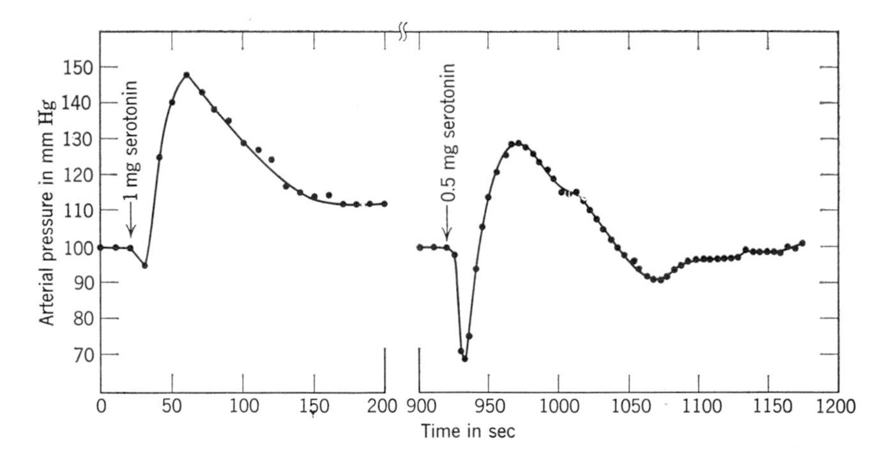

FIG. 4. *Arterial blood pressure of an anesthetized normal 13-kg dog given serotonin intravenously.*

augmented (90). When the injected serotonin reaches the carotid sinus a nerve impulse is sent to the central nervous system which evokes a parasympathetic reflex message for the blood vessels to expand. This presumably is the response to the knowledge that serotonin is inducing a contraction, and is an effort to compensate for it. In some individuals overcompensation takes place, and this is seen as the transient fall in blood pressure. The serotonin continues to act on the muscles of the blood vessel walls, causing them to contract so much that the compensatory process cannot stand against it, and the result is the succeeding rise in pressure.

The serotonin is short lived, since it is being destroyed by monoamine oxidase, and by other enzymes. Consequently, the pressure soon falls again to the original level. When the compensatory reflex is eliminated by cutting the proper nerves, or by blocking them chemically, one sees only the rise in pressure caused by the contraction of the blood vessel walls. In animals such as the rat and the cat, injection of serotonin intravenously causes only a fall in pressure and no rise. If, however, the compensatory nerves are inactivated, one gets the rise without the fall. Man responds to intravenous serotonin in the same way as does the dog. Some individuals show only the rise, some show the fall before the rise (91 and 92). In all species, if the serotonin is infused very slowly instead of being injected within a few seconds, the usual result is to produce only the fall in blood pressure. Under such conditions, the overcompensation of the parasympathetic nervous system wins out.

The vasoconstriction which results from injection of serotonin can have many repercussions. For example, when rats are injected intraperitoneally or subcutaneously with serotonin, the rate of excretion of water by the kidneys is reduced (93). This is seen particularly when the animals have been loaded with water by prior injection. The restricted flow of blood through the kidney reduces the volume of urine produced. Probably also some direct effects of the serotonin on the kidney per se are involved.

The effects of serotonin on all parts of the vascular system are not the same. Although the general effect is to cause contraction of blood vessel walls, this action can be modified or even reversed as we have just seen. Such modification need not apply to all parts of the vascular system. Many studies have been made of the effects of injected serotonin in various portions of the vascular tree (94). These have shown that it can for example cause dilation of the small capillaries in certain parts of the skin. Such a response may reflect only the backing up of blood because of constriction somewhere in the venous return.

However, there is still need for detailed exploration of many of the vascular responses to determine which are direct effects on the muscles of blood vessel walls and which are indirect effects, effects activated through the nervous system.

Intravenous injection of serotonin into dogs or men causes strong contractions of the intestines and the urinary bladder. The result is to elicit defecation and urination. These contractions cease within a minute or two, because of the destruction of the serotonin. However, as mentioned above, if a constant supply of serotonin is provided by injection of 5-hydroxytryptophan, the contractions of the intestines continue, with resultant diarrhea (95). Serotonin injection causes defecation but not diarrhea. In the human carcinoid syndrome, which is characterized by constant overproduction of serotonin by the cancerous argentaffin cells of the intestines, diarrhea is a prominent sign.

Injection of serotonin causes an increase in permeability of the capillaries of the vascular system. The result of such an injection may be to allow fluid to pass into the surrounding tissues. Thus, when serotonin is injected into the footpad of a rat, a marked edema occurs. It is not clear what part contraction of muscle cells in the capillary walls plays in this increase of permeability. Some recent work tends to suggest that the increase may be attributed more to other changes.

There are many more pharmacological effects of serotonin which, however, do not seem to be of direct concern for the subject matter of this book. They have been catalogued by Page (94) and by Erspamer (124).

Some effects on nerves. The principal effect which serotonin has been found to have on nerves when tested by the usual electrical techniques is to inhibit the transmission of impulses in the autonomic system, or in the brain. This is not to say that inhibition has been the only effect seen, but it has been encountered frequently. Thus, one of the earliest findings was that of Marrazzi and Hart (96, 97) who observed that when serotonin in very small amounts was injected into the blood supply to a cat's brain the transmission of electrical impulses was inhibited in the optic pathway from one side of the brain to the other through the corpus callosum. This transcallosal inhibition was also induced by epinephrine, but serotonin was considerably more potent.

Serotonin seems to have difficulty in passing from the blood into nerves, and probably for this reason, more success has been had with bufotenine than with it. The probable reasons for this will be discussed below in the section on blood-brain barrier. Thus, in the Janiculate nucleus of the optic circuit, serotonin applied externally causes no inhibition of transmission of electrical impulses. Bufotenine, however, does inhibit transmission (98). This problem of penetration of serotonin into nerves is a very important one in the designing of neurophysiological experiments, as well as in the understanding of natural processes in the brain. Experience shows that serotonin may often fail to evoke a response, but bufotenine does.

In addition to cases of inhibition caused by serotonin or its derivatives, examples are known of excitation initiated by it. Perhaps the earliest examples were somewhat crude but are noteworthy. These are represented by the respiratory arrest followed by gasping which always follows intravenous injection of serotonin (99 and 100), and by the itching which follows intradermal injection. The respiratory arrest and gasping are believed to result from the nerve impulse sent out when the serotonin reaches the carotid sinus (101). These electrical impulses can be monitored with suitable amplifying equipment (100).

An interesting but as yet incompletely explained effect on inhibition of nerve impulses can be observed in human beings suffering from the pains of angina pectoris or of arthritis. When such patients are given an inhibitor of monoamine oxidase (iproniazid, for example) the pains are no longer felt (102 and 103). The drug increases the amount of serotonin in the tissues, but it also increases the amounts of norepinephrine, epinephrine, and other amines. It is, thus, not clear as to which hormone the inhibition of the transmission of the pain impulse is to be attributed, although it could conceivably be due to the serotonin acting alone or in concert.

If the finding that some nerve systems can be inhibited by serotonin, and others can be excited by it, should seem paradoxical, remember that although most smooth muscles are caused to contract by serotonin, some are known which relax instead. Thus, muscular elements in isolated pieces of lung have been shown to relax rather than to contract, and the retractor muscle which holds the shells of some bivalvular shellfish closed can be made to relax by application of serotonin. Such opposites can be made understandable when we have considered the biochemical mechanism of action of this hormone. The apparent paradox is not unique to serotonin, because it has been observed with acetylcholine and with other hormones.

Effects on oligodendroglia and other brain cells. The oligodendroglial cells, which lie in the spaces between the blood capillaries and the neurons of the brain, can be observed to be in constant motion. They undergo a slow pulsating movement, expanding and contracting. The time scale for these motions is not greatly dissimilar to that seen in smooth muscles, for they have a systole of about 1.5 minutes, and a diastole of about 3 minutes (106). The movements of these cells can be seen to best advantage in a time-lapse motion picture, one of which was prepared by Lumsden and Pomerat at the University of Texas, and another by Margaret Murray at the College of Physicians and Surgeons, Columbia University. Three still photomicrographs of such cells are shown in Figure 5. By looking at the same cell, number 1, for instance, one can see it first in relaxation, then in movement with the fuzzy edges which result from the motion during the long exposure of the photographic film, and finally contracted.

These cells can be cultivated *in vitro,* and examined in tissue culture for the effects of serotonin and its analogs. This was done by Benitez, Murray, and Woolley (107), who found that added serotonin caused them to undergo a strong tetanic contraction. With about 5 gamma of hormone per ml of culture fluid a contraction would persist for about 30 minutes. Then the cell would slowly relax and begin to undergo once more its rhythmical motions. Presumably the excess serotonin had been destroyed at that time. So far as is known these cells do not contain actomyosin. At least, they do not show muscle fibers or fibrils.

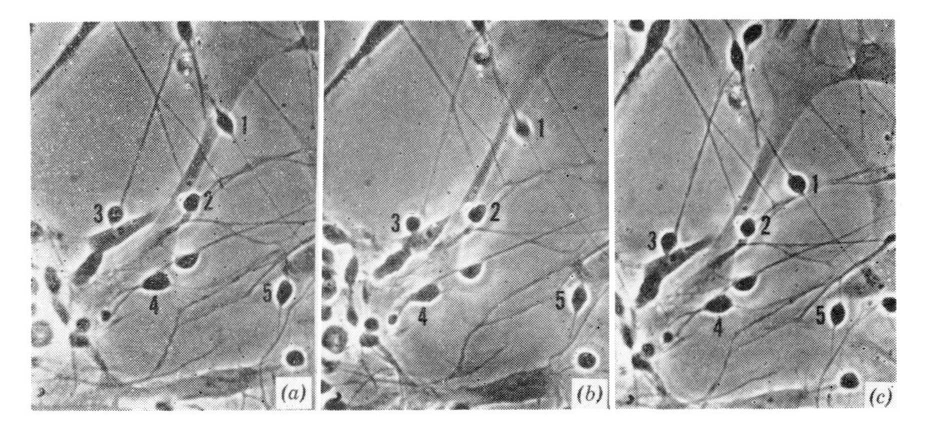

FIG. 5. *Photomicrographs of human oligodendroglia taken at intervals so as to illustrate the motions of these cells. The cells were cultivated* in vitro, *and the three frames were taken at short intervals so that the same cell (for example, the one numbered 1) could be seen first in relaxation, then during contraction, and finally contracted.*

All kinds of cells in the brain do not give a visible response to the addition of serotonin as oligodendroglia do. In fact, oligodendroglia are the only ones which have been seen to do it. Astrocytes, for example, do not contract with addition of serotonin (107). The responses of oligodendroglia may well play a role in the psychiatric involvement of serotonin, as we shall explain in Chapter 6.

It is not without interest that the original discovery of oligodendroglia in the brain depended on their staining properties with silver salts. These cells have a strong affinity for silver salts, which are reduced to metallic silver. Such affinity of serotonin-containing cells for silver stains was the reason for Erspamer's discovery of serotonin in the argentaffin cells of the intestinal tract, and it may be that the preferential staining of oligodendroglia by silver salts likewise is related to the importance of serotonin in them.

Physiological roles. A number of physiological roles for serotonin have been postulated, based on its pharmacological effects. There has been no unanimity about any of these roles. Thus, some have claimed that it plays a role in hemostasis after wounding. There can be no doubt that platelets break down at the site of a wound, and that they then liberate serotonin. One would logically suppose that such serotonin would cause local constriction of blood vessels which might aid in hemostasis. Indeed when an animal is treated with an antiserotonin such as 2-methyl-3-ethyl-5-nitroindole it can readily be shown that hemostasis is impaired. The animals bleed much longer from a wound. The antimetabolite prevents the action of the liberated serotonin. Yet there are some who declare that this hormone has no role in hemostasis, because partial depletion of the serotonin in platelets by administration of reserpine does not seem to influence bleeding time. The explanation probably is that reserpine does not release all of the serotonin from platelets, as is well known. Some evidence exists to show that serotonin also plays a role in the contraction of the clot, once it has been formed (108).

Erspamer and Ottolenghi have maintained that the only role for serotonin in normal physiology is to control the flow of liquids through the kidneys (93). The kidneys are undoubtedly sensitive to very low concentrations of serotonin, and this was the main basis for the deduction about role. However, further study has shown that there are other organs in the body which respond to very small concentrations of this hormone. The fundus of the stomach is an example (49). It will contract when treated with as little as 0.0002 μg serotonin per ml. Enough is not yet known about potentiating factors which may render a tissue supersensitive to serotonin to base the entire argument about physiological role on the idea that a minute dose must produce a response. Nevertheless, it is true that if one must use a dose very large in comparison to the concentration which would reach the tissue under physiological conditions, one may well be observing a pharmacological property of serotonin rather than a physiological one.

Considerable debate has taken place about the relation of serotonin to the physiological control of blood pressure. It is probably correct to say that it does not enter into the control of pressure in normal individuals at rest. This is borne out by the finding of Woolley and Shaw that a powerful antimetabolite of serotonin does not change the blood pressures of such individuals (109). However, in pathological states such as essential hypertension, these same authors have produced evidence that excess serotonin probably is contributing to the high blood pressure, because this same antimetabolite does reduce the pressure. Roles for this hormone in the motility of the gastrointestinal tract, in the beat of the heart, and in inflammatory processes by way of its effect on capillary permeability have been put forward, and each seems to have some experimental backing. A role in allergic responses has also been found to have some support (110 and 111).

The roles of serotonin in the nervous system are the main ones to be dealt with in this book. They will be described in succeeding chapters.

Blood-brain barrier to serotonin. Serotonin passes from the blood into the brain with difficulty. The body thus behaves as if it were composed of compartments insofar as serotonin is concerned. A barrier to the passage into the brain thus seems to exist as was first pointed out by Woolley and Shaw (29, 78, and 112). The principal evidence for this is that when large amounts of the hormone are injected peripherally, no increase in the serotonin content of the brain can be detected. The facts have been amply confirmed in several laboratories. By contrast, when the precursor—5-hydroxytryptophan—is similarly injected peripherally the serotonin content of the brain, as well as of peripheral tissues, is increased markedly (76 and 77). These facts are important for the designing of experiments having to do with psychiatry. It is futile to attempt to raise the serotonin content of the brain by peripheral administration of the hormone itself. The facts cited have led to the idea that some sort of barrier exists to the passage of serotonin from the periphery via the blood into the brain. Whether the barrier extends to all parts of the brain is not known.

The analyses have been done only on the whole organ. It is conceivable that some specialized parts do not possess it. In the experiment of Marrazzi and Hart (96), in which an effect of serotonin on the transmission of an electrical impulse through the corpus callosum was demonstrated, the serotonin was injected into the carotid artery and was then able to produce an effect in the corpus callosum of the brain. The barrier seemed not to extend to this corpus.

What constitutes the barrier anatomically and biochemically is not known. An idea which has some experimental support is that it may be located in the walls of the blood capillaries of the brain and may consist of a group of enzymes which destroy serotonin (113). The enzymes are monoamine oxidase, the phenol sulfatase, and, possibly, the other enzymes described earlier in this chapter. The enzymes would destroy serotonin as it diffused through the walls of the capillaries. The evidence which supports such a concept is that when an inhibitor of monoamine oxidase, such as iproniazid, is given to an animal, then serotonin injected peripherally does pass into the brain in measurable quantities (114). Furthermore, when the primary amino group of serotonin is protected from attack by this enzyme (as is the case in bufotenine) the derivative then can pass from the blood into the brain.

There is also some evidence to suggest that when the phenolic hydroxyl group of the hormone is protected by conversion to a methyl ether, this derivative produces an effect on the brain, and presumably must reach it, even though the primary amino group has not also been protected from monoamine oxidase. Much evidence for the increased activity of the methyl ethers of serotonin analogs over their non-etherified relatives has been pointed out in the studies of Woolley and Shaw. This evidence therefore adds to the idea that protection of the hydroxyl group as an ether can increase the actions on the brain. Finally, when both the hydroxyl group and the primary amino group are protected by methylation as in 5-methoxy-N,N-dimethyltryptamine (bufotenine methylether) one has a compound which will cause marked mental changes in trained mice when it is given peripherally (118). All such evidence is suggestive, but not conclusive. For example, the result with iproniazid could be explained as having arisen because of inhibition of monoamine oxidase in the lungs, a principal site of inactivation of serotonin which is in solution in the plasma instead of in safekeeping in the platelets. More critical experiments with refinements in techniques will be required to establish the location and the nature of the barrier.

Pathologic overproduction (carcinoid). One clearly defined disease of human beings is known to be the result of overproduction of serotonin. This is the carcinoid syndrome in which the argentaffin cells become cancerous. It will be remembered that the argentaffin cells of the gastrointestinal mucosa are the principal sites of serotonin synthesis. When these cells develop cancerous propensities the serotonin-manufacturing capacity of the body is greatly increased (115). The serotonin content of the blood of carcinoid patients is increased and may rise as high as 10 μg per ml. Normal human blood contains 0.4 μg per ml. The excretion of 5-hydroxyindoleacetic acid in the urine is very markedly increased. As mentioned earlier in this chapter, the daily output of this acid may be as high as 400 mg, whereas normal output is 2 to 5 mg. In carcinoid patients, therefore, the formation and excretion of hydroxyindoleacetic acid may become a major route of tryptophan metabolism. This can be appreciated when one remembers that all of it must come from tryptophan, and that the daily intake of tryptophan is 1 to 5 grams. Usually, however, patients with carcinoid excrete only ten to twenty times the normal amount of hydroxyindoleacetic acid.

Many of the clinical signs of carcinoid are those which might be expected from excess serotonin acting on tissues other than the central nervous system. Flushes of the skin due to vasodilation of blood capillaries are common. Severe diarrhea is usually present. High blood pressure is frequently seen although it is not always present. Because recent reviews on carcinoid have denied the existence of hypertension in carcinoids (116), it is interesting to note that the original description of the syndrome by Waldenstrom (117) recorded this sign in some of his patients. Furthermore, the present author has examined three patients with the disease, each of whom was admitted to the hospital because of hypertension. There are carcinoid patients who do not have high blood pressure just as there are some who lack one or more of the other signs, but there are many carcinoids who are hypertensive.

The understanding of why some fail to show all of the symptoms might prove to be of considerable importance. Especially is this true when one remembers that very powerful antimetabolites of serotonin such as BAS fail to control the diarrhea. These antimetabolites completely suppress diarrhea induced in normal animals by injection of 5-hydroxytryptophan (77 and 95). The fact that they control the effects on the intestines of excess serotonin induced with hydroxytryptophan, but fail to control this symptom of carcinoid suggests that more than serotonin is at fault in the disease. This is particularly noteworthy because the antimetabolites will control the flushing of the skin.

In addition to the signs of carcinoid just mentioned there may be anatomical abnormalities. For example, there may be damage to the valves of the heart and lesions of the stomach. It is particularly noteworthy for the subject of this book that carcinoid patients are not mental patients. They seem not to show any more psychiatric disturbance than would be expected from any person suffering from a protracted disagreeable infirmity. The measurements of serotonin which have been made show that, although the amount present in the blood and other peripheral tissues may be excessive, the amount in the central nervous system (for example, cerebrospinal fluid) is not. Presumably, the excess serotonin in the periphery does not pass into the central nervous system.

In addition to carcinoid there are other human diseases which seem to be connected with pathological changes in serotonin. This book is being written about some of these which affect the central nervous system. However, abnormalities involving this hormone in peripheral organs have been suggested. For example, it has been implicated in essential hypertension (119), and one treatment of this disease uses specific antimetabolites of serotonin (91 and 109). Nevertheless, there is much debate about its role in these conditions. By contrast its role in carcinoid is widely accepted because the overproduction there is great enough for all to see.

Biochemical mechanism of action. The basic mechanism of action of serotonin seems to be to arrange for the entry of calcium ions into cells (19 and 20). The concept to be outlined can be summarized by the following equations:

$$\text{Serotonin} + \text{specific lipid} \leftrightarrow \text{serotonin-receptor complex} \qquad \text{(a)}$$

$$\text{Serotonin-receptor complex} + \text{Ca}^{++} \leftrightarrow \text{Ca-complex} \qquad \text{(b)}$$

$$\text{Ca-complex} \xrightarrow{\text{receptor-enzyme}} \text{Ca}^{++} + \text{serotonin} + \text{degraded lipid} \qquad \text{(c)}$$

The question to be answered in attempts to understand mechanism is why does serotonin cause smooth muscles to contract and nerves to respond. By means of what series of chemical reactions are these physical effects produced? This is not an easy question to answer because for no hormone has anyone yet been able to do so. There are consequently no precedents to guide us. Each time someone has seemed on the road to the correct answer, as in the case of thyroxine or epinephrine or the estrogens, something has appeared which has made it seem finally that only an interesting property, or a biochemical transformation of the hormone was being studied, and not its mechanism of action as a hormone.

After it was discovered that most of the water-soluble vitamins were built into the several coenzymes and that they owed their biochemical and physiological importance to this fact, many biochemists explored a similar idea for the hormones. The postulate was that each hormone was an essential part of some coenzyme which might be functioning in the breakdown of glucose to yield energy or in the biosynthesis of various constituents of the cell. A large amount of work went into these explorations, but up to the present time it has not been possible to understand the mechanism of action of any hormone on the basis of this coenzyme working hypothesis. This may only be because no one yet has chanced upon the proper reaction to explore. It might also be because the working hypothesis is not correct.

Many of the hormones seem to be regulators of the activities of cells. Almost always their biological activities cannot be measured unless an organ, or a cell, or an organized fragment of a cell is used. When the organization is lost the hormonal effect is also lost.

Cells seem to maintain an "insulated" existence in the media in which they live. To a less marked degree the organelles inside the cells, such as nucleus and mitochondria, do this also. The means by which cells do this is the cell membrane. Much debate rages at the present time, as it has for decades, on the chemical nature of the cell membrane. Many maintain that it must be mostly protein. Their reason for thinking this is that it has now been shown that cells really do have the power to distinguish between various kinds of small molecules and can take in one kind and exclude others which are only slightly different. It is argued that such great specificity could only be achieved by making the membrane of protein. Also, since enzymes are so specific, and since enzymes are proteins, the specific membranes must be proteins too. Such an argument can never be conclusive.

In the past, studies of the penetration of various kinds of molecules into cells, especially red blood cells and cells of the plant *Nitella*, have led some to the conclusion that the membrane must be at least partly lipid (120). Fat-soluble molecules of all sorts seem to pass readily into cells, and even to partition themselves between the aqueous medium and the cell in accordance with the partition coefficient of the substance in mixtures of fat (triglyceride) and water.

Work of the last decade with the electron microscope has shown many new things about cell membranes. An electron micrograph of a smooth muscle cell, very kindly given to me by Dr. G. Palade, is shown in Figure 6. Here one sees that the outside of the cell exhibits a layer about 250 Å thick of material which stains rather lightly with osmium tetroxide. Inside of this is a very deeply staining band about 70 Å thick. This is the membrane which was invisible before the introduction of the electron microscope. The deep staining with osmium of this band might suggest that it is lipoidal, since unsaturated lipids are known to stain in this fashion. However, proteins also can be stained with osmium, and thus this membrane might be protein. However, if the section of the cell is dipped into a fat solvent such as toluene before the exposure to osmium tetroxide, this 70 Å band does not appear in the micrograph. This suggests that it is lipid.

Much study of this 70 Å band has led to the conclusion that it is not uniform. Some say that it is a sort of sandwich composed of an inner and an outer sheet of darkly staining material with a layer in between of less darkly staining material. The postulate has arisen that the less darkly staining material may be protein, but direct evidence for this is lacking. It may even be that the sandwich effect is no more than an optical illusion which can be accounted for on the basis of molecular alignment of lipid molecules.

What better insulation from the hostile world could a cell have than a lipid membrane of this sort? All of the numerous substances in the external medium, which are soluble in water, but insoluble in oil would not be able to diffuse through this membrane. The same could be said for the water-soluble substances inside the cell which are required to keep the cell operating. They would not leak out. The few nutrients which the cell must take in from outside and which are water-soluble could be brought in by a special mechanism, such as the one to be described. The desired specificity of entry could thus be achieved. Furthermore, if the entry of each substance were under the control of some hormone, not made by the cell, but sent to it from a distant cell for the express purpose of allowing the cell in question to take up a specific nutrient and thus to set some machinery inside to work on it, then the control mechanisms of which the hormones have long been felt to be a part would find an explanation.

The hormone-producing cell sends out its message in the form of a molecule of hormone. The target cell picks up this hormone with the result that its membrane is so modified that a specific nutrient can now dissolve in it, and thus enter the cell. When it is time to excite some other kind of activity in the cell another kind of hormone is sent

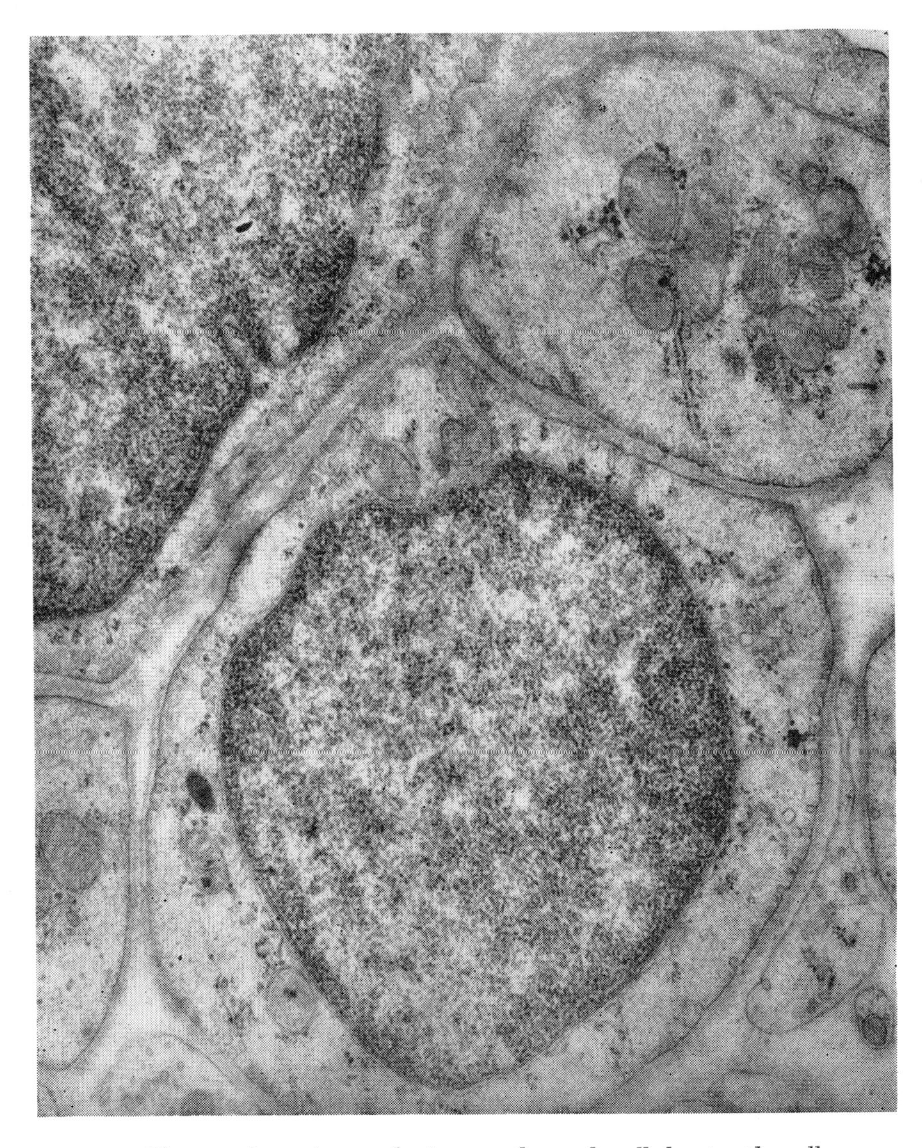

Fig. 6. *Electron photomicrograph of a smooth-muscle cell showing the cell membrane stained with osmium tetroxide. The membrane is the narrow band of heavily stained material which appears just inside the broader and more lightly stained area at the edge of the cell.*

out, which combines with some other constituent of the membrane of the target cell so that now a different molecule can be extracted from aqueous solution in the medium and allowed to diffuse into the target cell.

Such a concept is in agreement with several recent studies on the uptake of radioactive phosphate by cells stimulated by a particular hormone. Such studies show that the hormone is probably not built into part of the metabolic machinery inside. Rather, this machinery all seems to be there idling, waiting for a signal to turn out those products which the hormone is known to evoke. This seems to be the case for thyroid cells stimulated to produce thyroglobulin by the thyroid stimulating hormone of the pituitary, and for the adrenals stimulated to produce cortisone by the adrenocorticotropic hormone of the pituitary. The hormone in each case seems to allow the passage of something into the target cell which sets its specialized machinery in motion.

If this hypothesis is correct, what is it that serotonin carries into the cell, and how does it do it? The working hypothesis just outlined for the mechanism of action of hormones arose from the studies of the mechanism of action of serotonin on smooth muscles.

The first question to answer is what is being carried in by serotonin. Evidence was found which indicated that it was calcium ions. Large amounts of these ions had serotonin-like activity in causing contraction of the isolated rat uterus (19). A kymographic record to illustrate this point is shown in Figure 7. When serotonin is applied to the muscle a series of contractions and relaxations takes place. If a minimally effective dose is used the amplitude of each succeeding contraction grows less, and finally the contraction ceases. This is due to destruction of a fraction of the serotonin, because if small increments are added after each contraction, the gradual decline in amplitude does not take place. About 10 per cent of the minimally effective dose of serotonin is used up with each contraction of the muscle as judged by the amount required to maintain the amplitude. These last data show that although there is some loss of serotonin during contraction most of it remains unchanged.

When calcium chloride in relatively large amount is added, the muscle contracts just as it does with serotonin. The lag period between addition to the bath and the start of the contraction is longer than it is with serotonin, and the decline in amplitude does not take place with each succeeding contraction. The calcium chloride is about seventy thousand times (on a molar basis) less potent than is serotonin. A concentration of calcium ions sufficient to initiate contraction would thus never occur when the organ is in its place in a normal animal. If calcium ions are completely eliminated from the bathing fluid, then serotonin will not cause contraction. It has been known for a long time that calcium ions are essential for muscular contraction. The bathing fluid in these experiments contained 20 mg $CaCl_2$ per liter. From the experiment with additional calcium one can see that calcium ions alone will cause contraction if their concentration is great enough. If it is not, then serotonin will make up the deficiency and cause a contraction. The inability of serotonin to cause contraction in the absence of calcium ions can be shown easily by the use of versene (ethylenediaminetetraacetate). This is a chelating agent which strongly binds calcium in a soluble, but unionized form. The data given in the kymographic tracings of Figures 7 and 8 will show that in the presence of versene, serotonin was unable to

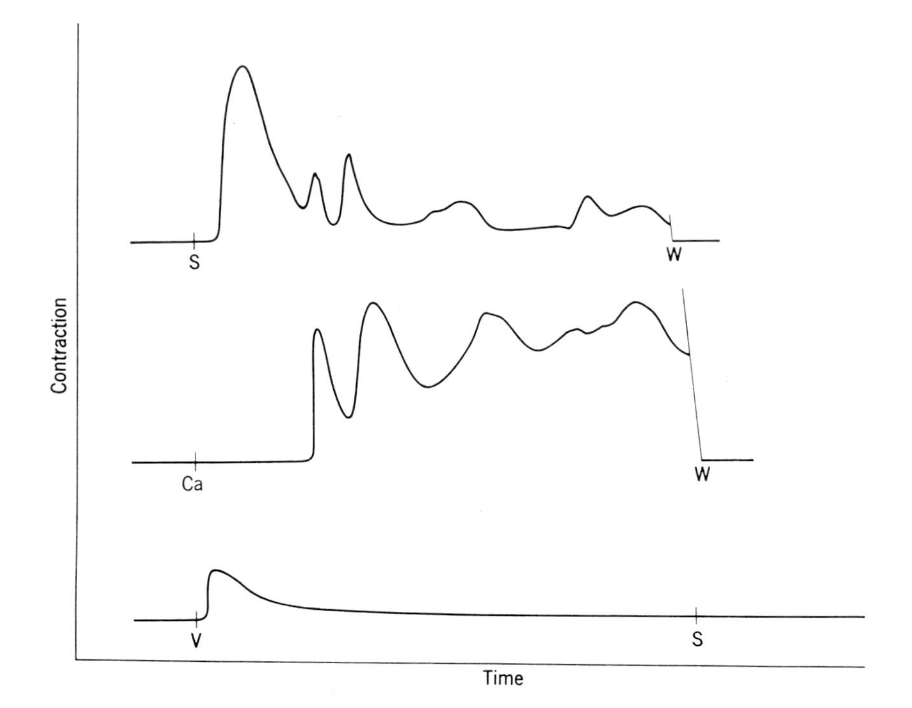

Fig. 7. *Comparison of responses of an isolated rat uterus to serotonin, calcium chloride, and versene. S = serotonin, 0.1 μg per 10 cc; W = wash; Ca = $CaCl_2$, 2 mg per 10 cc.; V = versene, 1 mg per 10 cc.*

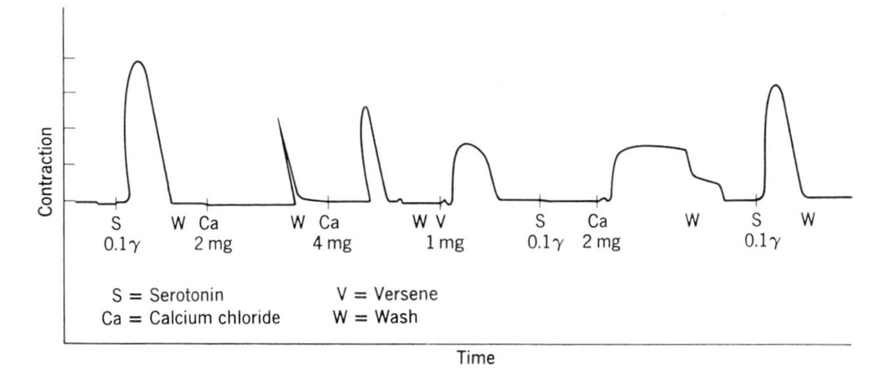

FIG. 8. *Prevention of serotonin-induced contraction of isolated rat uterus with versene and reversal of this effect. Amounts shown are per 10 cc.*

cause contraction. When the versene was washed away, or was neutralized with an equivalent of calcium, the ability to contract on addition of serotonin was restored.

If calcium ion is the thing transported into the cell with the aid of serotonin, how is this accomplished? One might say that serotonin changes the membrane so that all sorts of water-soluble substances, including calcium ions, leaked in easily. In order to understand why high concentrations of calcium ions will by themselves cause contraction it is necessary to picture the membrane as being slightly leaky. If it is, and if it allows one unit volume of aqueous medium to leak through, the amount of calcium transported in this unit volume of leakage is not enough when the calcium concentration of the medium is physiological (20 to 40 mg $CaCl_2$ per liter). If, however, the concentration in the medium is high enough, this unit volume of leakage will bring inside the cell sufficient calcium to incite contraction. Some will prefer to consider the leakage as not just a passive passage through a hole, but rather an active engulfment of tiny droplets by pinocytosis.[a] Either way the result would be the same. However,

[a] Pinocytosis is a term used to describe the uptake by cells of discrete microdroplets of fluid. It is a process of drinking or active engulfment by cells. It comes about by invagination of the cell membrane. The invaginations grow deeper and become balloon shaped. Finally, the neck of the invagination is sealed off by movement of the cell membrane across the opening. The little droplet of external medium is thus surrounded by a film of cell membrane, but finds itself as a vesicle inside the cell. When the film which surrounds this vesicle

if pinocytosis is the reason for the leakage, then one might say that serotonin increased the rate of pinocytosis and thereby put more calcium ions into the cell. The difficulty with any hypothesis which would explain the action of serotonin as arising from an increased leakage into the cell is that all substances in the surrounding medium would be carried in at the same rate as calcium ions, provided only that they were of the same size as these ions. There is no evidence that this takes place. In fact, some evidence suggests that it does not, and that calcium is taken up selectively. Nevertheless, crucial evidence is difficult to obtain.

The reason why the lag before initiation of contraction was longer with excess Ca^{++} than it was with serotonin in Figure 7, can be understood now. If the excess Ca^{++} entered by leakage, either actively through pinocytosis, or passively through tiny holes, more time would be required than if these ions were carried in by a rapid chemical reaction.

We might come at the problem in a different way; we might see it as a rapid chemical reaction. Suppose that the membrane should contain a substance which would combine with serotonin and render it fat-soluble (so that it would dissolve in the membrane). Suppose further that this compound should be able to form a salt or a chelate with calcium ions, so that the calcium now would be fat-soluble. A way would thus be provided for taking the calcium ions from the aqueous solution of the medium and getting them into the barrier which is the membrane. It would next be necessary to get them out and back into aqueous solution, but inside the cell. There would, thus, need to be an enzyme inside the membrane for which the calcium-serotonin-receptor complex would be the substrate. The substance in the membrane which combines with the serotonin would thus be a part of the serotonin receptor, and might be called the receptor substance. The enzyme might be called the receptor enzyme. This enzyme would destroy some part of the complex formed with the result that the calcium ion would no longer be bound by it, and would be liberated into the aqueous phase within the cell. There

is removed by enzyme action the droplet has in effect passed bodily into the cell without diffusion through the cell membrane. The motions of cells which give rise to such invaginations can be recorded readily by time-lapse motion pictures. In fact, this process is visible in Figure 6. Recently Palade and his associates have shown the uptake of particles of colloidal gold by cells, a process which their electronphotomicrographs suggest is accomplished by such engulfment of little droplets of external fluid containing the metallic particles.

would now be needed an enzyme to regenerate the receptor substance so that the next cycle of transport could take place. This would be the point at which energy would be required, and the likely candidate for this energy source is adenosine triphosphate. Since many of the complex lipids are phosphate esters, and many possess additional sites for the attachment of more phosphate groups the possible reactions are easily conceived.

Some way of getting calcium ions back out of the cell must exist, otherwise the concentration inside would soon be very high. One could picture this as happening by having the complex-destroying enzyme localize at certain spots inside the membrane, and the receptor-regenerating enzyme at other spots. If a similar network of these two enzymes existed on the outer surface of the membrane, but in reversed sequence, then calcium could be passed back out through the membrane in the same way in which it came in. A cyclic process would then be obtained which depended only on a supply of energy and of serotonin to keep it in motion.[b]

The scheme outlined contains a number of assumptions. What experimental evidence is there to support it? In the first place, with respect to the network arrangement of calcium-binding sites, it has been shown that when a smooth muscle is stimulated electrically to contract in a medium containing radioactive calcium ions, and a radioautogram of the cell is made, the radioactivity is not uniformly distributed on the surface, but rather is found in a network. This is only suggestive evidence. More direct evidence for the movements of calcium during contraction can be obtained in another way through the use of radioactive calcium. When muscle cells contract in medium containing Ca^{45}, radioactivity enters the cells and is not removed by

[b] The mechanism of action of serotonin just outlined allows one to understand the system by means of which blood platelets concentrate serotonin. This "serotonin pump" found in platelets as described in the section "Storage and sequestration" could be composed of the serotonin receptor substance present in the platelet membranes and the receptor destroying enzyme inside the platelets. It is only necessary to picture the lack of the returning system which in muscle cells carries calcium ions and serotonin back out of the cells. If this returning system were not present in platelets serotonin and calcium ions would accumulate inside them by the action of the lipoidal receptor substance and the receptor destroying enzyme in the way pictured for the entry into muscle cells. This idea would account for the presence of the serotonin receptor in the lipids extracted from platelets, and also for the need of bivalent metallic ions for the serotonin-concentrating activity of platelets. This need for the ions was found without any reference to the receptor idea (82).

washing so long as the muscle does not continue to contract. If, after the washing, the cells are stimulated to contract, radioactive calcium is again released into the surrounding fluid (121).

The evidence for the postulated receptor substance is the following. When fresh organs which respond to serotonin, as for example, stomach or intestine or brain, are extracted with chloroform and methanol, or ether and ethanol, the lipids which are extracted contain substances which combine with serotonin in a reversible fashion, and render it extractable from aqueous solution into a fat solvent such as benzene and butanol (20). These substances are lipids which can be fractionated and purified in the ways used for complex lipids, and appear in the phosphatide fraction. Several acidic lipids exhibit activity of this sort as can be seen from the data of Table 3. The activity for rendering serotonin extractable by fat solvents which some of these lipids show does not necessarily identify them as serotonin receptors. It merely shows that cells do contain certain lipids which have such activity. Whether the activity is great enough and specific enough to class these as parts of the receptor remains to be seen. In

TABLE 3. *Amounts of serotonin made extractable from aqueous solution by various lipids (The lipid solvent used was benzene-butanol (1:1). The concentration of serotonin in the aqueous phase was 25 μg per ml.* Ca^{++} *was omitted from the system because several of the lipids which were active formed the insoluble* Ca *salts which consequently interfered with the test*)

Lipid	Serotonin Extracted, μg per gram lipid
Cholesterol	Less than 3
Estradiol	8
Soybean lipositol	60
Beef brain sphingomyelin	Less than 40
Stearic acid	500
Cerebron sulfate	2,900
Cholesterol phosphate	19,200
α-Tocopherol phosphate	11,500
Phosphatidylcholine (synthetic)	Less than 500
Phosphatidylethanolamine (synthetic)	Less than 500
Gangliosides from brain	1,000

the absence of these lipids serotonin is not extractable from aqueous solution into fat-solvents. When the serotonin is made fat-soluble in this way, calcium ions are also picked up and carried into the fatty layer (21). Both the serotonin and the calcium can be recovered by shaking the fat solvent with dilute hydrochloric acid, after which they are found in the aqueous acid. Enzymes capable of destroying the active lipids in the presence of serotonin also have been detected. These might be the receptor enzymes of equation (c).

The machinery inside a muscle cell which does the actual contracting is actomyosin, and adenosine triphosphate is the source of the energy (19). This machinery can be taken out of the cell as Szent-Györgyi first did (122), and the actomyosin can be formed into threads suspended in an aqueous solution. When adenosine triphosphate is added to this preparation, the threads do not contract, but when calcium ions are also added, contraction takes place. The addition of serotonin instead of calcium ions to the actomyosin-adenosine triphosphate system does not cause contraction. This shows clearly that it is not the direct combination of the hormone with the contractile machinery which is the cause of the contraction. Rather, it seems that it is the admission of calcium ions which is brought about by the hormone.

The experiments of Heilbrunn and Wiercinski (123) bear directly on this point. When each of a variety of metallic ions was injected through the cell membrane directly into a single muscle cell by means of a micromanipulator, the only ion which caused the cell to contract was calcium. Potassium ions or sodium or magnesium ions were not able to induce contractions, although an occasional response to potassium ion was observed.

It must not be supposed that the only way of getting Ca^{++} through cell membranes is by intervention of serotonin. The mechanism under examination (19 and 20) envisions several independent systems for Ca^{++} entry and consequent cell contraction. Thus, the action of epinephrine, of acetylcholine and of other hormones which make smooth muscles contract could be of the same general kind. The lipid receptor might be different for each hormone. The receptor enzyme would probably be different for each. In this way hormonal specificity could be understood, but the basic mechanism for each hormone would be the same. It would be the union between hormone, specific lipid, and Ca^{++} to give a dissociable complex soluble in the lipoidal part of the membrane. Each complex would be the substrate for a special enzyme which would liberate the Ca^{++}. There would thus be a number of independent ways for transportation of

Ca^{++} into a cell. The experimental evidence for such mechanisms for other hormones is not as extensive as in the case of serotonin. It consists of demonstrations that removal of Ca^{++} by means of versene prevents each hormone from causing contraction, and that lipids can be extracted from susceptible cells which will render the hormone fat extractable.

The hypothesis about mechanism of action which has been presented above is still a working hypothesis. Although it has some evidence to support it one cannot say that it has been established. It was presented here because it is useful in the understanding of some matters relative to mental diseases which will be discussed in subsequent chapters, although it should be pointed out that the relationship of serotonin to most mental diseases is independent of this postulate about mechanism.

Another hypothesis about the mechanism of action of serotonin and of epinephrine requires description. This work was first done in relation to the mechanism of action of epinephrine (125 and 126) and was later extended to that of serotonin. When solid particles made by fragmentation of tissues such as liver are separated and suspended in a solution containing adenosine triphosphate (ATP) and epinephrine, the ATP is converted into a new compound which has been isolated and identified. It is the 3′,5′-cyclic phosphate of adenosine (126). This compound now can be used in an enzymic process to activate the enzyme phosphorylase. The phosphorylase is phosphorylated by the cyclic phosphate and thus made more active. The activated phosphorylase (phosphophosphorylase) produces glucose-1-phosphate from glycogen. It has long been known that one of the actions of epinephrine is to raise blood sugar levels. This effect might be explained in terms of the above demonstrations.

The connection of the reaction described above—that is, the formation of cyclic adenosine phosphate—to the reason why epinephrine causes muscles to contract has not yet been clarified. The fact that the enzyme or enzymes concerned in the formation of this cyclic phosphate have not been separated from particles of cells, may even allow room for a calcium ion or other divalent ion transport effect in these particles similar to the one discussed above for serotonin and whole cells. The epinephrine could owe its effect to the transport of calcium (or magnesium) ions through the membranes of the cell fragments. Inside the fragments the calcium (or magnesium) ions could activate the enzyme which makes cyclic adenosine phosphate from ATP. This idea has not been proved experimentally, but attempts are now underway to do so. If it can be proved, the stimulation of enzymic formation of cyclic adenosine phosphate would become understandable in terms of an effect on calcium (or magnesium) transport through a membrane.

Quite recently, a similar demonstration to that described for epinephrine has been made with serotonin (125). With cell particles separated from the parasitic liver fluke *Fasciola hepatica,* serotonin has been found to catalyze the formation of the cyclic phosphate from ATP just as epinephrine does in mammalian cell particles. What has been said about epinephrine for the relation of phosphorylase activation by cyclic adenosine phosphate in relation to Ca ion transport could be repeated here for serotonin.

Antimetabolites of serotonin. A large number of structural analogs of serotonin are known which act as antimetabolites of it. That is, they specifically interfere in the biological actions of the hormone. Sometimes they can also act like the hormone in some tissues, but not in all. Many have been shown to be competitively reversible antagonists; others are known which are non-competitive, and still others have been found to be completely irreversible, but nevertheless specific antagonists. In other words, all of the variations of antimetabolite action has been observed with these structural analogs of serotonin.

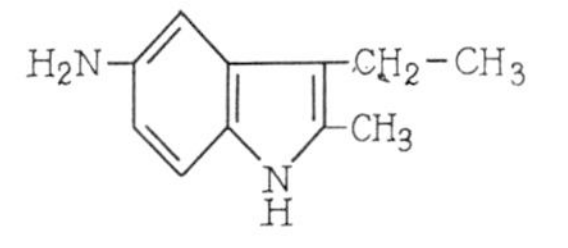

2-Methyl-3-ethyl-5-aminoindole

FIG. 9. *Structure of the first antimetabolite of serotonin.*

The simplest test for an antimetabolite of serotonin is to determine whether the compound in question will overcome the contraction caused by serotonin in a piece of smooth muscle. Thus, ring-shaped sections of carotid arteries may be immersed in Ringer's solution in a glass dish and caused to contract by addition of small amounts of serotonin. The contraction can be overcome by addition of an antimetabolite of serotonin such as 2-methyl-3-ethyl-5-aminoindole (119, 127). This was one of the first testing methods used to demonstrate antiserotonin action, and the analog mentioned was the first to be found active as an antiserotonin (119). Its structure is shown in Figure 9. Many other tests may be used however. A favorite one has been to suspend one horn of the uterus taken from an estrogenized rat in a glass vessel in such a way that the contractions of the tissue can be recorded on a kymograph. When serotonin is added to the Ringer's solution in which the tissue is suspended it contracts rhythmically as was shown in Figure 3. If an antimetabolite is added before the serotonin is applied, the contractions are prevented. The degree of inhibition can be measured accurately in either the artery ring or the uterus by determination of the quantity of analog required to reduce the contractions caused by a unit dose of serotonin. Usually the end point is taken as that at which the contractions are reduced to half their amount in the absence of the inhibitor. The relative potencies of various analogs can be readily established by parallel assays of the two analogs. When the analogs act as competitive antagonists this fact can be established by determination of how much analog is required to overcome let us say 0.1 μg serotonin, and how much is required to overcome ten or a hundred times this amount. The ratio of antimetabolite to serotonin is constant if the antagonism is competitive.

If the antagonism is non-competitive or irreversible it is not possible to use the same piece of tissue to compare the potencies of two analogs. A useful technique then is to use one horn of the uterus of a given rat to measure the potency of analog A, and to use the other horn of the same rat to measure the potency of analog B. The tissues of individual rats vary in responsiveness to a given dose of serotonin and of a given analog. The use of comparable tissues from the same animal minimizes errors when two compounds are to be compared.

Many kinds of tissues can be used for assays of this sort. In fact any test system suitable for the bioassay of serotonin can eaily be adapted for meaurement of potencies of antimetabolites of the hormone. The rat stomach, the clam heart, the rat intestine, and many other tissues have been used for this purpose. However, the potency of a given analog will not necessarily be the same in the artery ring test as it is in the rat uterus test or rat stomach test. This point was discussed and illustrated in Chapter 3. Receptors of different tissues differ in their affinities for a given analog.

The assays just described all use isolated tissues. There are others which depend on a response in a living animal, and there are a variety of these. For example, the intravenous injection of serotonin into a dog causes a rise in arterial blood pressure, which can be measured quantitatively as was shown in Figure 4. If the dog is treated previously with an antimetabolite of serotonin, the rise in blood pressure induced by serotonin can be prevented. By use of graded doses of the analog a quantitative measure of its potency can be obtained. The dog can then be rested and used to obtain comparable data on a second analog. In this way potencies may be compared directly.

Just as with the *in vitro* assays with isolated tissues, so also with the *in vivo* assays there are many kinds which have been found useful. The dog blood-pressure test was the first one used for evaluation of antimetabolites of serotonin (120 and 128). Another one which has given very useful results depends on a somewhat different response in living animals. This is the mouse diarrhea assay (95). When mice are injected with 5-hydroxytryptophan they develop a severe and persistent diarrhea. This arises from the sustained production of serotonin from the 5-hydroxytryptophan, and the action of the serotonin on the smooth muscles of the intestines. If an antimetabolite of serotonin is given prior to the 5-hydroxytryptophan the diarrhea is prevented. This has been developed into perhaps the most quantitative and simple assay for comparison of potencies of antiserotonins in living animals.

The choice of an assay system for antiserotonins, of course, is influenced largely by the purpose one has in mind. If one wished to find a good analog for the control of blood pressure one would naturally choose the blood-pressure assay. If he wished to find the best analog for control of intestinal contractions he would use the diarrhea assay or some other similar method which employed intestinal tissue. Nevertheless, the potency of an analog in one system may be reflected accurately by its potency in another, so that several antiserotonins which are very active in the diarrhea test have been found first by use of the blood-pressure test, in which they are also very potent.

The assays which use isolated tissues rather than living animals often show an analog to be a good antimetabolite, but the same analog may fail to show any potency at all in living animals. The reasons for this are readily understood. The analog may not reach the desired tissues in the living animal. It may be excreted or destroyed during its passage through the blood. It may be absorbed and inactivated by one of the proteins of the blood. For example, although medmain (2-methyl-3-ethyl-5-dimethylaminoindole) was very potent when tested *in vitro* in the artery ring assay, it was quite inactive in the assay with dog's blood pressure. It could be shown that one of the globulins of the blood adsorbed and inactivated the analog (29, 129).

To illustrate the importance of getting the analog to the proper tissue in the living animal the case of BAS (1-benzyl-2-methyl-5-methoxytryptamine) is noteworthy. This analog showed the same potency on isolated muscles as did its near relative known as BAB (1-benzyl-2-methyl-5-methoxy-N,N-dimethyltryptamine) which differed from it only by having two methyl groups on the $—NH_2$ group. BAB had practically the same potency as BAS in the blood pressure test with living dogs (130). BAB however, because of its structural difference, can penetrate into the nervous system. It exerts effects there whereas

TABLE 4. *Some antimetabolites of serotonin with their potencies in various assay systems*

Analog		Potencies in				
Trivial Name	Chemical Name	Artery Rings,* μg per ml	Rat Uterus,† μg per ml	Dog's ‡ Blood Pressure, mg per kg	Mouse Diarrhea,§ mg per kg	Literature
	3-ethyl-5-aminoindole	30	—	—	—	127
	2-methyl-3-ethyl-5-aminoindole	9	10	20	—	127, 89
	1,2,3,4-tetrahydro-6-aminocarbazole	11	—	—	—	127
Medmain	2-methyl-3-ethyl-5-dimethylaminoindole	0.04	2.0	inactive at 50	—	29
Methylmedmain	1,2-dimethyl-3-ethyl-5-dimethylaminoindole	0.04	1.5	inactive at 50	—	29
Dimethylthamca	1,2,3,4-tetrahydro-6-dimethylaminomethylcarbazole	0.2	1	1.6	—	129
Pathcole	1,2,3,4-tetrahydro-6-phenylcarboxamidinocarbazole	20	5	0.4	1.2	129
Benzyldimethylthamca	1,2,3,4-tetrahydro-6-dimethylaminomethyl-9-benzylcarbazole	—	30	Less than 2.5	—	129
	2-methyl-5-methoxytryptamine	—	30	1.0	—	131
BAS	1-benzyl-2-methyl-5-methoxytryptamine	—	0.2	1.0	10	131, 95
BAS phenol	1-benzyl-2-methylserotonin	—	—	0.4	2	132, 95
BAB	1-benzyl-2-methyl-5-methoxy-*N*-dimethyltryptamine	—	1	0.5	8	130, 95

Hydrazindole	1-benzyl-2-methyl-3-aminoethyl-5-indol-oxyacethydrazide	—	0.05	—	0.3	133
	1-benzyl-2-methyl-5-(*p*-methoxy-benzyloxy)-tryptamine	—	0.02	—	0.15	133
LSD	Lysergic acid diethylamide	0.2	0.004	0.3	—	52, 141, 9
BOL	2-bromo-lysergic acid diethylamide	—	0.004	—	—	142

* The amounts shown are those required to antagonize by 50 per cent the contractions induced by 0.2 μg serotonin per ml.

† The amounts shown are those required to antagonize by 50 per cent the contractions induced by 0.1 μg serotonin per 10 ml bath fluid.

‡ The amounts shown are those required to reduce by 50 per cent the rise in arterial blood pressure which followed the intravenous injection of enough serotonin to give a rise of at least 30 mm of mercury in the untreated dog. This was usually 25 to 50 μg serotonin per kg body weight.

§ The amounts shown are those which protected 50 per cent of a group of six mice from the diarrhea which followed intraperitoneal injection of 1 mg DL-5-hydroxytryptophan per mouse (30 mg per kg) 30 minutes after administration of the analog. All analogs were injected intraperitoneally.

‖ General footnote. The route of administration of the analogs sometimes influenced potency markedly. The values shown for effects on blood pressure of dogs were determined by intravenous administration. Each analog was also assayed by oral administration. In this test, some analogs (such as dimethylthamca) were inactive, and others (such as 2-methyl-3-ethyl-5-aminoindole and 2-methyl-5-methoxytryptamine) were much less active than when given intravenously. On the contrary, BAS and BAB were as active when fed as when injected. The potency of a given analog in every kind of assay was influenced by the time relationships of administration. The longer time of exposure of a tissue to the analog the more active the analog was. For this reason the values for all compounds shown were determined under identical conditions so that comparisons could be made of relative potency. The analogs differed markedly in reversibility by serotonin. Analogs 1 to 5 and 9 were competitive antagonists in all systems. Compounds 6, 15, and 16 were partially reversible in some systems. All others were irreversible.

BAS, which enters with difficulty, does not. The easiest way to show this difference is to taste the two analogs. BAB has a strong and persistent taste, whereas BAS has none (130), but there are more sophisticated ways also of demonstrating an effect on the nervous system.

The consequence of these facts is that there are scores of analogs which act as antimetabolites in various isolated tissues. There are many less which act as antimetabolites when injected intravenously into whole animals, but there are only a few which are active in whole animals when taken orally. Furthermore, all active antimetabolites of serotonin do not exert identical effects on the whole animal. Not only do the receptors in various organs differ in their affinities for the various analogs, the qualitative effects are not the same. For some receptors, a given analog may act as an antimetabolite, but for others it may act like serotonin. A case in point is lysergic acid diethylamide which acts like serotonin in the blood-pressure test, but antagonistically in the uterus (9). Much more will be said about such differences in activity in Chapter 6 when we consider the relationship of antimetabolites of serotonin to schizophrenia.

In Table 4 are listed a few of the antimetabolites of serotonin along with some data to show their relative potencies. Only a small number of the total list of antimetabolites of serotonin is given in this table, because the numbers of antimetabolites and the varieties of test methods are so great. All of the values shown in Table 4 (except for some for BOL) were determined by the same experimenters in a single laboratory. The data thus have comparative significance.

Some of the antimetabolites of serotonin show a remarkable degree of specificity. They protect a tissue or a living animal against the actions of serotonin, but not against the actions of other hormones. Two such examples are 1-benzyl-2-methyl-5-methoxytryptamine (BAS) and 1-benzyl-2-methylserotonin (BAS-phenol or 1-benzyl-2-methyl-5-hydroxytryptamine). When either of these compounds is fed to (or injected into) a dog at 1 to 5 mg per kg per day, the animal becomes insensitive to rises in blood pressure induced by the injection of serotonin. However, the pressor actions of epinephrine and norepinephrine are not interfered with and even the pressor effect of tryptamine is not affected (134). Data to illustrate this point are shown in Table 5. This ability of the analog to protect against serotonin (5-hydroxytryptamine) but not against tryptamine illustrates well the high degree of specificity which can be built into these compounds. Prior to demonstrations of this sort it had been widely maintained that serotonin and tryptamine acted on the same receptor which had been called the tryptamine receptor (135). It is now quite plain that there are sero-

TABLE 5. *Pressor responses in a dog before and after injection of BAS-phenol (1-benzyl-2-methyl-5-hydroxytryptamine hydrochloride) (2.2 mg per kg)*

Pressor Agent	Amount, μg per kg	Rise in Pressure before BAS-phenol, mm Hg	Rise in Pressure after BAS-phenol, mm Hg
Serotonin	30	36	6 *
Tryptamine	220	46	68
Epinephrine	2	72	98
Norepinephrine	1	50	58

* The fall in pressure which accompanies injection of serotonin into a protected dog was observed.

tonin receptors and tryptamine receptors, and they are not the same. One can be blocked without blockade of the other.

Probable evolutionary relationship of serotonin and the plant growth hormone (indoleacetic acid). Several kinds of evidence suggest that serotonin plays a role in animals (and a few plants which contain it) similar to that of the growth hormone of plants, auxin, or indoleacetic acid (136). Both compounds are quite similar in structure (see Figure 10). The plant growth hormone is an acid, whereas the animal hormone is the corresponding base to which has been added an hydroxyl group. Possibly the reason for use of the acid in plants and the base in animals is related to the fact that the pH of the tissue fluids of plants tends to be more acidic than it is in animals. Serotonin would be functioning in animals at a pH at which indoleacetic acid would be completely ionized. At that pH serotonin would still have a very small percentage of its molecules unionized. Possibly it is these unionized molecules which exert the biological effect. In plants, on the other hand, where the pH is usually much lower than in animals, serotonin would be completely ionized. Indoleacetic acid, on the other hand, at these lower pH values exists partly as unionized molecules. We might ask whether nature has provided most plants with the indole acid and most animals with the indole base to conform with the differences in acidity of the tissues in the two kingdoms.

Both serotonin and indoleacetic acid have been found to influence the

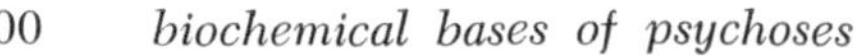

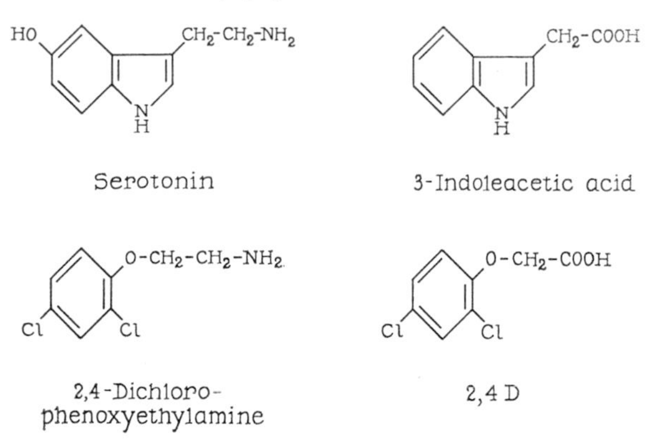

FIG. 10. *Structures of serotonin and indoleacetic acid, and the corresponding chlorophenoxy compounds.*

permeability of cells to certain substances. Thus, for indoleacetic acid there is some evidence to suggest that the entry of calcium ions into plant cells is accelerated by addition of the hormone. We have just seen that there is evidence for the effects of serotonin on calcium transport into animal cells. The effects on cell permeability can be shown in other ways. Either indoleacetic acid or serotonin cause increased loss of the red pigment of beet root slices suspended in aqueous solution (137).

In plants, indoleacetic acid seems to promote the incorporation of methyl groups into the methyl ester groups of the pectins of the cell walls (138). If the esterification of the pectins by use of the methyl groups donated by methionine is an enzymic reaction catalyzed by calcium ions the role of the hormone would be an indirect result of the entry of these ions. One might picture the formation of cyclic adenosine phosphate in particles from the cells of liver flukes catalyzed by serotonin as an analogous situation in animals. At present these roles of calcium ions are speculations.

The final result, the one which is measured, in the determination of the actions of both hormones on cells is different. In plants, the indoleacetic acid causes imbibition of water with consequent increase in size of the cells. In animals, the serotonin causes a contraction of a muscle cell. The sensitive machinery is different in the two kinds of cells. These differences in final result may only reflect this difference in the machinery inside the two kinds of cells. When that in the plant cell is set in motion the cell expands. When that in muscle cells is set in motion the result is contraction. The entry of calcium ions could set both types of machinery in motion in the respective cell types.

Many years ago it was found that phenoxyacetic acids with chlorine atoms or methyl groups in the 4-position or the 2,4-positions of the phenyl ring acted on some plants like indoleacetic acid, and on others as antagonists to the hormone (see Figure 10). The corresponding phenoxyethylamines were accordingly made and tested for effects on animal tissues. If the postulate being discussed had merit, these compounds would be expected to show serotonin-like actions on some tissues, and antiserotonin potencies on others. They were found to act like serotonin on the clam heart, and as antagonists to it on the rat uterus (136). Data to illustrate these points are shown in Table 6.

The reason for the insertion of the hydroxyl group into serotonin, and not into indoleacetic acid invites speculations. When the hydroxyl group is introduced into indoleacetic acid to give 5-hydroxyindoleacetic acid, the compound is found to have lost about 95 per cent of its potency as a plant-growth hormone in the single plant species where it has been tested (oats). On the other hand, when the hydroxyl group is removed from serotonin (to give tryptamine), it is found that the potency is reduced. Thus, tryptamine is usually less potent than

TABLE 6. *Activity of various phenoxyethylamines as pro- and antiserotonin*

Phenoxy-ethylamine Hydrochloride	Serotonin-Like Potency *	Anti-serotonin Potency †
2,4-Dichloro-	1	150
2,4,6-Trichloro-	10	100
4-Methoxy-	0.1	1,500
2,6-Dimethoxy-	0.5	90
3,4,5-Trimethoxy-	1	200

* Measured on clam heart and expressed as a percentage of the activity of serotonin creatinine sulfate.

† Measured on rat uterus and expressed as the quantity of compound required to overcome the action of a unit weight of serotonin creatinine sulfate. The smaller the inhibition index, the more potent is the compound as an antiserotonin.

serotonin in causing smooth muscles to contract, but the ratios of the potencies vary greatly from tissue to tissue. If one descends low enough in the evolutionary scale one can even find a species (the sea anemone) for which serotonin is almost inactive in comparison to tryptamine (139 and 140). One might justifiably reason that in lower animals the needs of the organism could be met with tryptamine just as in the plants unhydroxylated indoleacetic acid was sufficient. Receptors for these unhydroxylated compounds were therefore developed by the usual evolutionary means. In the higher animals, the insertion of an hydroxyl group into the tryptamine to give serotonin probably had some special usefulness, and receptors for it were evolved and used more and more as the animals became more differentiated. We have already seen in a preceding section that the tryptamine receptors, separate from serotonin receptors, can still be found in dogs and other mammals (134). No means is available to tell without doubt what the advantage of having the hydroxyl group was. It may have been a device to provide for the compartmentalization, so that serotonin in the periphery would not pass freely into the nervous system. The only evidence which can be offered to support such a concept is that when the hydroxyl group is removed from serotonin or bufotenine, or when it is covered with a methyl ether group, the resulting compounds seem to have increased ability to pass into the central nervous system, and even into peripheral nerves. However, the judging of relative potencies for these activities is open to much debate.

chapter 5

Some other hormones which act on nerves and smooth muscles

Several hormones in addition to serotonin are known which cause smooth muscles to contract and which are of great importance in the actions of nerves. These hormones are found in the brain as well as in peripheral nerves. There is evidence to indicate that when the actions of these in the central nervous system are interfered with, psychiatric changes ensue. There is also evidence to show that the biological actions of serotonin are somehow intimately connected with those of these other hormones. These matters will be dealt with in Chapters 8 and 9. The present chapter will tell briefly some of the chemical, biochemical, and pharmacological properties of these compounds.

To some it will seem presumptuous to say that in addition to serotonin there are other hormones which are associated with the actions of nerves. Actually, serotonin was a latecomer to the list of "neuromuscular" hormones. As early as 1904, Elliot (143) presented evidence for the liberation of epinephrine from peripheral nerves when stimulated electrically, and suggested that the liberation of this substance was in fact the reason for the physiological effect of the stimulated nerve. Loewi's discovery in 1926 (144 and 145) that acetylcholine was the substance liberated from the vagus nerve which caused slowing of the heart had established this hormone as the first clear case of chemical mediation of the actions of nerves. Another 30 years passed before serotonin was demonstrated to be of importance in the nervous system (62 and 78). Nevertheless, it was with serotonin that the first clear relationship of the neural hormones to a widespread mental disease of unknown etiology was made plain.

Acetylcholine. The chemical structure of this hormone is shown in Figure 2 of Chapter 2. It is an ester and a quaternary base. Both of these chemical facts are of great importance in the establishment of some of its biological properties. The ester linkage, for example, makes it rather unstable in aqueous solutions, and renders it subject to attack by esterases.

Acetylcholine is liberated at the endings of certain peripheral nerves when they are stimulated electrically. Mainly these nerves are of the parasympathetic system, but not exclusively so. Because a few sympathetic nerves, in addition to the parasympathetic ones, may contain fibers which give rise to acetylcholine (156) the term "cholinergic nerves" has been used to designate those which liberate this hormone.

Acetylcholine is synthesized biochemically in at least two ways. The principal route seems to be the reaction of choline with acetyl-coenzyme A which is catalyzed by an enzyme found in brain. This enzyme transfers the acetyl group from coenzyme A to the alcoholic group of choline (146). A second manner of enzymic synthesis starts with choline and acetate, and uses the enzyme choline esterase. The equilibrium of this reaction, however, is shifted so far in favor of hydrolysis rather than synthesis that it is doubtful if any acetylcholine is actually made in this way in living organisms. There is some evidence to suggest that once synthesized, acetylcholine is sequestered in tiny vesicles (147 and 148). In this form it is biologically inactive, but it becomes active when liberated by mechanical or enzymic rupture of the vesicles. A similar sequestering of serotonin in platelets of the blood, and in microscopic particles of adrenal and brain cells, and of epinephrine and norepinephrine in similar particles has been demonstrated. From such findings it seems likely that such storage is found useful for several of these hormones.

Acetylcholine is destroyed in living tissues by at least two kinds of enzymes. These are the true choline esterase and the pseudocholine esterases. The true esterase hydrolyzes acetylcholine to acetate and choline at a rate much greater than is the case for other esters of choline. The pseudoesterase does not show such a preference for the acetate ester, although the products of hydrolysis are the same as for the true esterase. The two enzymes frequently occur in different tissues. The reason why animals need these two kinds of enzymes is not known.

The need of an animal, however, for enzymes to destroy acetylcholine is obvious. Once the hormone has been liberated and has exerted its biological effect (such as the contraction of a voluntary muscle), it is imperative that this effect be stopped. Otherwise, the biological action would continue, and the result might be undesirable.[a] Choline esterase does for acetylcholine what monoamine oxidase does for serotonin and for norepinephrine. It destroys it when it is no longer wanted.

The liberation of acetylcholine from nerve endings causes muscles to contract. This ability to induce contraction is used as the basis for the bioassay of the hormone.

Quantitative measurement. This can be done pharmacologically (by bioassay), or chemically, but because the bioassay methods are much more sensitive and considerably more specific, they are usually employed. In the bioassay an isolated muscle such as the *rectus abdominus* of the frog, or the uterus of a rat in estrus, or the muscle of a leech is suspended in a bath and attached to a lever arranged to record contractions. The contractions of the tissue are standardized with graded doses of acetylcholine. Comparison of the contractions called forth by application of an unknown solution are made with those elicited by the standard, and the amount of acetylcholine in the unknown is thus deduced. Because other substances may be present which cause contraction of the muscle it is necessary to prove that the contractions observed are actually due to this hormone. An antagonist of acetylcholine such as atropine, must be shown to overcome the biological effect of the unknown solution just as it does for acetylcholine.

Several chemical methods are known for the quantitative measurement of acetylcholine. One very useful colorimetric procedure utilizes the fact that the hormone is an ester and consequently yields a colored ferric hydroxamate when treated with hydroxylamine and then with acidic ferric chloride (149). The chemical methods, however, require the presence of considerable quantities of acetylcholine and consequently are not sensitive enough for use in the assay of tissue extracts. They find their chief use in enzymic experiments.

Mechanism. The reason why acetylcholine causes contraction of muscles is not known. Many bits of evidence point to the idea that it changes the permeability of the cell membrane. The mechanism by means of which this is accomplished is not defined. Some (such as Nachmansohn) feel that the membrane is composed of protein, and that the acetylcholine receptor is a protein which curls up around a molecule of the hormone, thus opening holes in the membrane. It is

[a] In fact, when the esterases are inactivated specifically in living animals (as, for example, by treatment with diisopropylfluorophosphate) death results.

not stated why this opening of holes in the membrane should cause the cell to contract. Others think that the membrane is largely composed of lipid, and that acetylcholine reacts with a component of it in such a way as to allow calcium ions to pass through. This concept was discussed in the chapter on serotonin. It has the advantage of conferring specificity on the change in permeability, and of making understandable why the muscle contracts when the hormone is added. In all of these postulates it is felt that the mechanism of action of the hormone on muscles will be a model of its action on nerves.

There is considerable direct and indirect evidence to indicate that acetylcholine does actually alter the permeability of cell membranes, and that it does so selectively. The first postulate mentioned in the preceding paragraph, namely that the hormone causes the opening of tiny holes in the membrane, would not explain the specificity of the changes in permeability. The postulated holes would allow passage of small molecules indiscriminately. By contrast, much of the evidence indicates that acetylcholine more or less specifically changes the permeability to potassium ions and to calcium ions. It is conceivable that the direct effect has to do with the passage of calcium ions through the membrane. The mechanism would be basically the same as that described in Chapter 4 for serotonin. The only difference would be that the lipid receptor would be different from that for serotonin, and the receptor enzyme would be different. Actual experimental evidence for a lipid which fulfills such requirements has been found (19 and 150). Furthermore, it has been shown that the presence of calcium ions is required before acetylcholine will produce a contraction in a muscle (19 and 185). The effect on permeability to potassium ions may be merely the result of competition (ion exchange) of potassium and calcium ions with the receptor lipid acting as the ion exchanger. This would make the effect on potassium ion permeability a secondary one to the transport of calcium ions. Nevertheless, the precise chemical reasons for the actions of acetylcholine on muscles and nerves are not understood, aside from the demonstrated changes in permeability.

Discovery. Acetylcholine was known as a synthetic organic chemical which caused muscles to contract long before it was known to be a constituent of living matter. Hunt in 1915 (151) acetylated choline chemically and observed that this greatly enhanced its activity on muscles. After Loewi demonstrated in 1926 that acetylcholine did occur in animals and was the hormone liberated by the vagus nerve, the realization that it was something more than a synthetic organic chemical grew slowly. An entire new generation had to grow up before this concept superseded the old view of acetylcholine as just another drug. The mere fact that it was made in the laboratory before it was found in living matter thus had much importance in delaying the understanding of this hormone. Somewhat similar situations plagued the early histories of norepinephrine and histamine.

Naturally occurring analogs of acetylcholine with similar biological actions. Acetylcholine is not the only substance present in the animal body which exerts the biological actions described in the preceding sections. Spleen and some other tissues contain propionylcholine as well as acetylcholine. Both of these substances are present in suitable aqueous extracts of brain.

Recently, three other compounds with biological actions resembling those of acetylcholine have been isolated from aqueous extracts of the brains of animals in convulsions (152). These compounds are not present in aqueous extracts of normal brains. If, however, normal brains are first treated with chloroform before the aqueous extraction, these new substances can be found in the extract. There is thus evidence to suggest that the liberation of these compounds may be intimately related with the production of convulsions. Presumably, the three compounds were present in normal brain, but were sequestered in lipoidal vesicles. These vesicles were ruptured by treatment with chloroform or (in the living animals) by induction of convulsions. The three compounds are the coenzyme A esters of the betaine of γ-aminobutyric acid, of crotonbetaine, and of carnitine. The free betaines lacked pharmacological action, but the esters possessed it.

Antimetabolites of acetylcholine. A large number of antimetabolites of acetylcholine are known. Most of these were discovered quite accidentally. Only after they were known did the antimetabolite concept arise, and it was realized that these existing drugs were structural analogs of and antagonists to this hormone.

The analog which is nearest in structure to acetylcholine is succinylcholine, which is shown in Figure 1. This antimetabolite is a clinically useful antagonist of acetylcholine which paralyzes the diaphragm and blocks transmission of parasympathetic nerve impulses at the neuromuscular junction in certain other muscles. It was discovered after the establishment of the antimetabolite concept, and this concept played a role in the designing of it.

One of the earliest antagonists of acetylcholine was atropine, the structure of which is also shown in Figure 1. It is a naturally occurring

$(CH_3)_3-\overset{+}{N}-CH_2-CH_2-O-CO-CH_3$

Acetylcholine

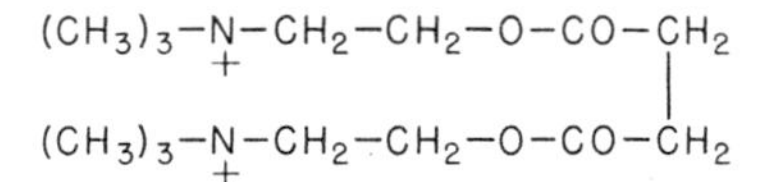

Succinylcholine

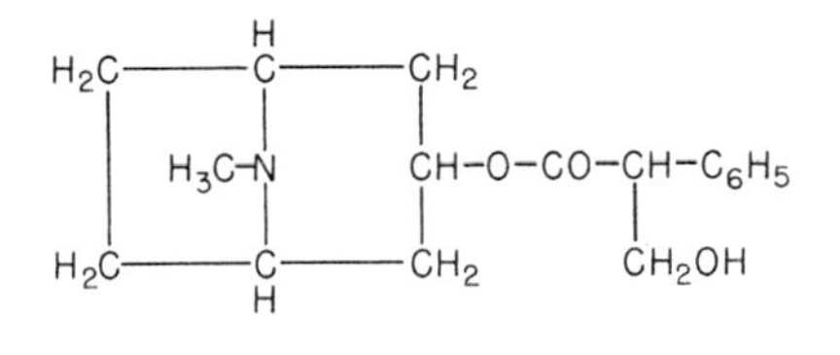

Atropine

FIG. 1. *Some antimetabolites of acetylcholine.*

plant alkaloid which was found accidentally. Its antagonism to acetylcholine was not elucidated by use of the antimetabolite concept. In fact, the antiacetylcholine activity of atropine was known long before the antimetabolite concept arose. Although the structural resemblance of atropine to acetylcholine is somewhat remote, the fact that there is some resemblance was of some importance in the development of the antimetabolite concept about 20 years ago. The spasmolytic drugs such as trasentine were made synthetically by chemical alterations in the structure of atropine. These alterations consisted of making the nitrogen-containing portion much more similar to the choline part of acetylcholine, and of making the acyl part more like the acetyl portion of the hormone. The spasmolytic drugs were developed by empirical means but when a number of them were produced, it was plain that they were analogs of acetylcholine, and, in fact, resembled it much more than atropine did in chemical structure.

All of the antimetabolites of acetylcholine do not affect nerves, but there are some which do. A few of them produce changes in the functioning of the central nervous system and these changes are reflected in emotional and behavioral disturbances. These will be dealt with in later chapters.

Epinephrine and norepinephrine, or adrenaline and noradrenaline. Although these two hormones are officially called (in the United States) epinephrine and norepinephrine, the names adrenaline and noradrenaline are widely used and understood. Their chemical structures were shown in Figure 2 of Chapter 2. They will be treated together because of their similarity of pharmacological action and occurrence in tissues, and because existing evidence indicates that norepinephrine is the biological precursor from which epinephrine is made (153). These two hormones and their precursor dopamine are known collectively as catechol amines because they are derivatives of catechol (1,2-dihydroxybenzene). Because several reviews of the history and properties of these compounds are available [as in Gaddum and Holzbauer (154)] only a brief statement of the salient points pertinent to the subject of this book will be given here.

Both of these hormones occur in adrenal glands and in brains of animals and man. The proportions vary with the past treatment of the animals. In some species no norepinephrine may be found in the adrenals unless the supply of epinephrine has recently been depleted, as, for example, by injection of insulin. In brain and many other parts of the nervous system there is more norepinephrine than epinephrine.

Epinephrine was the earlier of these two hormones to be involved in the actions of nerves. The suggestion of Elliot that sympathetic nerves liberated epinephrine when stimulated electrically, and subsequent experimental findings of Dale and of Cannon established this substance as a chemical mediator of the sympathetic nerves. It was recognized, however, that more than one substance was needed to explain the pharmacological findings, and for several years attempts were made to identify the other active substances. Von Euler (155) was the first to recognize that norepinephrine was the principal substance liberated from sympathetic nerve endings when these nerves were stimulated electrically. Small amounts of epinephrine also may be liberated. As mentioned at the start of this chapter, some of the parasympathetic nerve fibers may liberate norepinephrine[b] instead of acetylcholine, but in general the adrenergic nerves are the sympathetics.

In speaking about epinephrine and norepinephrine both in the nervous system and elsewhere in the body one must take into consideration that both substances exert pharmacological effects which are

[b] Sympathetic nerves may also contain a few fibers which liberate acetylcholine instead of the epinephrines (156). For this reason, the name adrenergic nerves may be preferable to the term sympathetic nerves because the anatomical classification does not correspond rigorously to the biochemical (hormonal) behavior.

TABLE 1. *Relative amounts of epinephrine and norepinephrine in the adrenal glands of various animals (The values are expressed as per cents of the total hormones methylated—that is, amount of epinephrine times 100 and divided by the amounts of epinephrine plus norepinephrine)*

Species	Methylated Per Cent	Species	Methylated Per Cent
Whale	17	Cow	80
Fowl	30	Man	85
Cat	60	Rat	85
Horse	80	Rabbit	97

rather similar. Quantitatively they differ in potency from tissue to tissue, but qualitatively they are quite similar. Because epinephrine is merely norepinephrine which has been methylated in the amino group, some investigators determine the content of both hormones in a tissue, and then determine the fraction of this which is methylated. The data of Table 1 will show the per cent methylated (that is, the per cent of epinephrine) in adult adrenal glands of various species. In mammals the per cent methylated increases as the animal matures (157).

Storage. Just as with serotonin and acetylcholine the epinephrines in tissues are held in storage inside of tiny vesicles within the cells. Such sequestered hormones are pharmacologically inactive. They are in solution in the free state, but are held away from the other parts of the cells by the membranes of the vesicles. Once these membranes are broken (as, for example, by osmotic shock) or damaged, the hormones are released and can then exert their biological effects. In adrenal cells separate vesicles contain the epinephrine and the norepinephrine. It has been possible to separate these two kinds of cell particles by differential centrifugation (80, 81, and 158) and to obtain those which contain norepinephrine and others which contain epinephrine.

Formation. The biochemical source of both of these hormones is the amino acid phenylalanine. This is oxidized first to tyrosine and then to 3,4-dihydroxyphenylalanine, or dopa. Dopa is then decarboxylated to the corresponding amine known as dopamine (see Figure 2), or 3,4-

dihydroxyphenylethylamine. The final step in the formation of nor-epinephrine is the insertion of the hydroxyl group into the aliphatic side chain. Epinephrine is then formed by the methylation of nor-epinephrine. These biochemical reactions were first mapped out by Gurin and Dellura and later studied in more detail by Udenfriend and his collaborators and by others (153, 159, 160, and 161). This pathway of metabolism was established by administration of radioactive precursors. Thus, when radioactive phenylalanine or tyrosine is injected

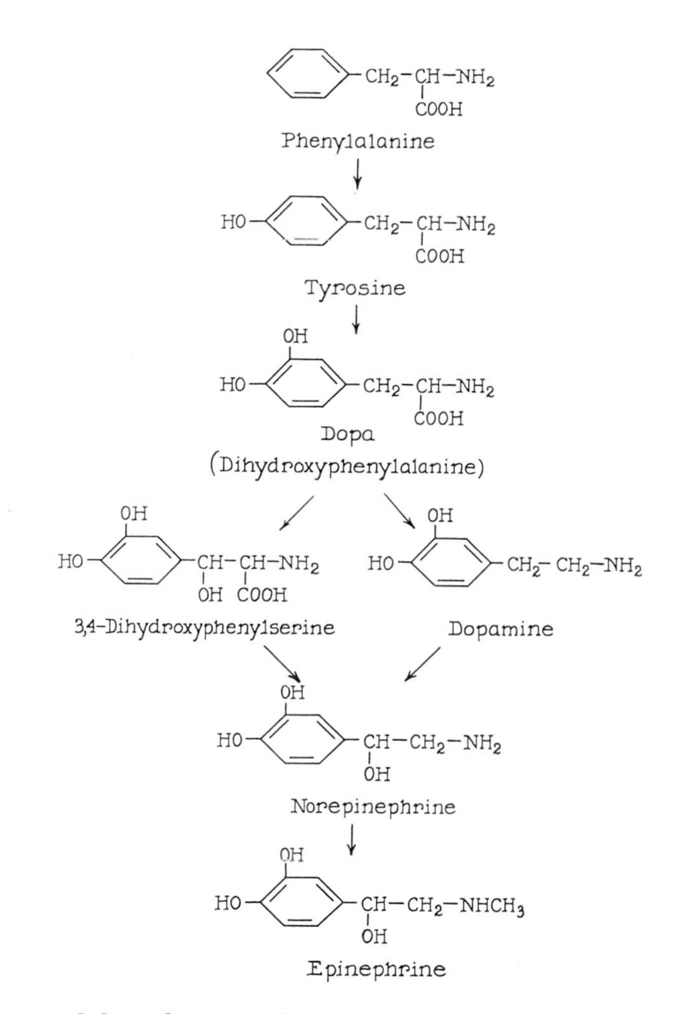

FIG. 2. *Metabolic pathways for the formation of dopamine, epinephrine and norepinephrine.*

into animals the radioactive label can be found abundantly in the epinephrine and norepinephrine of the tissues. In like fashion, labeled dopamine can be traced to these hormones. However, when phenylethylamine with radioactive label was given, no labeled hormones were found. This shows that the phenolic hydroxyls are not inserted after the decarboxylation step. The major mechanism for biosynthesis of epinephrine and norepinephrine is the one just outlined.

A minor pathway to the hormones also seems to exist which goes by way of 3,4-dihydroxyphenylserine. The decarboxylating enzyme attacks this substrate, although less vigorously than is the case with dopa (162). When radioactive dihydroxyphenylserine is injected into animals some labeling of the epinephrine does occur (163), although not as much as when dopa is administered.

Some of the enzymes involved in the major pathway have been studied rather extensively. The decarboxylase which converts dopa to dopamine has been much studied. As was mentioned in Chapter 4 this enzyme is the same one which forms serotonin from 5-hydroxytryptophan. The hydroxylating enzymes are less well understood because they are contained in particles formed when cells are broken, and therefore cannot be purified as readily as can soluble enzymes. However, it can be shown that these hydroxylases depend on triphosphopyridine nucleotide (TPN).

Destruction. Once formed and liberated into the fluids surrounding susceptible tissues, it is important that these two hormones be destroyed. The reasons for this were discussed in the section on acetylcholine and in the chapter on serotonin. Several different enzymes for this purpose are found in tissues. One of the principal enzymes for the destruction of norepinephrine is monoamine oxidase. This is assumed to be the same enzyme which also destroys much of the serotonin in the body. Monoamine oxidase also attacks epinephrine, even though this hormone is not a primary amine. The rate of attack is less than it is with norepinephrine, but it does occur. Two decades ago, before the biological importance of norepinephrine and serotonin was widely recognized, epinephrine was thought to be a principal substrate for this enzyme (or group of enzymes).

In addition to the oxidative pathway of destruction of epinephrine and norepinephrine others are known to be functional in animals. Thus, epinephrine is conjugated through one of its phenolic hydroxyl groups with glucuronic acid. The pharmacologically inactive glucuronide has been isolated from urine (164 and 165). Conjugation with sulfuric acid is to be expected, but although this route has been suggested (166) the evidence for it is not conclusive. The glucuronide and sulfate can be detected when large doses of the hormone are administered. Without such an external supply of hormone, however, the amounts of conjugated hormones excreted in the urine are small. This indicates that under physiological conditions conjugation is a minor pathway of inactivation.

Methylation of the phenolic hydroxyl in position 3 takes place when norepinephrine is given to animals. The resulting methoxy derivative, which has lost much of its biological action as norepinephrine, is then attacked by monoamine oxidase and finally excreted as 3-methoxy-4-hydroxymandelic acid in the urine (167). This same urinary excretion product might also arise by methylation of the hydroxyl group subsequent to the oxidation of the amino group, but recent enzymic investigations have made this possibility seem unlikely. The 3-methyl ether of norepinephrine can be isolated from tissues.

Blood-brain barrier. After it was shown that serotonin injected into the blood failed to pass into the brain in measurable quantities, the idea was entertained that epinephrine and norepinephrine also might encounter a barrier to their free entry into the brain. Such a barrier can be demonstrated. Perhaps the most elegant way is that of Weil-Malherbe, et al. (174), in which radioactive epinephrine was injected intravenously and the radioactivity in various parts of the brain was measured. Small amounts were found in the hypothalamus and adjacent structures, but none had entered most of the brain.

Actions. Either norepinephrine or epinephrine causes various smooth muscles to contract. The sharp increases in blood pressure which follow intravenous injections of very small doses of either are presumably due to contractions induced in the muscles of the walls of blood vessels. The data of Table 5, Chapter 4, will show the extremely small doses required for this response. Norepinephrine is more potent than epinephrine in this test system. Other kinds of smooth muscles also respond but several kinds do not. Thus, the uterus does not contract with either hormone. The uterus is in fact rendered insensitive to other hormones which ordinarily cause it to contract. Neither acetylcholine nor serotonin will cause a contraction in the presence of epinephrine or norepinephrine. This antiacetylcholine effect on uterus is used as the basis for one kind of assay of the catechol amines. Very small amounts are quite sufficient to block the action of either acetylcholine or serotonin on this tissue. We shall see in a later chapter that this fact of antagonism between serotonin and the epinephrines has considerable importance in the understanding of the evidence on the causation of schizophrenia.

Quantitative measurement. The bioassay of epinephrine in the presence of norepinephrine, or vice versa, is not easy. Most tissues which respond to one also respond to the other. There are, however, quantitative differences in the potencies of the two hormones on two kinds of tissue. By use of two kinds of tissue it is thus possible to employ a differential assay. If an unknown also contains serotonin, the results of such an assay may be open to question. The pharmacological methods fall into two categories. In one, a muscular contraction which is induced by the hormone is measured. An example is the blood pressure assay. In the other kind, the inhibition of a muscular contraction incited by acetylcholine or serotonin is the basis of measurement. For example, small amounts of epinephrine prevent the contraction normally induced by acetylcholine in an isolated rat uterus.

Chemical methods of measurement of these two hormones have also been devised and enjoy widespread use at the present time. These also suffer from the fact that the two substances are so nearly alike that both undergo the chemical reactions on which the assays depend. What is usually done is to separate the two hormones chromatographically, and then measure the amount of each by the chemical method. Three types of chemical methods may be used. One of these involves reaction of the epinephrines with ethylenediamine to produce a fluorescent substance (169). Catechol itself and several catechol derivatives interfere and must be removed prior to testing. A second type involves the production of a blue color with alkaline arsenomolybdate (170, 171). Various reducing agents can interfere with this test. The preferred method at the present time is to oxidize with alkaline ferricyanide. Norepinephrine is converted to trihydroxyindole and epinephrine to adrenolutin, the corresponding N-methyl compound. These products fluoresce in light of suitable wavelength (for example, the trihydroxyindole from norepinephrine, when activated with light of 400 mμ, emits a fluorescence with a maximum at 505 mμ). With a fluorospectrophotometer quantitative measurements can be made of the amounts present in unknowns (168). The ability to distinguish the two hormones depends primarily on the ability [c] to separate them chromatographically, and to do so without loss by oxidation of the minute quantities involved. This is sometimes difficult.

[c] Some of the chemical methods detect much less epinephrine than norepinephrine. Consequently, small amounts of norepinephrine relative to epinephrine may not cause appreciable interference in the assay of tissue extracts for epinephrine.

TABLE 2. *Sensitivity of various analytical methods*

Methods of Assay	Amount ($m\mu g$) Required for Each Test *	
	Epinephrine	Norepinephrine
Biological		
Cat's blood pressure	200	100
Rat's blood pressure (C_6)	50	3
Rat's blood pressure (pithed)	7	5
Rat's uterus (2-ml bath)	0.1	15
Rabbit's ear (perfused)	0.5	1
Rabbit's gut (10-ml bath)	40	40
Fowl rectal cecum (2-ml bath)	2	50
Chemical		
Formation of adrenolutin by oxidation with ferricyanide	100	—
Formation of trihydroxyindole by oxidation with ferricyanide	—	100
Coupling with ethylenediamine	2.5	2.5

* The amounts required for an accurate assay would be five to ten times the amounts given in the table.

The various pharmacological and chemical methods for the quantitative determination of these hormones differ not only in specificity, but also in the amounts required for a determination. The data of Table 2, which have been taken partly from the paper of Gaddum and Holzbauer (154) (and corrected for obvious errors), show this variation in sensitivity.

The biochemical mechanism of action of epinephrine. One of the mysteries of biochemistry is to understand in terms of chemical reactions why hormones exert their effects on tissues. The reason why this is still a mystery for every hormone is not the lack of trying to understand. A vast amount of thought and experimentation has gone into this problem during the last 25 years.

In Chapter 4, the calcium permeability hypothesis to explain the mechanism of action of serotonin was outlined, and supporting evidence on which it was based was given. Possibly this mechanism may represent a beginning in the understanding of the biochemistry of hormonal action. A similar mechanism for the action of epinephrine and norepinephrine can also be invoked, but the supporting evidence is less extensive than for serotonin. It is not even certain that the transport of calcium ions is the important point, because it could be either calcium ions or magnesium ions which are being transported. The evidence is not yet sufficient to make the distinction. The divalent cation-permeability mechanism would envision a lipid in the cell membrane which forms a complex with one of the epinephrines and with Ca^{++} (or Mg^{++}) and an enzyme inside the membrane for which this complex is substrate. Either the lipid or the enzyme or both would be different from the ones concerned with serotonin.

An apparently different biochemical mechanism for the action of epinephrine has been explored by Sutherland and his collaborators (126, 172, and 173). We shall see presently that this mechanism can be reconciled to the cation-permeability idea, but first the Sutherland findings should be stated. These throw considerable light on one aspect of the action of this hormone—why it increases the glucose content of the blood.

The enzyme phosphorylase, which converts glycogen to hexose-1-phosphate, exists in two forms. These two forms differ in enzymic potency, because one is more active than the other in bringing about the phosphorolysis of glycogen. The more active form is a phosphorylated derivative of the less potent one, and may be called phosphophosphorylase.

An enzyme exists which will convert the less active phosphorylase into the more active one. The source of the phosphate for this transformation involves a specific substrate—the cyclic 3′,5′-phosphate of adenosine.

The action of epinephrine which Sutherland et al. have found is to promote the formation of this cyclic adenosine phosphate from adenosine triphosphate. As one might expect, the conversion of ATP to the cyclic phosphate is an enzymic reaction. The enzyme which brings it about is found in liver. An important point is that this enzyme is not a soluble one, but instead is found in the coarse fragments of ruptured liver cells. It has not yet been solubilized. One must use the particles of tissue for the demonstration of the effect of epinephrine. When epinephrine is added to a suspension of these particles in ATP, the cyclic adenosine phosphate is formed. Without addition of epinephrine, much less cyclic phosphate is formed, and consequently much less phosphorylase is activated, and much less glucose phosphate is produced from glycogen.

Once the cyclic phosphate has been formed, the influence of epinephrine is at an end. Without the hormone the cyclic phosphate converts the relatively inactive phosphorylase into the active enzyme, presumably by addition of adenylic acid to some group in the enzyme. The more active phosphorylase then can attack glycogen at a more rapid rate, and can form glucose phosphate from it. This then may be hydrolyzed by a suitable phosphatase, and lead to an increased outpouring of glucose into the blood. The fact that epinephrine increases blood sugar is one of the well-established actions of this hormone.

The specificity of these biochemical reactions, or more specifically, the lack of specificity, may raise some doubt as to whether the formation of the cyclic adenosine phosphate is the primary reaction which is to be attributed to epinephrine. The lack of specificity falls into two categories.

a. It is not only epinephrine which promotes the formation of the cyclic phosphate. Either glucagon or ACTH (adrenocorticotrophic hormone) will replace epinephrine for this effect (173). Serotonin also will cause formation of the cyclic phosphate (see Chapter 4). The effect of glucagon can be demonstrated on the same cell fragments (those from liver) as are used for the epinephrine effect. The action of ACTH has been demonstrated on adrenal particles and that of serotonin on fragments of liver flukes.

b. It is not only phosphorylase which is activated by the cyclic phosphate. Other enzymes also can be activated, as, for example, those concerned with amino acid incorporation into cells, and other enzymes of carbohydrate metabolism.

Although these discoveries of the action of epinephrine in relation to the activation of phosphorylase make understandable some of the biochemical effects of this hormone on living animals, they do not clearly mark out the chemical reaction which is basically responsible for the actions of this hormone. They do show clearly how an event far up a metabolic pathway (the formation of the cyclic phosphate) can have profound effects, although indirect ones, much further down. In this case the event seen is the increase in blood sugar. The complexity of chemical events attributable to a hormone is thus plain.

One could make understandable the lack of specificity just discussed if one were to picture the action of epinephrine on the various cell particles as being akin to that discussed in Chapter 4 in connection with the mechanism of action of serotonin. Let us assume that the enzyme in the cell particles which forms the cyclic phosphate from ATP requires calcium or magnesium ions for its activity. Once these ions enter the particles the enzyme is activated and forms the cyclic phosphate. The role of epinephrine then would be to cause the entry of calcium or magnesium ions into the particles through their lipoidal membranes. The particles would be pictured as having receptors for epinephrine in their membranes. Similarly, one would envision appropriate receptors for the other hormones (glucagon, ACTH, etc.) in those particles which form the cyclic phosphate in response to these hormones. These receptors would bring about the entry of calcium or magnesium ions in response to activation by the appropriate hormone.

The carrying of calcium ions into muscle cells would adequately explain why epinephrine makes them contract. Those which do not contract (for instance, those of uterus) would be pictured as lacking either the specific receptor lipid for epinephrine or the receptor enzyme. In addition, it is well-known that epinephrine prevents the contraction of uterus which is caused by acetylcholine or serotonin. Another explanation to the ones just mentioned (lack of the lipid or the enzyme) therefore might be that the epinephrine causes the entry of magnesium ions. The magnesium so introduced might then exert its well-known antagonism to calcium ions in the contraction of actomyosin with ATP in these special cases. Consequently, the idea of calcium or magnesium ion transport into the cell, or into particles from the cell, would account for all of the observed actions of epinephrine and would make understandable the problems of specificity discussed above. Whether or not this explanation is valid remains to be seen. As matters stand now, however, it is not possible to understand why epinephrine causes certain smooth muscles to contract merely by thinking of the formation of cyclic adenosine phosphate. The muscles which do contract in response to the hormones are not suffering from lack of glucose as a source of energy, nor are they lacking in ATP or the components of the contractile machinery.

The biochemical mechanism of action of the epinephrines on nerves could be pictured in terms of calcium or magnesium ion transport, as was done for serotonin in Chapter 4. Here, however, in contrast to the effects on muscles and on blood sugar, the exact chemical reaction in the nerves for which calcium ions are needed is not known. One cannot point to the actomyosin-ATP system or to the phosphorylase system but instead must await the chemical understanding of the mechanism of nerve impulse conduction.

Inhibitors. Although some drugs are known which will prevent the actions of epinephrine or norepinephrine on nerves or muscles, there has been no systematic development of antimetabolites of these hormones. A variety of kinds of drugs has been discovered empirically to be able to protect tissues from the actions of one or both of these hormones, but although some of these enjoy widespread use in medicine, they have not arisen because they are specific antagonists to these hormones alone.

The classical antagonists of epinephrine are the ergot alkaloids. In recent years, however, it has been shown (35) that these drugs are also antimetabolites of serotonin. Other drugs which interfere with the actions of the epinephrines are Dibenamine (2-chloroethyldibenzylamine), and chlorpromazine. These also owe their effects to more than one cause.

A few antimetabolites of dopa have been investigated. These would be expected to prevent the formation of all catechol amines because of their inhibition of the decarboxylating enzyme in the biosynthetic scheme. One of the best of these inhibitors is α-methyl dopa. However, such an inhibitor is not suitable for the blocking of the actions of the epinephrines, once they have been formed.

Dopamine. Dopamine has the structure of norepinephrine except that the hydroxyl group on the aliphatic side chain has been replaced by a hydrogen atom (see Figure 2). As mentioned in the section on the epinephrines, dopamine is the immediate precursor of norepinephrine in the biosynthetic pathway.

Dopamine occurs in normal brains, peripheral nerves, adrenal glands, and hearts (175–178). It is, however, not clear whether it is there for any reason other than as a source of raw material for the synthesis of norepinephrine. That is, it is not clear whether or not it has an independent physiological role.[d] It does have pharmacologi-

[d] During publication of this book a discovery was reported (403) which may well indicate a physiological role for dopamine. The excitation of a nerve impulse caused by pulling the tail of a crayfish can be inhibited by application of certain substances to the nerves. It had been known for several years that γ-aminobutyric acid exhibited such inhibitory activity, but there had been reluctance to relate this discovery to nerve function in higher animals because of the large amount required. Dopamine has now been found to be very active (about a hundred times more than γ-aminobutyric acid) in causing this inhibition of the passage of nerve impulses. This finding suggests that dopamine may play a role in the nervous system in causing inhibition. The quantities present in certain parts of the brain (e.g., the basal ganglia) are large enough when compared to the amounts needed to induce inhibition in the crayfish stretch receptor test. In

cal action on several of the tissues which respond to the epinephrines, but it is of considerably lower potency. Nevertheless, its occurrence in the brain in relatively large amounts may suggest that it is of importance for the functioning of this organ in a way not yet discovered.

Quite possibly someone may find that for certain specialized tissues it has a unique function which is not fulfilled by the epinephrines. Such a situation is not unknown, as the experience with melatonin described in Chapter 4 will show.

Histamine. This substance, the chemical structure of which is shown in Figure 2 of Chapter 2, is known to occur in tissues of animals and man and to exert pharmacological effects on certain smooth muscles and nerves. Nevertheless, it is not quite in good standing with many physiologists. They have not accepted it as a compound of physiological importance but tend to regard it more as an unphysiological drug than as a hormone. Because an excellent review is available (182), only a brief summary of points pertinent to the subject of this book will be made here.

For a long time it has been known that histamine is of importance in some pathological processes, especially with allergic reactions and anaphylactic shock. It is released from cells in which it has been stored (usually mast cells) when an animal previously rendered sensitive to some antigen is injected with that antigen. Thus, if a guinea pig has been rendered sensitive to egg albumin by several previous injections of that protein, the injection of an additional dose of egg albumin may cause an anaphylactic shock. This shock is in part due to the release of histamine from the mast cells. The shocking of the animal can be prevented by administration of a specific antimetabolite of histamine. Furthermore, the symptomatology of the shock can be duplicated at least in many of the essential features by injection of histamine into a normal (unsensitized) guinea pig.

Histamine apparently has a role in the stimulation of secretion of gastric juice. It has been known for a long time that injection of it does cause such stimulation. For this reason, some have concluded that physiological release of histamine is part of the normal mechanism for the flow of gastric juice.

Histamine causes certain kinds of smooth muscles to contract. The muscle which is often used for demonstration of this property is the uterus of guinea pigs. This tissue contracts when very small quantities of histamine are applied to it. By contrast the uterus of the rat

this test norepinephrine and epinephrine were almost inactive (0.1 per cent of the activity of dopamine).

is almost insensitive to histamine. This species difference in the muscles correlates well with the fact that although guinea pigs are made anaphylactic by relatively small amounts of histamine, rats tolerate quite large doses without showing signs of shock.

There are several ways in which the relationship of histamine to actions of nerves can be demonstrated. None of these demonstrations is entirely free from equivocation about how directly the response seen is the result of nervous stimulation, but in several instances the connections with nerves seem evident. Thus, the injection into the skin of very small amounts of histamine will cause a sensation of itching. The injection must be made intradermally and not subcutaneously. One way to accomplish this is to coat fine glass wool with a very small amount of histamine. Handling of the treated wool then causes itching of the skin which can be very marked, and greatly in excess of any slight irritation caused by the untreated wool. Histamine and serotonin have been isolated from the stingers of wasps and of scorpions, and it is well known that a suitable inunction of an antimetabolite of histamine such as pyribenzamine will stop the itching of mosquito bites and wasp stings.

The injection of histamine into animals causes stimulation of gastric secretion as was mentioned earlier. It is believed that liberation of histamine in normal stomach takes place as the result of nerve impulses which arrive at nerve endings in the secreting cells. In guinea pigs, the injection of relatively large amounts can lead to the formation of gastric ulcers and perforations. This can be seen best in animals treated with an antihistamine such as benadryl. The antimetabolite protects most of the tissues against the excess histamine, but fails to protect the stomach. However, it is possible to construct an antimetabolite which will protect the stomach as well as the rest of the body (179). The ulceration is presumably due to excessive stimulation of the secreting structures.

Perhaps the most important factor in the establishment of histamine as a naturally occurring substance of physiological importance was the discovery and clinical use of the antihistamines. These antagonists were found quite empirically (that is, by chance) in the days before antimetabolites were known. As better antihistamines were developed, and as the antimetabolite concept became established, investigators recognized that these drugs were structural analogs of histamine, and could be shown to act as antimetabolites of it (1, 180, and 181). The structural analogy of some of these drugs to histamine is rather remote, but with others it is much closer, so that just as with antimetabolites of serotonin or of *p*-aminobenzoic acid, a sequence can be seen. This sequence starts with close relatives and ends with substances rather dissimilar in structure to histamine. The use of these antihistamines to protect animals against anaphylactic shock, and certain other allergic phenomena, was the strongest reason for the change in attitude which has led many to include histamine as one of the hormones.

More will be said about antimetabolites of histamine in Chapters 6, 7, and 8. In these, the induction of mental abberations with some of these drugs will be described. Furthermore, the fact that some antihistamines are also antiserotonins and antiepinephrines will be discussed in relation to the interconnections of these hormones.

Formation and destruction. Histamine is made biochemically by the decarboxylation of the amino acid histidine just as serotonin arises by decarboxylation of the amino acid 5-hydroxytryptophan, and dopamine from dihydroxyphenylalanine. It is stored in specialized cells such as the mast cells just as serotonin can be found in the platelets of the blood, or particles of the argentaffin cells of the gastric and intestinal mucosa. It is destroyed by the enzyme histaminase, also called diamine oxidase, and to some extent by monoamine oxidase. The actions of these two enzymes on histamine are quite dissimilar. Diamine oxidase leaves the side chain intact, but cleaves the imidazole ring. Monoamine oxidase leaves the ring intact, but oxidizes the $—CH_2NH_2$ of the side chain to an aldehyde, which is then converted to a carboxylic acid group by a second enzyme. These are not the only ways in which an animal inactivates this hormone. Part of an injected dose of histamine is excreted in the urine as 1-methyl-imidazole-4-acetic acid, and some as 1-ribosylimidazole-4-acetic acid. These end products arise from the methylation or ribosidation of histamine, followed by the action of monoamine oxidase to convert the side chain from $—CH_2NH_2$ to $—COOH$ as just mentioned (183). The ribose is probably attached by the action of the enzyme diphosphopyridine nucleotidase. This enzyme has been shown to catalyze a reaction between histamine and diphosphopyridine nucleotide (184) to replace the adenine portion of DPN with histamine. Thus, just as with serotonin and with acetylcholine and the epinephrines several enzymes, not just one, are provided for inactivation.

Peptide hormones. In addition to the amine hormones which have just been described, and which affect smooth muscles and nerves, there are several peptides which likewise cause contractions in smooth muscles. The action of these on nerve tissue has not been explored extensively, but there are a few experiments which suggest that they do actually play a role there. These peptides each contain 8 or 9 amino acid residues per molecule, and are thus about the same size. Their biological specificities are reminiscent of the situations described earlier for the amine hormones. That is, it is possible to arrange relatively specific test systems for each individual peptide, but it is usual to find that any one of them will cause a response in several kinds of muscles. These peptide hormones include oxytocin, vasopressin, bradykinin, angiotensin, and substance P. The problem of specificity can be illustrated by the fact that, although oxytocin will cause an isolated uterus to contract in a characterisic slow way, bradykinin or angiotensin will also cause contractions of the same slow kind. It will be remembered that in an analogous way serotonin will cause a rapid contraction of the uterus, and that acetylcholine will do the same. One rationalizes this by postulation of individual receptors in the muscle, one for serotonin, and another for acetylcholine. The same idea may be applied to the peptide hormones, but it is a postulate and not a demonstrated fact.

Bradykinin and kallidin. Bradykinin is a nonapeptide of the structure shown in Figure 3. It is composed of five different amino acids, some of which are repeated, arranged in the sequence arginyl prolyl prolyl glycyl phenylalanyl seryl prolyl phenylalanyl arginine as Elliott et al. have shown (186). Quite recently this structure has been confirmed by a synthesis of the active peptide (187).

Bradykinin is the name of a specific peptide, but there are other peptides with similar pharmacological properties which are formed by proteolytic action on plasma proteins. For these peptides, the generalized name of plasma-kinins has been proposed.

When bradykinin is applied to certain smooth muscles, such as those of an isolated rat uterus or guinea pig ileum (188 and 189), a contraction is produced. Very small amounts of the peptide suffice (0.01 μg per ml of bathing solution) (186). The contraction is qualitatively different from that caused by serotonin or acetylcholine or histamine. With bradykinin the contraction begins slowly and slowly increases in intensity, and lasts for a much longer time than does that induced by one of the amine hormones. This slow action was the reason for the name bradykinin, which means slow action or movement.

Bradykinin is formed from one of the proteins of blood when certain proteolytic enzymes act on it. The α_2 globulins of blood serum can be digested with trypsin to give rise to bradykinin. Snake venom

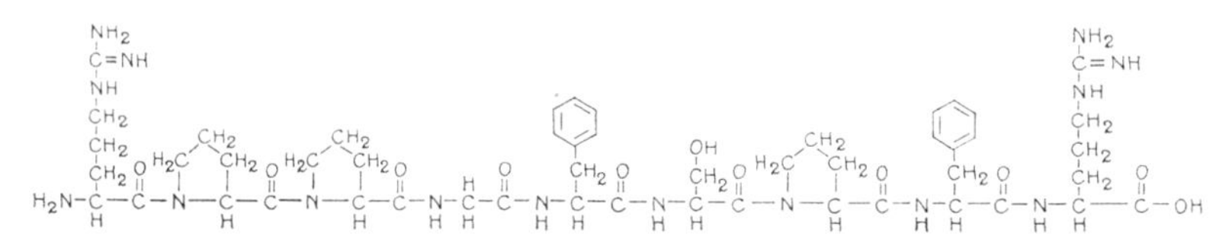

Bradykinin

Arginyl prolyl prolyl glycyl phenylalanyl seryl prolyl phenylalanyl arginine

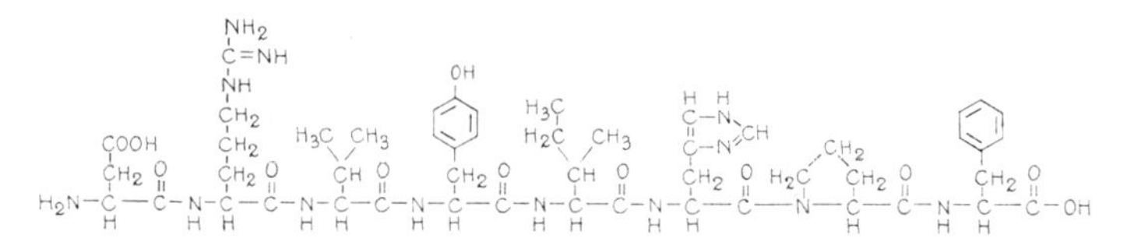

Angiotensin

Aspartyl arginyl valyl tyrosyl isoleucyl histidyl prolyl phenylalanine

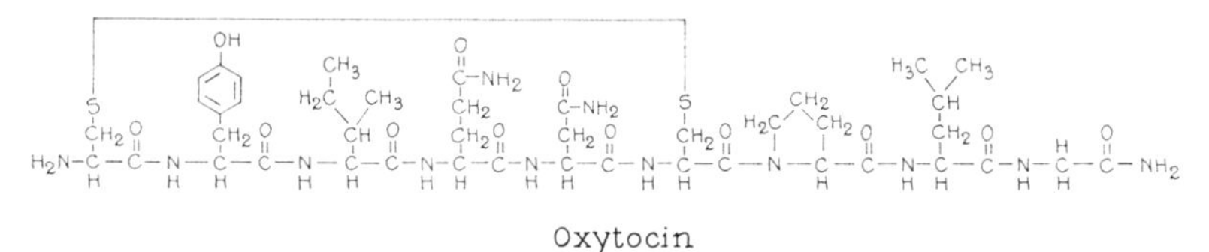

Oxytocin

Cyclic disulfide of

Cysteinyl tyrosyl isoleucyl glutaminyl asparaginyl cysteinyl prolyl leucyl glycinamide

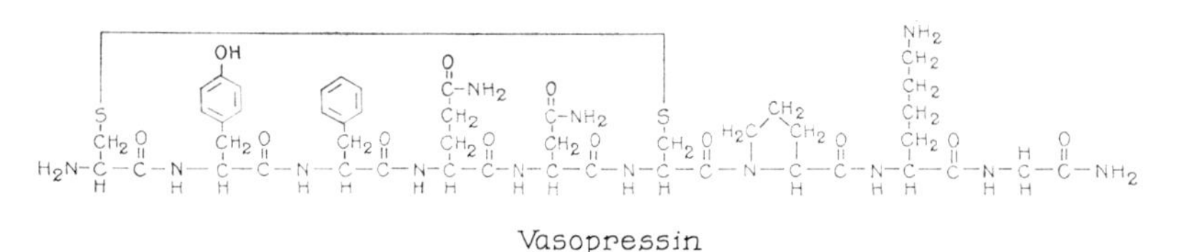

Vasopressin

Cyclic disulfide of

Cysteinyl tyrosyl phenylalanyl glutaminyl asparaginyl cysteinyl prolyl lysyl glycinamide

FIG. 3. *Chemical structures of peptide hormones.*

can also be used as the source of enzyme (190).[e] The proteolytic enzymes of the parasite *Clostridium histolyticum* give rise to a similar if not identical peptide (191) which is said to account for some of the pathogenic properties of this microorganism.

A derivative of bradykinin known as kallidin also occurs in tissues. Kallidin is lysylbradykinin—that is, bradykinin to which a lysine

[e] Since this book was written it has been demonstrated that snake venom does in fact give rise to bradykinin identical to that formed by trypsin.

residue has been attached at the amino end of the peptide chain (404 and 405). There is an enzyme (called kallikrein) present in blood and certain other tissues in an inactive state. When it becomes activated, it attacks the α_2 globulins of the blood and liberates kallidin from which bradykinin can arise. There is thus a system nicely balanced in a state of suspended animation. When the balance is disturbed as the result of cell injury or nerve impulse, the net result is the release of the pharmacologically active peptides. Kallidin is converted to bradykinin by enzymic action, and consequently bradykinin is the final active product in these reactions. Both kallidin and bradykinin are biologically active on the smooth muscles and sensory nerves. As might be expected, tissues contain enzymes which readily inactivate these peptides, usually by cleavage of the arginine residue from the carboxyl end.

The physiological roles of bradykinin and kallidin are not yet established, because these peptides have so recently been obtained in pure condition. In fact, a prevalent opinion has been that, although they might participate in pathogenic processes (as the result of snake bite or microbial infection), they might not actually have a physiological as opposed to a pathological role. However, recent discoveries of their relation to salivary secretion and to vasodilation in response to mild heat have made physiological roles seem quite probable (406).

The evidence that bradykinin affects nerves is quite meager. It can cause pain when injected into the skin. This is evidence for ability to act on sensory nerves. Chapman and Wolff (192) have sought to show that a bradykinin-like substance may be present in the cerebrospinal fluids of schizophrenic patients, and that it may be formed there as the result of entry of a proteolytic enzyme which normally is not found in that tissue. It must be admitted, however, that the evidence to support the presence of bradykinin was not impressive. The pharmacologically active substance which they detected could have been a plasma-kinin different from bradykinin, although it may have been that peptide.

Angiotensin. This octapeptide, formerly known as angiotonin and as hypertensin, has the structure shown in Figure 3. It was isolated, after many years of intensive effort, by Page and his collaborators and has been synthesized by them (193 and 194), and by others.

Angiotensin is believed to be a causative agent in the human disease hypertension (high blood pressure). Decisive proof of this is still lacking, but some believe that a substance which can sometimes be detected in the blood of hypertensive patients, and which increases blood pressure when injected into normal dogs, actually is angiotensin. In any event, the discovery of angiotensin was the result of studies of hypertension.

Angiotensin is formed when the α_2 globulins of blood serum are digested with renin, a proteolytic enzyme extracted from kidneys (195). The peptide, along with a derivative of it which contains two extra amino acid residues, can be isolated from the digested proteins, just as bradykinin can be isolated from digests of these same proteins when trypsin is used rather than the kidney enzyme renin.

Angiotensin can be detected and measured quantitatively because it causes an increase in blood pressure when injected intravenously. This increase is slow to ensue, and long-lasting once established, and is thus in contrast to the sharp and fleeting rises in blood pressure called forth by serotonin or the epinephrines. Angiotensin is five to ten times more potent on a weight basis than is norepinephrine in this test. A good rise in blood pressure can be found after injection of 0.1 μg per kg of body weight. Angiotensin also can be detected because it causes an isolated rat uterus to contract. Just as with bradykinin, the contraction is slow to begin, increases slowly, and persists for a considerable time.

Although the contractile action of angiotensin on certain smooth muscles (those of blood vessels and of uterus for example) is well established, there has been little direct evidence of its action on nerve tissue. Page and co-workers had demonstrated some actions of crude concentrates of the peptide on the central nervous system. Recently, however, by means of cross circulation established between two dogs, the pure peptide was shown to have a central action. The increase in blood pressure was partly the result of nerve impulses engendered by the peptide in the central nervous system of one of the animals (196). The action there was then relayed through the autonomic nervous system to the vascular bed. Such experiments suggest that specific actions of this peptide in nerve tissue can be found.

The clinical evidence about hypertension may also give a valid clue. Careful observers of this disease (as for example Dr. R. Wilkins) have recognized that it is partly a mental disease, even though the patients are able to adjust to society for a considerable time. If the cause of hypertension is angiotensin (and this is by no means clearly established) then it may be that the mental component is a reflection of the action of angiotensin on the brain. It must be recognized that all of this is far from being established, but it would be a mistake to discard clinical evidence of this sort merely because it is based only on clinical experiences without detailed proof.

Angiotensin may not be of any physiological importance in normal animals, but may be only a pathogenic agent. If this be true, it cannot be called a hormone. The situation is akin to that mentioned for bradykinin. It is, however, difficult to make these distinctions between normal and pathological roles, as the past histories of histamine, acetylcholine, and norepinephrine have shown. What is lacking for angiotensin and for bradykinin are demonstrations that they occur in normal individuals. They may be present only in pathological states and some may even debate whether they are present then. The only thing which is above any question is that they can be found to form in the laboratory when enzymes extracted from a normal tissue are allowed to react with normal proteins of the blood.

Oxytocin and vasopressin. We may now pass from peptides of uncertain occurrence in normal animals to those which are definitely known to be present. These are oxytocin, vasopressin, and substance P. Normal hormonal functions for the first two are well established, but for substance P all that is available is the knowledge that it occurs in normal tissues and causes certain smooth muscles to contract. Its physiological role is unknown.

Oxytocin and vasopressin are nonapeptides which have the structures shown in Figure 3. The vasopressin pictured there is lysinevasopressin, which is present in pig pituitaries as well as in those of some other species. In the corresponding hormone of cattle, the lysine residue (197) of the peptide is replaced by an arginine residue.

A similar situation may be said to exist with oxytocin because in amphibia there seems to be in addition to oxytocin a hormone which has the same structure except that leucine has been replaced by arginine (198).

These peptide hormones were first isolated from pituitary glands, and their chemical structures were established by du Vigneaud and his associates (197) after many years of intensive effort. They also confirmed the structures by chemical synthesis of the hormones.

Oxytocin is the hormone liberated from the pituitary gland, which causes contractions of the gravid uterus, thus initiating birth. The name oxytocin denotes the initiation of birth. It has other physiological actions as well. For example, it causes the "letting down" of milk in the mammary gland, and in chickens a fall in blood pressure.

Oxytocin can be measured quantitatively by taking advantage of the fact that it will cause the isolated uterus of a rat to contract, or that it changes blood pressure in an animal. In other words, it may cause contractions of certain smooth muscles. These pharmacological responses can be made the basis of bioassays.

Vasopressin is a hormone released from the pituitary gland which affects blood pressure, urinary output by the kidneys, and other functions. In the kidney this hormone brings about a decrease in the formation of urine. It is the antidiuretic hormone of the pituitary. As its name indicates it also brings about increases in blood pressure. This fact is sometimes used as the basis of a bioassay. When coupled with two additional amino acid residues vasopressin becomes another hormone, namely the corticotropin releasing factor (CRF), which is sent out from the median eminence of the hypothalamus to the pituitary gland. CRF excites the pituitary gland to release adrenocorticotrophic hormone (ACTH) (199 and 200).

When either of these two hormones causes contractions of smooth muscles the contraction induced is of the slow kind described for bradykinin and angiotensin. This slow response thus seems to be characteristic of the actions of all of these peptides and is in contrast to the type of response caused by the hormonal amines.

The biochemical mechanism of action of oxytocin and vasopressin is unknown. In the case of vasopressin it has been demonstrated that the kidneys are able to bind the hormone by formation of a mixed disulfide bond (201 and 202). This bond seems to be formed between the cysteine residues of the hormone (which must be rendered reactive by opening of the disulfide bridge in the hormone) and some —SH groups in the kidneys. A similar type of disulfide binding takes place when the hormone acts on the isolated bladder of the toad (203). Very recently a role of calcium ions in the functioning of this hormone has been detected, although it is not yet clear that the transport of calcium ions through cell membranes is the actual event which causes the physiological effect. In fact, thinking seems more to revolve around the idea that the formation of the mixed disulfide bond between hormone and receptor results in the appearance of tiny holes through which water and other small molecules pass merely by diffusion. No attempt has yet been made to extract from cells a lipid which would function in calcium transport in the way shown for the action of serotonin or acetylcholine. It is of course not necessary that this be done. These peptide hormones could influence the entry of calcium ions in other ways.

Vasopressin has been shown to influence the permeability of various bodily structures to water and to sodium and potassium ions. The skin of the frog is often used for such demonstrations. The urinary bladder of the toad can also be used. What is measured in many of these experiments is the passage of the ions through or around cells. The passage into cells is less often studied, because of the technical problems this involves.

Any relationship of oxytocin or vasopressin to the nervous system has been seen only dimly. Both of these hormones are released from the pituitary gland which is akin to and near to the brain. There is some reason to entertain the idea that they are actually formed in the brain proper, and only stored in the pituitary gland for use. Changes in emotional state of women or animals can bring about behavioral changes as a result of release of oxytocin into the blood, but so also can emotional upheavals influence the functioning of a variety of peripheral organs. These effects of oxytocin therefore have no special relevance. Nevertheless, the demonstration that the corticotropin-releasing factor (CRF) of the hypothalamus is a derivative of vasopressin has some special interest. CRF is formed in the midbrain and acts on the pituitary gland, causing it to release ACTH. The ACTH then acts on the adrenal glands to cause them to release steroid hormones. CRF thus seems to be a chemical messenger sent out from the hypothalamus. Its message is amplified in the pituitary and again in the adrenal glands with the final effect that steroid hormones capable of affecting behavior are sent into the blood stream. These relationships probably are of great importance but as yet their details and ramifications are not understood. We must therefore conclude with the remark that the relation, if any, of oxytocin and vasopressin to the nervous system is yet to be divulged.

Substance P. This substance is a peptide, which has only very recently been isolated in pure condition (407 and 408). Its chemical structure is not yet elucidated. Pharmacologically, it differs from bradykinin in its relative effects on chicken cecum, guinea pig ileum, and rabbit blood pressure.

Substance P, as an extract of various tissues (usually intestines) causes smooth muscles to contract in the slow fashion described for bradykinin or angiotensin or oxytocin. It has been found in extracts of various parts of the brain (65). At least, a peptide-like substance with biological activity on smooth muscles has been found there. Gaddum has observed that an enzyme system which will destroy it can be found in the brain, and that one of the hallucinogenic drugs (LSD) will inhibit this system (204). These are the reasons for entertaining a postulate that substance P may have some relationship to the nervous system. However, as stated in the preceding paragraph, it will be necessary to establish its chemical identity as being apart from known peptides before much can be said about it. There are several peptides of unknown chemical composition which have been detected in extracts of tissues. Because the biological tests used for their detection lack specificity, it is not possible to distinguish by them alone whether a new and distinct substance is being dealt with. The contractions of smooth muscles can be induced by bradykinin, or angiotensin, or oxytocin.[f] Eventually it may be possible to devise a series of bioassays which will allow clear differentiation of a peptide like substance P from known biologically active peptides. Such tests are much needed if new peptides of importance are to be found.

Other hormones. Other hormones are known to be of importance in mental processes. The evidence for this is that in diseases in which they are in excess or are deficient, changes in personality may be prominent, and frank mental deficiency may be found. However, these hormones do not function in smooth muscles and nerves as is the case for those described earlier in this chapter. Furthermore, they do not show the interrelationships which exist between serotonin, acetylcholine, the epinephrines, and histamine. They will be described in later chapters. They include thyroxine, cortisone, and certain other steroidal hormones.

[f] Despite this lack of specificity it is possible by suitable differential assays to recognize some of these hormones as distinct from others. It is true that in certain tissues any one of them will cause contraction of smooth muscles. Nevertheless, tests can be devised to distinguish some of them. Thus, intravenous injection of bradykinin causes a fall in blood pressure due to vasodilation, whereas angiotensin causes a rise. Such individual differences are useful to decide whether bradykinin or angiotensin is the active peptide in a given solution, but to decide whether it is bradykinin or oxytocin or substance P or angiotensin may be much more difficult.

chapter 6

Relationship of serotonin to mental diseases, especially to schizophrenia

When normal human beings are given small doses of any one of a variety of analogs of serotonin, they develop temporarily some of the mental changes characteristic of schizophrenia. The recognition of this fact was the origin of the idea that serotonin has a causal relationship to mental diseases, an idea first put forward in 1954 by Woolley and Shaw (78, 112). Any single analog of serotonin may not necessarily call forth all the manifestations of schizophrenia. It is well known among psychiatrists that the symptomatology of this disease is not identical in various individuals, and that at least four subdivisions can be recognized; these are simple (or undifferentiated), hebephrenic, catatonic, and paranoid. It would therefore be asking too much to expect to see all the manifestations in a single individual treated with a single analog of serotonin. However, when tests are done with a variety of analogs and with a variety of individual subjects, most of the manifestations of schizophrenia can be called forth for short periods in normal people. The changes may not be identical with those of schizophrenia, but they are very closely related to them.

Briefly, the kinds of evidence which link malfunctioning of serotonin to the etiology of schizophrenia are the following:

a. Structural analogs of serotonin can call forth in normal people some of the signs of schizophrenia, as just mentioned. These analogs act like serotonin on some tissues and as antimetabolites of it in others.

b. Tranquilizing drugs interfere with the functioning of serotonin. For example, reserpine decreases the serotonin content of the brain; chlorpromazine can be shown to prevent the normal action of serotonin on tissues.

c. A variety of drugs which relieve certain kinds of depressions can be shown to increase the serotonin content of the brain and to owe at least part of their psychiatric effect to this increase.

d. Increases of the serotonin content of the brain which have been induced by a variety of independent methods seem to make labile schizophrenic patients worse.

The tentative conclusion which these facts suggest is that in schizophrenia something has gone wrong with the control of the functioning of serotonin in the brain. The facts further tend to suggest that hallucinations and other forms of excitement and agitation may be connected with excessive serotonin in the brain. Mental depression may be the result of a deficiency of it there.

The object of this chapter is to discuss the evidence which led to this concept. It is also intended to point out some of the shortcomings and the complications of this evidence. When all of it is considered together the concept mentioned above seems to make an understandable and logical explanation of existing facts.

Psychotomimetic and hallucinogenic drugs. Chemical substances which when given to normal men call forth some or all of the symptoms of a psychosis are called psychotomimetic substances. Their effects mimic the symptoms of a psychosis. Substances which induce hallucinations are said to be hallucinogenic. Because hallucinations are only one of the symptoms of a psychosis, and not the only one, the name psychotomimetic is one of broader meaning than is hallucinogenic. There are psychoses in which hallucinations do not occur. Depression, withdrawal from reality, and distortion of the body image are more characteristic of schizophrenia than are hallucinations. Drugs which induce any of these changes may be said to be psychotomimetic. The psychiatric changes induced by psychotomimetic drugs in normal persons are sometimes called model psychoses.

A. *Lysergic acid diethylamide or LSD.* The analog of serotonin which has been most widely studied for its psychotomimetic effects on normal human beings is lysergic acid diethylamide or LSD (Figure 1). It is important to note that LSD is the diethylamide, not lysergic acid. Lysergic acid itself does not cause mental changes. Many statements in the literature have created the impression that LSD is lysergic acid, and that this acid therefore causes the mental changes. It is unfortunate that the name of lysergic acid diethylamide is so long that many who are not familiar with chemistry apparently grow tired and stop after the first syllables. Perhaps the difficulty could be overcome if one were to speak of LSD as the diethylamide of lysergic acid or of diethyllysergamide, rather than of lysergic acid

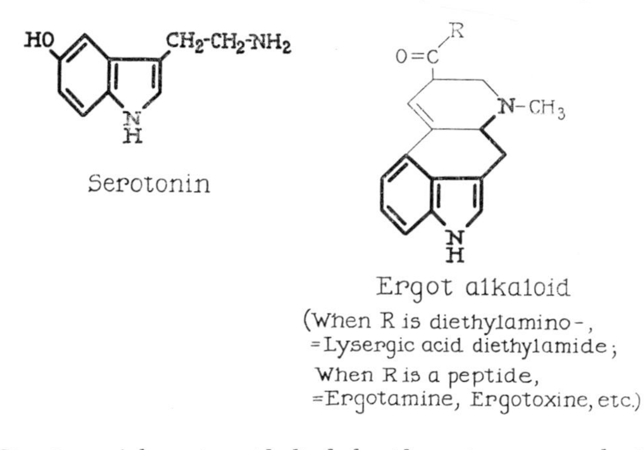

FIG. 1. *Structure of lysergic acid diethylamide, written to emphasize the relationship to serotonin.*

diethylamide. Actually the diethylamide is such an important part of the molecule for the causation of mental disturbances that the simple amide of lysergic acid, and even the monoethylamide of it have little, if any, psychotomimetic effect (205). Optical specificity is also involved because only the D-isomer is psychiatrically active.

When a normal man is given an oral dose of LSD, ranging from 1 to 2 μg per kg of body weight, mental changes ensue rather rapidly. Visual hallucinations, frequently in brilliant colors, are almost always present. However, auditory hallucinations (for example, the hearing of voices, reproachful or admonitory) are almost never experienced. A variety of delusions may occur, some of them clearly giving evidence of distortion of the normal body image or of marked depersonalization. Thus, one subject had the impression that he was being flushed down the sewer. In most individuals the delusions have some connection with falling or of going down. This is of much interest when we come to consider the effects of LSD on the behavior of normal animals of various genera, because always there seems to be a distortion of the sense of balance. Mice act as if they were sliding down a steep incline, and Siamese fighting fish tilt their bodies upward at a considerable angle from the horizontal. In general, the changes which LSD brings about both in men and in lower animals are those which might be termed excitement. Mental depression is not seen in the early phases of the experience. The changes in mood and behavior of a normal man given LSD are noticeable to his close associates. For example, members of his family can detect the difference even when they have had no foreknowledge of the administration of the drug. It is, however, possible to function in a minimal fashion under the influence of LSD. One subject, for example, attended a governmental committee meeting while under the influence of the drug, and no one detected his discomfiture. The mental changes last for only a few hours and usually have disappeared after about 8 hours.

Perhaps the most literary description of the psychiatric changes induced by LSD is to be found in a small work by Aldous Huxley (206). This description is particularly noteworthy because it brings out the fact that hallucinations are not the only psychiatric changes produced. The LSD psychosis at one stage can be attended by a pleasurable increase in insight. In Huxley's expressive phrase, "the doors of perception" are opened wider. This also can occur in some other model psychoses, but it is not a major feature and is of fleeting existence.

The dosage of LSD required to cause mental changes is exceedingly small. No other hallucinogenic drug is as potent as it is because in some individuals the changes can be induced with less than 1 μg per kg. Usually, however, slightly larger doses are needed. All individuals seem to be susceptible to its actions. In doing an experiment with it, however, one must always be aware of the fact that when a hundred normal persons are given tap water to drink, about thirty-five will report hallucinations and other subjective phenomena if they suspect that they have been given an hallucinogenic drug. This placebo effect is well known in psychological experiments with human beings, but it is sometimes neglected in psychopharmacological studies. One of the ways to guard against it is to carry out a so-called double blind experiment. In such a one neither the subjects nor the experimenters know which are the controls and which the individuals receiving the drug. In such double blind tests the effects of LSD can always be found clearly.

The mental changes brought about by LSD were discovered quite by chance, and were first described in 1947 by Stoll (207). The first experience with it was had by Hofmann, the chemist who first synthesized it (208 and 209). He and his associates noted the change in his mood and affect after he had worked with this new substance. The changes were traced to the accidental ingestion of minute amounts of it. As was the case in the discovery of the sweet taste of saccharin, enough LSD was accidentally transferred from fingers to mouth to affect the unsuspecting experimenter. The discovery of the relationship of LSD to serotonin came several years after LSD was known to be a psychotomimetic drug.

Laboratory animals as well as man are affected by LSD in a way which suggests strongly that their emotions and bodily sensations have been altered. This statement may sound unjustifiable to some who will ask, and rightly so, how one can get evidence of psychiatric changes in lower animals. The fact is, however, that despite the manifest difficulties and uncertainties involved, the behavioral changes shown by animals treated with LSD are of such a kind as to allow some conclusion to be made that aberrations of perception and of emotion are being experienced.

When mice are injected intraperitoneally with LSD, 0.1 mg per mouse, a change in behavior is noted in about 10 minutes (210). The animal looks rapidly from side to side as if it were apprehensive. It flattens itself to the floor, vibrates its vibrisae rapidly, spreads its forelegs and the toes of its forepaws, and begins to push backwards with the forelegs. Soon these motions of the forelegs begin to make the animal walk backwards. It will traverse a space of many meters in this backwards motion without turning its head to look backwards. Tremors also appear and the hair stands on end. The motions which cause the walking backwards can be seen in a normal untreated mouse if it is placed on a large sheet of glass which is then rapidly raised to form a steeply inclined plane with the mouse at the top edge looking downhill. Just before the inclination of the plane becomes great enough that the mouse begins to slide downhill it executes the motions described above for the LSD-treated mouse which is resting on a horizontal surface. All of this suggests that the treatment with LSD creates in the brain of the animal the sensation of slipping downhill when in fact it is on a horizontal surface. If now the surface on which the LSD-treated mouse is resting is tilted so that the animal is facing uphill, the motions of walking backwards immediately cease, and return again when the surface is returned to the horizontal. It is impossible to know what a mouse is thinking, but the evidence is plain that the LSD-treated one may be experiencing the false sensation that it is in danger of sliding downhill.

When a normal cat is injected with LSD, it exhibits sham rage (211). It arches its back, hisses and spits, and may strike at the air with a forepaw.

When a Siamese fighting fish is placed in a very dilute solution of LSD, its normal motions are changed (212). The fish tends to change its major axis from horizontal to a tilted position with the head pointing upwards. It may remain in this position for long periods. If now a second fish is placed near it, the two will fight in the normal manner, but, when the excitement has subsided, it may again resume the rather motionless, tilted position.

When spiders are fed LSD, their characteristic instinctive performance of web-spinning is altered. They still spin, but, whereas the normal spider always constructs a web with angles between radii and circumferential threads constant, the treated animals no longer produce the normal angles.

A number of other kinds of experiments have been done with animals treated with LSD. Thus, it is possible to alter permanently the behavior of mice by injecting them with LSD plus indole (213). The animals so treated develop a nervous tic such that when the head is touched lightly between the ears with a pencil a strong jerking of the head is elicited. This difference from normal behavior is permanent. The animals also exhibit a tendency to cower in the back corners of the cage instead of being more alert. These are vague changes which are difficult to evaluate or to measure.

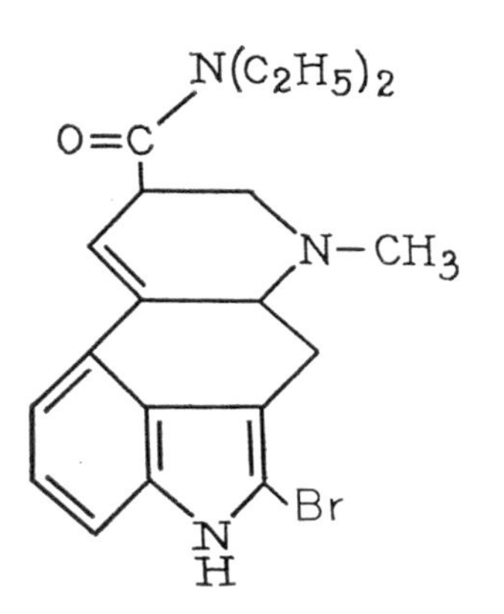

FIG. 2. *Structure of BOL.*

The dose of LSD required to elicit the changes in animals are much larger than those used to cause hallucinations in man. One might also remark, however, that the changes evoked in the animals are much more marked than those induced in man. Remember, for example, the subject who attended the committee meeting and functioned adequately.

B. *2-Bromolysergic acid diethylamide or BOL.* When the hydrogen atom at position 2 of the indole nucleus of LSD is replaced by a bromine atom, BOL is obtained (see Figure 2). BOL does not call forth, in normal men, the visual hallucinations and other forms of excitement which are produced by LSD (142 and 205). Instead, it brings about profound mental depression (215). It is not correct to say, as has been done on several occasions (142 and 205), that BOL does not cause mental changes. It does not cause the same ones as LSD, but it does cause changes. Failure to recognize this point has been the source of much confusion in thinking about the relationship of serotonin to schizophrenia, as we shall see later in this chapter.

C. *Other ergot alkaloids.* In past centuries, the eating of large amounts of rye which was infested with the fungus ergot led to the occurrence of a disease known as ergotism. This disease sometimes became widespread in lands where rye formed a principal article of diet. One of the features of ergotism was the psychiatric changes. Barger (214) in his monograph on ergotism in 1931 gives a striking description of these psychiatric events. Today we might characterize them as withdrawal from reality, insensitivity to pain, lethargy, and some of the other features of catatonia.

Ergot contains a number of alkaloids. These include ergotoxine (itself a mixture of three alkaloids) and ergotamine. Each of these alkaloids is a derivative of lysergic acid, in which the acid is combined as an amide with a peptide of somewhat unusual chemical structure (see Figure 1). LSD can be made from each of these alkaloids by removal of the lysergic acid and conversion of it into the diethylamide. LSD, however, does not occur in ergot so far as is known.

It is not known which of the natural alkaloids of ergot is responsible for the psychosis of ergotism. Some may object that it could not be ergotamine because this compound has been used in the past for the treatment of schizophrenia with results, which, though they leave much to be desired, were made the basis of an international prize. How then could we possibly accuse this compound, especially since it has also been used widely in medicine for the treatment of migraine headache, essential hypertension, and other conditions, without induction of psychoses. Still, one must remember that the hallucinogenic drug LSD has been used and recommended for an aid in the treatment of schizophrenia, so that ergotamine is not totally above suspicion. Nevertheless, some of the ergot alkaloids other than ergotamine seem more likely as the causative agent of the psychosis.

Nowadays the enthusiasm for LSD as a psychotomimetic agent has almost blotted out the memory that a psychosis does occur in ergotism from the eating of ergot alkaloids which do not contain LSD per se. It is true that LSD is probably much more potent than the natural constituents of ergot. However, the character of the psychosis induced by ergot differs in detail from that caused by LSD. Still, this point has not been tested adequately, since all of the experiments with LSD have been of short duration, whereas with ergot the administration has been prolonged. The acute effects of LSD are principally those of agitation, whereas in ergotism apathy and withdrawal are prominent. One remembers how in schizophrenia agitation or even frenzy in the early stages can gradually recede into catatonia as time goes by.

D. *Harmine.* When harmine, the chemical structure of which is shown in Figure 6, Chapter 3, is given in relatively large doses to normal men, psychotic changes are produced (216). These are noteworthy principally because they include auditory hallucinations. Most of the other analogs of serotonin which cause mental changes do not bring out auditory hallucinations which are so common a feature in mental diseases such as schizophrenia. Harmine, however, has been said to do so. With harmine only a very few experiments have been done on normal human beings. The mental changes which it produces are therefore much less thoroughly documented than are those caused by LSD.

The changes in behavior produced in dogs by harmine were studied a long time before any psychotomimetic effect was known in man. In dogs relatively large doses clearly derange the animals. They will attempt to walk through solid walls as if they saw openings in them and will bark at objects which are not there.

E. *Yohimbine.* Yohimbine, the structure of which is shown in Figure 6, Chapter 3, may be regarded as the parent alkaloid of a considerable group of related substances which occur in certain tropical vines. One of these is reserpine, of which more will be said later because of its special effects on the mind. The African plants *Corynanthe johimbe* and *Rubiaceae* from which yohimbine usually is obtained were used by the aborigines as aphrodisiacs. Although the crude extract of the plants does bring about sexual arousal, there is controversy as to whether or not pure yohimbine exerts this effect on the nervous system. Several investigators assert that it does.

F. *Ibogaine.* This alkaloid has been isolated in pure condition from the African plant *Tabernanthe iboga.* Its chemical structure, which is shown in Figure 3 (217), was established only after the serotonin hypothesis of mental diseases was put forward. The plant from which ibogaine is obtained has been used by the aborigines of Africa to stay awake and induce mental changes desired for certain ceremonies. It was because of this that the work was done on its chemical structure. The pure alkaloid, in relatively large doses (200 mg) brings about in normal men mental changes in which anxiety, excitement of an unpleasant kind and visual hallucinations occur. Sleeplessness is a prominent sequel (218).

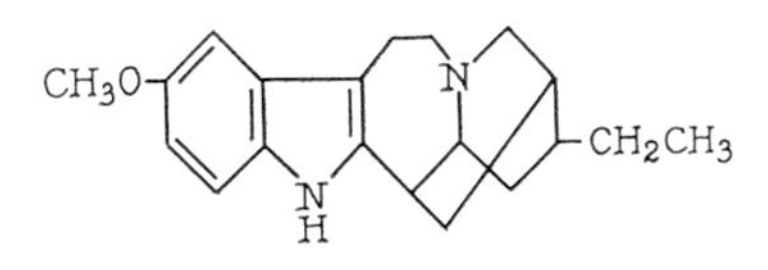

FIG. 3. *Structure of ibogaine.*

G. *Reserpine.* If anyone wonders why the tranquilizing drug reserpine is being discussed as a psychotomimetic compound, it is necessary only to recall that depression is a prominent feature of many psychoses, and that reserpine can cause serious depression. The chemical structure of reserpine is shown in Figure 6 of Chapter 3. It may be regarded as a more complicated yohimbine. Some twenty-seven alkaloids of related chemical structure, including yohimbine, have been isolated from the Indian vine *Rauwolfia serpentina* from which reserpine was first isolated.

When reserpine in quite small doses is given to normal men or laboratory animals it brings about tranquilization. The state it induces is not quite what has previously been called sedation, such as one experiences after using barbituric acid derivatives. The change in character is well illustrated by the effects of this drug on normal monkeys. These animals are usually quite aggressive so that, in the laboratory, one must use gloves to handle them if he does not want to be bitten, and must be quick in action. After treatment with reserpine, a monkey becomes quite docile, although still quite wide awake. It can be handled easily and without gloves. One might say that the condition induced by reserpine in man and other animals is almost a state of depression, although it is not quite that. However, when human beings are maintained for long periods of time on small doses of reserpine, as they are for the treatment of essential hypertension, frank and profound mental depression may develop. This is one of the handicaps in the use of this drug for the control of high blood pressure. The tranquilizing or depressing property of reserpine was soon put to work after its discovery in laboratory animals, to control the frenzy or agitation of many patients in mental hospitals. It was one of the first tranquilizing drugs to be used for this puropse. Although it makes mental patients easier to handle it does not seem to overcome the schizophrenic process.

H. ***Bufotenine.*** In Figure 2, Chapter 4, the structure of bufotenine, which is N,N-dimethylserotonin, was given. As mentioned there, bufotenine occurs naturally in the skins of toads (from which the name is derived), in the poisonous mushroom *Amanita mappa* (66) and in other creatures. Of special interest for the present discussion is its occurrence in the cahobe bean. These beans are found around the shores of the Caribbean Sea, and in those lands they have been used in aboriginal rites to induce mental changes. For this purpose the beans are powdered and packed in the nostrils. The mental changes produced by cahobe are ill defined, but seem to include a dream-like state in which there is some insensitivity to pain. For this reason, one finds it being used by the aborigines before amputation of limbs.

It is by no means certain that the psychotomimetic effects of cahobe are to be attributed to the bufotenine which it contains. Shortly after the discovery of bufotenine in cahobe, and while the serotonin hypothesis of mental diseases was exciting discussion, an enthusiastic report was made (219) in which the results of treatment of normal men with pure bufotenine were described. The subjects had been given intravenously doses of up to 15 mg of the pure bufotenine. It was stated that hallucinations were induced, but the only description of these was that some of the men saw flashes of light after the injection (that is, "saw stars"). When one remembers that bufotenine, like serotonin, causes sharp increases in blood pressure when it is injected intravenously, as well as strong actions on the heart and respiration, one can be somewhat skeptical about the evidence cited in support of the contention that visual hallucinations were induced. Nevertheless, subsequent studies using the double blind method of testing did indicate that intravenous bufotenine caused some mental changes of temporary nature in normal men. These were difficult to describe precisely. However, it will be remembered that cahobe is taken by nostril, and not intravenously. When relatively large amounts of pure bufotenine were given by installation into the nostril, no mental changes were found (220). It would thus seem that the principal psychotomimetic agent of cahobe is not bufotenine, but that bufotenine does cause some mental changes when injected into normal men.

In laboratory animals bufotenine causes neurological changes which may result in changes in behavior. It brings about inhibition of the passage of nerve impulses in the Janiculate nucleus of the optic tract, and may cause temporary blindness in dogs (221).

I. *N,N-Dimethyltryptamine.* When normal human beings are fed or injected with relatively small amounts of this compound they experience mental changes temporarily. The changes are said to be somewhat like those induced by LSD (220 and 231). Unsubstituted tryptamine, however, does not have this activity. The psychiatric experiments with dimethyltryptamine have been done with the pure synthetic compound, but this substance is known to occur in at least two species of South American plants (220). Thus, it is found in cahobe along with bufotenine. It is still uncertain whether dimethyltryptamine is the only hallucinogenic compound in these plants.

J. *Psilocybin.* The aborigines of Southern Mexico use a mushroom found in that land for the induction of trances (223). A medicine man may eat this mushroom before giving advice on some matter of grave concern. Two active agents of this mushroom have very recently been isolated in pure form, and their chemical structures have been shown to be those given in Figure 4 (222). Psilocybin is the more abundant in the mushroom. The ingestion of about 10 mg of pure psilocybin

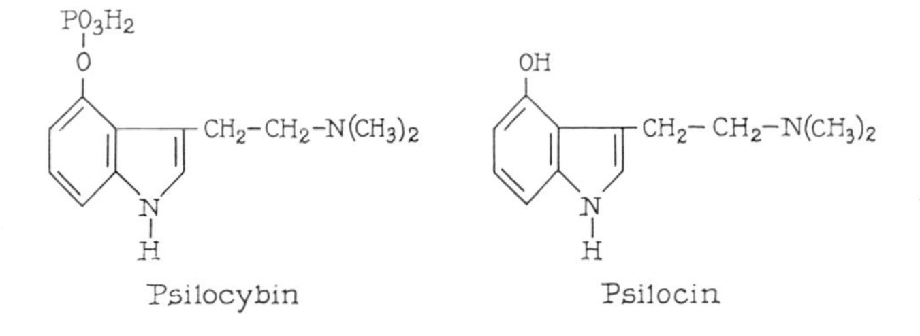

FIG. 4. *Psilocybin and psilocin.*

by a normal man will induce mental changes which resemble many of those induced by LSD. They are not, however, identical in so far as can be judged from brief descriptions which have been published for the psilocybin psychosis (223).

K. ***Synthetic analogs of serotonin, not of natural occurrence, with strong actions on the mind and the central nervous system.*** A considerable number of analogs of serotonin designed as antimetabolites of that hormone have been tested in animals, and some have been tested in man. These have given rise to behavioral changes in the animals, and to psychic changes in human beings. The ones which have proved to be most baleful in laboratory animals have not of course been tried in men. The findings with the first few of these synthetic analogs, which were given to men in the mistaken belief that they were harmless will now be mentioned. The analogs which have shown the production of frank behavioral changes in laboratory animals, and which have not been given to men, were developed after the discovery of the weaker first members of the series. The induction of mental changes by these synthetic analogs along with the related mental effects induced by the serotonin analogs of natural occurrence described above, were the first evidence which gave rise to the serotonin concept about mental diseases.

L. ***2-Methyl-3-ethyl-5-nitroindole.*** The chemical structure of this indole, which may be called the nitro analog of serotonin for brevity, is shown in Figure 5. When it was given in a clinical trial to human beings suffering from essential hypertension, but otherwise of sound mind it brought about rather profound depression (224). The dose used was rather large (about 10 gm per day orally).

Mice or dogs which had been fed large doses of this analog in the laboratory experiments which preceded the clinical trial had tolerated it well (225). When the feeding of it to mice was continued for many weeks, however, a few of them showed a change in character. They

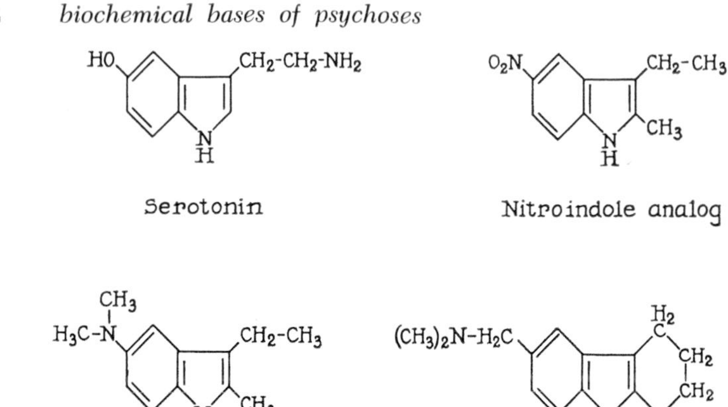

FIG. 5. *Synthetic, psychiatrically active, analogs of serotonin.*

became savage and would run forward and bite anyone who opened the cage to feed them (224). A few became very excitable, and could be made to convulse when a sharp noise was sounded. The train of events in the convulsions was much like that in medmain-induced seizures—a sharp cry, a violent seizure, followed by unconciousness and finally, return to normal. These were signs hard to interpret and were seen in only a few of the animals, but they took on new significance when it was discovered that this nitro analog caused mental changes in human beings. This was true despite the fact that in mice the symptom produced was excitement, whereas in men it was depression. More will be said later about the variation in type of response in different species.

M. *Medmain.* Medmain is a close relative of the nitro analog just described, as can be seen from Figure 5. This compound has never been used in man because its actions in laboratory animals have been so violent. When mice, for example, are given a rather large dose of it (200 mg per kg) they invariably exhibit a train of signs rather similar to those seen in grand mal epilepsy of human beings. They make a sharp cry just before being seized by a convulsion which is usually clonic. The details of this convulsion differ from those of the electrically induced convulsions in mice which are often said to be the replica of a grand mal seizure in man. Nevertheless, the resemblance to the seizures of epilepsy is clear (29). After the convulsion has passed the mouse lies quietly in a stupor for a time. It then arouses and moves about normally.

Some psychiatrists may be alarmed at the inclusion in a chapter which deals with schizophrenia of a compound which induces epileptiform convulsions. The author is aware, despite statements of some critics to the contrary (226), that epilepsy is not schizophrenia. Nevertheless, epilepsy is a mental disease not only recognized as such in standard textbooks of psychiatry but also certified as insanity by the legal code in several states of the United States (227). The possible relationship of serotonin to epilepsy will be discussed briefly in Chapter 7.

N. *Benzyldimethylthamca.* The structure of this compound, which is closely related to medmain and to the nitro analog, is shown in Figure 5. Its full chemical name is 9-benzyl-6-dimethylaminomethyl-1,2,3,4-tetrahydrocarbazole. It is a baleful compound. When dogs are fed it at about 25 mg per kg, they eat it readily and show no harmful effects for about 3 days (129). Then they develop a profound distaste for it and will very vehemently spit out food or drink which contains any of it. At the same time they develop behavioral changes. Some animals become disoriented and very excited and show bizarre behavior. One, for example, constantly attempted to dig into the concrete floor of the cage. In mice a constant repetitive motion of the head is called forth. The animal turns its head to the left, rests it on a paw, then turns it to the right, rests it on the other paw, and then repeats the whole process over and over again at regular periods for hours. The same behavioral trait may be seen in dogs but is not as marked as in mice. Most of the effects of this compound wear off in a few days following the cessation of administration, but the effects on blood pressure, that is, the antagonism of the pressor action of serotonin, may last for many weeks (129). Needless to say this compound has not been tested in man.

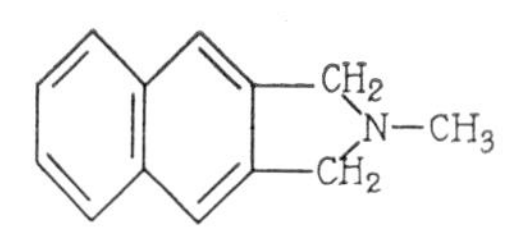

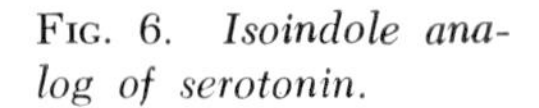

Fig. 6. *Isoindole analog of serotonin.*

O. *N-methylbenzisoindoline.* This compound, the structure of which is shown in Figure 6, was designed as an antimetabolite of serotonin (228), which it is, and was tested clinically in essential hypertension before it was recognized that some analogs of serotonin may cause mental disturbances. In the clinical trial it was quickly found that this compound was unusable because it brought forth strong mental changes in which excitement or even mania was prominent.

P. *Apresoline.* This drug was developed quite empirically for the treatment of essential hypertension. It is now widely used in attempts to control that disease. During its use for this purpose there have been occasional instances of the production of a marked psychosis in which agitation and confusion were prominent. The psychosis was causally related to the use of the drug (229).

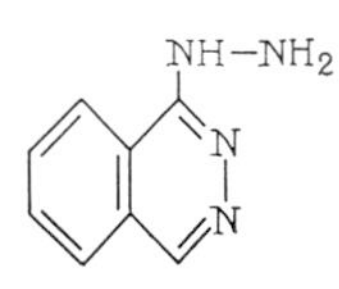

FIG. 7. *Apresoline, hydrazinophthalazine, or hydralazine.*

Apresoline is not a very close structural analog of serotonin, although it does have some resemblance (see Figure 7). It is, however, capable of protecting a dog against the rises in blood pressure brought about by injection of serotonin (230), and does not protect against similar rises induced by epinephrine. There is thus some reason to regard apresoline as a specific antagonist of serotonin, and possibly even as an antimetabolite of it, although this last relationship has not been studied sufficiently to make a conclusion possible.

Q. *Other psychotomimetic drugs related to serotonin.* The above list of analogs and antagonists of serotonin which have been found to cause mental and behavioral changes is not a complete one. There are others, some of which will be mentioned in later chapters. However, the ones just described are either the ones which led to the formulation of the serotonin hypothesis about schizophrenia, or were ones found after the enunciation of the hypothesis, and which because of the circumstances of their discovery and the arguments which were advanced from their effects, tended to lend support to the idea.

Functional relationships of hallucinogenic drugs to serotonin. The drugs just described, which cause either hallucinations or other psychic changes in normal people, are antimetabolites of serotonin. In several kinds of tissues they antagonize the actions of this hormone. In addition the drugs which cause primarily excitement (hallucinations, agitation, etc.) can also be shown to have serotonin-like actions. These substances which induce in normal persons mental changes similar to those of schizophrenia are thus all able to interfere in the biological actions of serotonin. They can act like it or against it.

A. *LSD and serotonin.* These relationships to serotonin can be demonstrated readily with lysergic acid diethylamide (LSD). Certain isolated smooth muscles—for example, those of the rat uterus or of arteries, can be used to show the antiserotonin actions. The muscles in these tissues contract when small amounts of serotonin are applied to

TABLE 1. *Serotonin versus LSD in the contraction of carotid artery rings*

Serotonin, (μg per ml)	LSD, (μg per ml)	Decrease in Diameter of Ring, (per cent)
0	0	0
0.2	0	31
0.2	0.03	23
0.2	0.1	15
0.2	0.3	12
0.2	1.0	6
0	10.0	−3

them. Such contraction can be either prevented or overcome by application of LSD. Data to illustrate this point with sections of arteries are shown in Table 1. These have been taken from the paper of Woolley (210). Gaddum and Hameed (52) have shown the same thing in isolated rat uterus. Demonstrations of this kind have been made with many kinds of test systems. In these, serotonin causes a response (usually a contraction) and LSD prevents or abolishes it.

In some biological tests, however, LSD acts like serotonin instead of as an antagonist. This was first shown by Marrazzi and Hart in the inhibition of nerve impulse transmission in the brain of a cat (232), and by Shaw and Woolley (9) in the blood pressure test with dogs, and with the clam heart test. The serotonin-like action on clam hearts was likewise shown by Welsh and Hart (233). In other systems too, LSD has been found to act like serotonin, as, for example, in causing contraction of the liver fluke (234). It is well to note, however, that LSD does not exhibit serotonin-like actions in all tissues. The data of Table 1 (last line) will show that it does not have such action on rings of carotid arteries.

The serotonin-like action is illustrated in Figure 8, which has been taken from the paper of Shaw and Woolley (9). As was pointed out in Chapter 4, a dog responds to intravenous injection of serotonin by an increase in arterial pressure. Sometimes the rise in pressure is preceded by a brief fall, occasioned as we have seen in Chapter 4 by a reflex nerve impulse through the cholinergic nerves. When LSD is similarly injected intravenously it likewise causes a rise in blood pres-

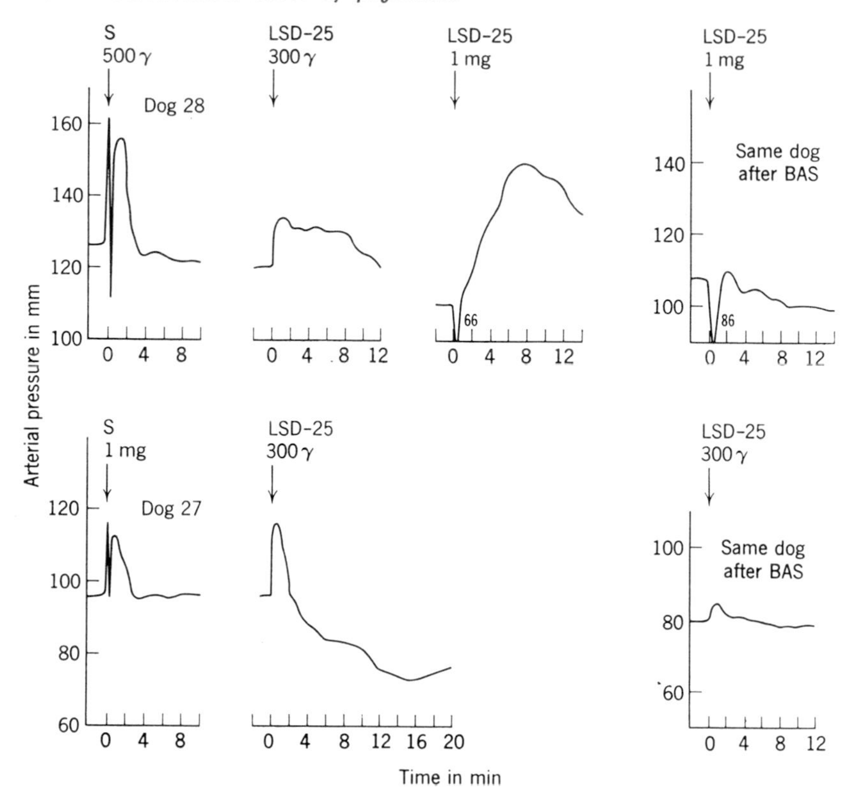

FIG. 8. *Serotonin-like action of LSD on the arterial blood pressure of an anesthetized dog, and its antagonism by the antiserotonin BAS. (1-benzyl-2-methyl-5-methoxytryptamine.) Fifty mg BAS was given intravenously 1 hour before the last LSD-25 injection. Numbers under the profound pressure drops indicate the lowest pressure obtained.* S = *serotonin, LSD-25* = *lysergic acid diethylamide. All compounds injected intravenously.*

sure. Often the rise is preceded by a transient fall. The main qualitative difference in the response to LSD and to serotonin is that with LSD the time scale is longer. The rise in pressure takes longer to reach the maximum, and lasts longer. The same is true for the fall. This is probably because LSD is not destroyed as rapidly as is serotonin in the circulation. The fact that the rise in blood pressure caused by LSD really is due to a serotonin-like action can be shown best by the use of a specific antimetabolite. Such a compound is BAS (1-benzyl-2-methyl-5-methoxytryptamine). This antimetabolite is so specific for serotonin, that although it will block the actions of the hormone it will not interfere with those of tryptamine (a very close relative of serotonin). Data to illustrate this point were shown in Table 5 of Chapter 4. The fact that BAS will overcome the rise in blood pressure when LSD is injected (as can be seen in Figure 8) means that LSD was in fact acting like serotonin in bringing about the rise.

One wonders why the transient fall in pressure is not prevented by BAS as the rise is. One principal reason probably is that BAS does not affect most parts of the nervous system. It is excluded by the blood-brain barrier, as will be discussed below. Because the transient fall is caused by a nerve impulse probably initiated by serotonin in the carotid sinus, and carried back from the brain to the blood vessels by cholinergic nerves, it persists despite the administration of BAS. It does so because BAS does not antagonize the actions of serotonin on most nerves.

The serotonin-like actions of LSD can be found in some tissues only within a limited range of concentration. If too much LSD is used one sees only an antiserotonin action. The serotonin-like effect is obscured. This is not true in all tissues. In tests with the clam heart, for example, LSD shows only the serotonin-like action. In the blood pressure test in the dog which was just described, however, doses of LSD greater than 10 mg per dog will result in protection of the animal against the pressor actions of serotonin which may be subsequently injected.[a] According to Costa (36) one can even find some serotonin-like action of LSD in the isolated rat uterus if sufficient attention is given to the dose used. The usual finding in this tissue is just that LSD is an antagonist to serotonin.

The functional relationship of serotonin and LSD can be seen in the central nervous system as well as with smooth muscles. In this tissue also one finds both serotonin-like and antiserotonin effects. We might call these pro- and antieffects for brevity. The serotonin-like action (proeffect) of LSD was noticed by Marrazzi and Hart as mentioned above. They were studying the inhibition of the passage of a nerve impulse in the optic tract, through the corpus callosum of a cat's brain and found that either serotonin or LSD caused such inhibition. One can also see the actions of LSD, perhaps even to better advantage, if one studies the specialized cells of the brain which are visibly affected by serotonin, as Benitez et al. (107) did. These are the oligodendroglial cells. These cells were cultivated *in vitro* from both human and rat brains. As described in Chapter 4, they can be seen under the

[a] This double action of LSD is not peculiar to it alone. The same thing can be seen with large doses of serotonin itself, as will be discussed in more detail later.

microscope to contract in response to added serotonin. LSD in small concentration likewise will cause oligodendroglia to contract tetanically. The action was more severe than that of serotonin and seemed to be more complex. The following description is quoted from Benitez et al. and illustrates the pro- and antieffects.

> The responses of oligodendrogliocytes to LSD are complex. When exposed to the compound alone at 5γ per ml the cells run a gamut of changes over a period of 3 hours. During the first 30 minutes there is relaxation, apparent loss of viscosity expressed as spreading, the production of clear vacuoles and a dull exudate. In approximately the next half-hour the cells return to normal size and tonicity. In the third half-hour, a tonic contraction seems to occur. Following this there is a period of active cell migration, and finally normal pulsation seems to be resumed. When applied in tenfold strength (50γ per 1 ml) with serotonin at 5γ per ml, LSD increases and prolongs the serotonin-induced contraction, whether both compounds are applied together or LSD is introduced after 35 minutes. This serotonin-induced contraction is prolonged even when both compounds are used at a concentration of 5γ per ml, and LSD is applied after a 52-minute interval. . . . Cultures were exposed to serotonin at the subthreshold concentration of 2γ per ml for 37 minutes, after which time LSD was added in tenfold strength (20γ per ml). There was no apparent interference with normal pulsation. . . . On the contrary, it appears that a small amount of serotonin may inhibit the early osmotic effects of LSD.

Many of the effects of LSD on behavior cannot be antagonized by serotonin. The most extensive studies have been made with mice which are caused to walk backwards with LSD (210). Peripheral injection of serotonin did not prevent the behavioral change, but one would expect this because of the failure of the hormone to penetrate into the brain. Furthermore, intracerebral injection of serotonin or peripheral injection of 5-hydroxytryptophan likewise failed. The combined intracerebral injection of large amounts of serotonin and carbamylcholine was found to prevent the LSD-induced behavioral change. In man the peripheral injection of serotonin also (as one might expect) has failed to prevent or to erase the LSD psychosis in most experiments, although there is one contrary report (283). However, both in rats and in men the behavioral and psychic effects of LSD can be prevented either partially or totally by certain steroid hormones. Cortisone and its derivative prednisone, have been found effective (284 and 285). Speculation about the reason for this unexpected result will be discussed in the chapter on steroid hormones. They may change the serotonin receptor.

The fact that LSD shows both pro- and antiserotonin actions should not be surprising. This is the typical behavior of many antimetabolites as discussed in Chapter 3. One understands this sort of behavior by saying that in some tissues the serotonin receptors are not as specific as in others. In these less specific ones LSD can combine with the receptor and carry out the physiological role of serotonin. In other tissues, the receptors are more specific. The LSD combines with them, but cannot then proceed to fulfill the hormonal role. Consequently, it acts as an antagonist to the hormone.

LSD is not a close structural analog of serotonin. Although the drug is an indole derivative, and may be visualized as being related to serotonin in the ways indicated by the bold face type of Figure 1, there are some who say that the analogy in structure is not close enough. This has been advanced as a reason against thinking of LSD and the other ergot alkaloids as antimetabolites of serotonin. To the present author this does not seem to be a valid objection. It will be recalled that this general problem of deciding when two structures are analogous was discussed at the end of Chapter 3. If phthalylsulfathiazole is an analog of *p*-aminobenzoic acid, as everyone agrees that it is, then LSD is an analog of serotonin.

B. *Prevention of the hallucinogenic action of LSD with BOL.* BOL, the 2-bromo derivative of LSD, does not induce visual hallucinations and other forms of excitement in normal people. Instead, it depresses them and induces some feelings of depersonalization, as was described earlier in this chapter. BOL like LSD is an antagonist to the action of serotonin on isolated rat uterus (142 and 235). It can be shown to act as an antimetabolite of serotonin (that is, to have antieffects) on other kinds of tissues as well. In contrast to LSD, however, its serotonin-like action (proeffect) is much less prominent. Thus, in the blood pressure test with dogs BOL has no serotonin-like action, but only an antiserotonin effect.

Ginzel and Mayer-Gross (236) administered BOL to normal people for 3 days and then gave them LSD. The visual hallucinations which LSD had produced in them before taking BOL were prevented. The BOL was not capable of terminating the LSD-induced hallucinations if it was given after the LSD. All that it would do was to prevent them from taking place. It had to be given first to confer any protection.

One can consider this experiment as being somewhat analogous to the one in dogs with BAS and LSD shown in Figure 8. The BAS protected the vascular muscles of the dog against the serotonin-like actions of LSD. The BOL seemed to protect the brains of human beings against the psychiatric effects of LSD in the experiment of Ginzel and Mayer-Gross. Possibly the psychic effects (the excitement and hallucinations) were an expression of the serotonin-like actions of LSD.

C. *Serotonin and other ergot derivatives.* LSD was not the first ergot derivative which was shown to function as an antimetabolite of serotonin. The naturally occurring ergot alkaloids, ergotamine and ergotoxine, were the first to be recognized as owing much of their pharmacological actions to the fact that they were antiserotonins. This was first done in 1953 (35). Subsequently other ergot derivatives, as, for example, ergonovine and LSD, were found to have similar antiserotonin effects on various smooth muscles. The structural resemblance to the hormone resides in the ring system which is present in all ergot alkaloids of this class (see Figure 1). Consequently, one would expect all of them to be antimetabolites of serotonin. The potency of individual members of the series would be expected to differ, and this is actually what is found experimentally. Thus, LSD is by far the most active antagonist of serotonin of any ergot alkaloid when tested on a smooth muscle such as that of artery walls. LSD is also the most active by far in causing hallucinations and other forms of excitement. In fact, the very small dose required to cause these psychic effects has been one of the reasons why LSD has attracted so much attention. There is, thus, good correlation between the relative potencies with respect to serotonin and to psychic changes.

The various ergot derivatives also differ in the prominence of their serotonin-like actions. As we have seen earlier, this property is quite prominent with LSD, and much less so with BOL. This fact may be of much significance in understanding the relationship of serotonin to psychiatry, as will be discussed later.

D. *Serotonin and harmine.* The structural analogies of harmine and serotonin are quite close, as can be seen from Figure 6, Chapter 3. In some smooth muscles, as, for example, in the isolated rat uterus, harmine acts as an antimetabolite of the hormone, and shows only the anti-effect. The kymographic tracing given in Figure 9 illustrates this. In other pharmacological test systems, however, harmine may show some serotonin-like actions. For example, when it is injected intravenously into a dog, it causes no rise in blood pressure. Consequently, it cannot be said to have real serotonin-like action in this test. Nevertheless, if serotonin is subsequently injected one finds evidence for some kind of serotonin-like action. Instead of preventing the rise in blood pressure, which it should do if it were acting as an antagonist, harmine enhances the rise (237). It adds to the serotonin response, even though by itself it had not shown serotonin-like powers.

E. *Serotonin and yohimbine.* Yohimbine has a structure which may be regarded as just a more complicated harmine (see Figure 6, Chapter 3). The analogy to serotonin is of the same kind as for harmine.

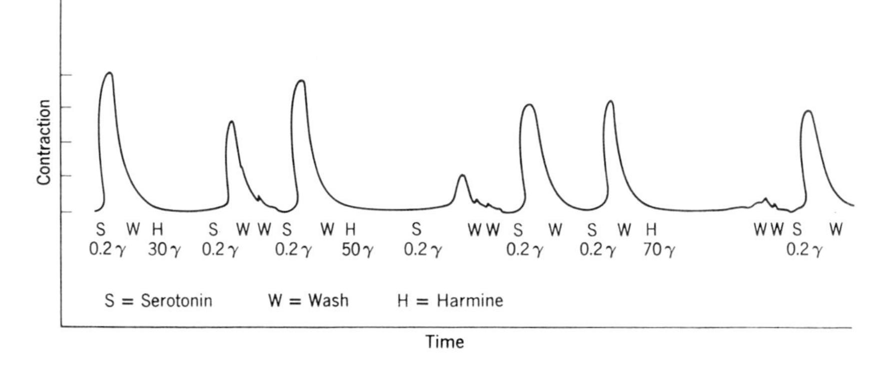

FIG. 9. *Contractions of an isolated rat uterus when treated with serotonin, harmine, or mixtures of the two.*

Yohimbine acts as an antagonist to the contracting action of serotonin on smooth muscles such as those of artery walls. The data of Table 2 will illustrate this, and will show that it is a very potent antimetabolite. The inhibition index was about 1 in this tissue. In fact, at the time the antiserotonin activity of yohimbine was discovered (35) it was the most potent antimetabolite known. Subsequently, more active synthetic antimetabolites were produced. Yohimbine is a competitively

TABLE 2. *Antagonism by yohimbine of the contracting action of serotonin on sheep carotid artery rings*

Serotonin, μg per ml	Yohimbine Hydrochloride, μg per ml	Contraction in Major Axis, per cent
0	0	0
0.2	0	20
0.2	0.06	28
0.2	0.2	6
0.2	1.0	4
0	4.0	0
2.0	0	26
2.0	0.2	26

reversible antagonist of serotonin in this tissue. However, some derivatives of yohimbine, notably reserpine, are by contrast completely irreversible.

Because Shaw and Woolley (35) were concerned over the fact that yohimbine was less analogous to serotonin than harmine was, they synthesized and tested chemical substances which were intermediate in structure between these two drugs. They wanted to learn whether or not an unbroken sequence of compounds existed, each of which was of greater complexity than its predecessor, but each of which was an antimetabolite of the hormone. If this were to be the case the evidence that yohimbine actually was an antimetabolite of serotonin would be greater. They found that intermediate structures also were in fact antagonists of the hormone.

F. *Serotonin and ibogaine.* The chemical structure of ibogaine (Figure 3) was established after the enunciation of the serotonin hypothesis of mental disorders, and probably for that reason it has not been investigated thoroughly as an antimetabolite of this hormone. If the fact had been known that it was a structural analog of serotonin, and if its psychotomimetic actions on human beings had also been known then, a concerted effort would surely have been made to demonstrate its functional relationship to the hormone. Instead, the serotonin hypothesis was being widely discussed then, and in fact urged on the study of ibogaine. When the structure of this psychotropic drug was established, and it was seen to be a new kind of analog of serotonin, investigators said merely, "Of course, it is a serotonin derivative," and no concerted effort was made to explore its functional relationship to the hormone. This should be done.

G. *Serotonin and bufotenine.* Bufotenine is so closely related in chemical structure to serotonin that there is no possible argument about the analogy. If we follow the idea of the blood-brain barrier to be discussed below we realize that bufotenine may be just serotonin, so modified that it can pass this barrier and thus can affect the mind. Bufotenine has the pharmacological actions of serotonin. It causes smooth muscles to contract. Much more than serotonin can, it can act on nerves, as was discussed in Chapter 4.

There are qualitative and quantitative differences in the actions of bufotenine and of serotonin on a series of tissues. These are of the same kind as are found, let us say, between epinephrine and norepinephrine. Some tissues respond better to a given dose of serotonin than to the same dose of bufotenine. Other tissues show the reverse effect, but there should now be no mystery about the causes of these differences.

In addition to its serotonin-like effects, which are quite prominent, bufotenine can act as an antagonist to the hormone in some tissues. Very often, the antiserotonin effect is found when relatively large doses are used. If the dose is reduced it is frequently possible to demonstrate a serotonin-like component of action as well.

H. *Serotonin and psilocybin.* Just as with bufotenine, the structure of psilocybin (and especially that of psilocin) is so close to that of serotonin that it would be expected that this drug would owe much of its pharmacological effects to pro- and antiserotonin properties. These can be demonstrated on certain smooth muscles. For example, psilocybin has a weak serotonin-like action on the isolated stomach of a rat (238). If the dosage is increased, it can be shown to act as an irreversible antagonist to the hormone on that tissue.

When the phosphate ester grouping is removed from psilocybin, by chemical or enzymic hydrolysis, psilocin is formed. This is a more potent antagonist of serotonin on the rat stomach (238). The removal of the phosphate group enhances the antiserotonin potency, but does not change the irreversible character of its antiserotonin property.

It is not without interest that the discovery of the chemical structure of psilocybin was made in a laboratory which in former years had been very critical of the idea that serotonin had a part in schizophrenia or other mental diseases. The fact that BOL did not cause hallucinations had led Cerletti and Rothlin (142) to reject the serotonin concept of mental disorders, and their conclusion exerted considerable influence on thinking for several years. However, it was plain that there actually were psychotomimetic drugs, whatever might be the explanation of their action. Partly for this reason the laboratory of Cerletti and Rothlin continued to work with them. Hofmann in this laboratory succeeded in the isolation of psilocybin, and in the determination of its chemical structure. One can imagine the surprise of Cerletti and Rothlin when psilocybin turned out to be such a close structural relative of serotonin. Their organization recently has supported the idea that serotonin may have some relationship to mental disease. Conversions in thinking of this sort carry weight far greater than if psilocybin had been discovered in the laboratory which had formerly believed in the relationship.

I. *Synthetic analogs of serotonin which are psychotomimetic agents.* All of the synthetic psychotomimetic agents described at the start of this chapter (with the exception of apresoline) were designed and made because they were to be antimetabolites of this hormone. Each of them did prove to be an antiserotonin when tested on various kinds of smooth muscles. Consequently, it would be superfluous to enumerate again their relationships to this hormone. They were originally designed to antagonize the action of excess serotonin on the muscles of blood vessel walls in the hope that they would be useful in the treatment of hypertension. Their effects on the mind were discovered accidentally in the course of the research on the treatment of hypertension. However, it was the fact that they had been made as antagonists to serotonin which allowed the idea to arise that serotonin was of importance in mental diseases. Interference with its functioning in the brain by means of these specific antiserotonins revealed that serotonin was somehow connected to the normal actions of the mind. The findings with the synthetic analogs were what allowed the connection of serotonin with the naturally occurring psychotomimetic drugs to be conceived.

The synthetic antimetabolites of serotonin were developed in a sequence (shown in Figure 5) which began with 2-methyl-3-ethyl-5-nitroindole and 2-methyl-3-ethyl-5-aminoindole (Figure 9 of Chapter 4). The aminoindole was modified to yield medmain or 2-methyl-3-ethyl-5-dimethylaminoindole and close congeners of it. The methyl and ethyl side chains were fused into a cyclohexane ring for ease in chemical synthesis, and the dimethylamino group of medmain was moved out from the indole ring by one $—CH_2$ group. These maneuvers stabilized the molecule towards destructive enzymes in the animal body, and thus enhanced potency. Finally, a benzyl group was attached to the indole nitrogen atom to confer ability to last for a long time in tissues and to give irreversible character to the antagonism. In this way benzyldimethylthamca was reached. All these compounds affect behavior of animals to a greater or lesser degree, but medmain and benzyldimethylthamca produce violent neurological and behavioral diseases, as described above. The two which have been tried in normal human beings (the nitro and the amino analogs) have both been psychiatrically disturbing.

Serotonin-like actions of several of these synthetic antimetabolites can be demonstrated on certain tissues in addition to their antiserotonin effects. For example, medmain can be shown to have both a pro- and an antieffect (29). In the isolated rat uterus some specimens respond to it as they do to serotonin, whereas others do not and show only the antiserotonin action. In the artery ring test, on the other hand, no serotonin-like action is found, but only the antieffect.

The actions of medmain can be demonstrated on specific nerve cells as well as in various smooth muscles. Thus, when human oligodendroglia were cultivated in tissue culture and used for testing in the manner described in Chapter 4, Benitez, Murray and Woolley (107) found that medmain had both a serotonin-like as well as an antiserotonin action. The analog could completely protect these cells from the contracting actions of serotonin (antiserotonin action), but if sufficiently high doses were used, the medmain by itself had serotonin-like action (proeffect). Data to illustrate these points are summarized in Table 3.

A most illuminating comparison was made between the actions of two closely related analogs both *in vitro* and *in vivo*. The two analogs were medmain and 1-methylmedmain. These two had identical potencies as antimetabolites of serotonin in the artery ring test (see Table 4, Chapter 4). Medmain caused epileptiform convulsions in mice, whereas 1-methylmedmain did not. When these two analogs were compared in the test with oligodendroglia, both were again found to be of equal potency as antimetabolites of serotonin. However, al-

TABLE 3. *Effects of medmain and 1-methylmedmain on human oligodendroglia cultivated* in vitro

Compound	Concentration, per ml	Results
Serotonin	2 μg	Ineffective (normal pulsation)
Serotonin	5 μg	Prolonged contraction for 60 to 90 minutes
Medmain	100 μg	Contractions starting after 3 hours (toxic)
Medmain	200 μg	Immediate contractions (toxic)
Serotonin + medmain simultaneously	5 μg 50 μg	Prevents serotonin effect—normal pulsation
Serotonin + medmain after 33 minutes	5 μg 50 μg	Releases serotonin contracted cells
1-Methylmedmain	5 μg	Ineffective (normal pulsation)
1-Methylmedmain	50 μg	Ineffective (normal pulsation)
1-Methylmedmain	200 μg	(Toxic)
Serotonin + 1-methylmedmain simultaneously	5 μg 50 μg	Prevents serotonin effect—normal pulsation
Serotonin + 1-methylmedmain after 30 minutes	5 μg 50 μg	Releases serotonin contracted cells

though medmain acted like serotonin at high concentration, 1-methylmedmain did not show this serotonin-like action. This correlated well with the ability to cause convulsions in living animals, and may shed some light on a question soon to be examined. This question is: are mental changes induced by analogs of serotonin to be ascribed to an excess or deficiency of the hormone?

All antimetabolites of serotonin are not psychotomimetic. This fact cannot be overemphasized for clarity of thinking. It was well recognized by Woolley and Shaw when they first put forward the serotonin hypothesis about schizophrenia (78), and yet critics of the hypothesis continue to gain an audience by producing an antimetabolite of serotonin which does not cause mental changes.

One way to produce an antimetabolite of serotonin which will not cause psychiatric effects is to design it so that it does not pass into the brain. If the analog could be kept out in the same way as serotonin itself is kept out, that is, by the blood-brain barrier to serotonin, then an antagonist could be realized which would protect only the peripheral tissues from the hormone and which should not act on the brain. In fact, the only hope of making useful therapeutic agents for the treatment of diseases arising from excess serotonin in the periphery is to make an antimetabolite which does not affect the brain. If it does affect that organ, the treatment of the peripheral complaint may well prove to be more harmful than the disease.

Such an antimetabolite of serotonin is shown in Figure 10. It is 1-benzyl-2-methyl-5-methoxytryptamine, the benzyl analog of serotonin, or BAS. It was designed with the idea of avoiding effects on the mind and of arriving at a highly potent compound for the protection of peripheral organs against excess serotonin. It does these things (109).

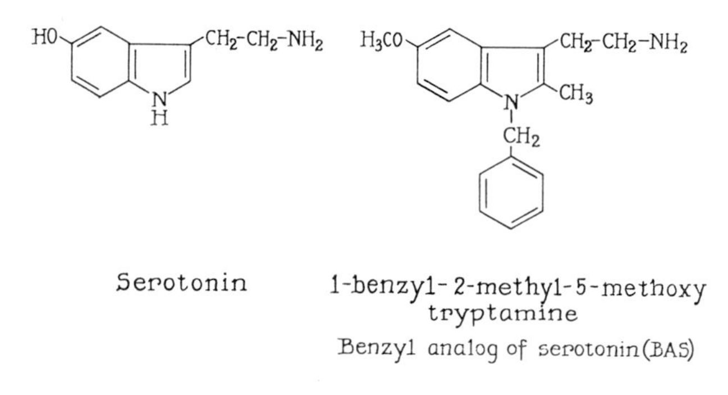

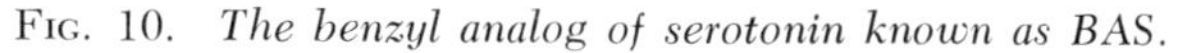

tryptamine

Benzyl analog of serotonin (BAS)

FIG. 10. *The benzyl analog of serotonin known as BAS.*

It has been given to a considerable number of human beings daily over a period of several years without causing mental disturbances. It has been found useful in the treatment of patients suffering from some kinds of hypertension (239, 240).

The relationship of penetration into the brain to the ability of an antimetabolite of serotonin to cause behavioral changes is well illustrated by the following experiment with BAS (77, 224). When the drug is injected peripherally into mice they show no behavioral change except a mild degree of tranquilization. However, if the drug is injected directly into the lateral ventricle of the brain (in the same dose per kg of brain tissue as used for the peripheral injection) marked behavioral changes are produced. These are characterized primarily by excitement.

Failure to penetrate into the brain is not the only reason why some antimetabolites of serotonin do not cause hallucinations. Consider the case of BOL. Cerletti and Rothlin showed that this antimetabolite of serotonin did in fact enter the brain (142) and yet it did not cause hallucinations as did its close relative LSD. We know now that BOL does in fact cause mental changes, although not hallucinations, and this again is evidence that it does reach the brain. Possibly the fact that BOL lacks most of the serotonin-like component of action which LSD possesses may account for the failure of BOL to cause the hallucinations and other forms of excitement. Such an idea would accord with the concept which will be explored later that excitement is associated with an excess, and depression with a deficiency of cerebral serotonin. If an antimetabolite has little or no serotonin-like action on brain structures, and yet penetrates into these parts, one might expect to find it to cause no hallucinations or other excitement, but only depression. If it failed to penetrate into serotonin-sensitive regions, one would expect to find that it exerted no psychotomimetic effects, not even depression.

All psychotomimetic agents are not analogs of serotonin. The best known example is ethyl alcohol which can induce psychoses and yet has no known connection with serotonin either structurally or functionally. Another example is mescaline (3,4,5-trimethoxyphenylethylamine). There are several other examples. In fact, some of them which are antimetabolites of acetylcholine and of epinephrine will be discussed in Chapters 8 and 9.

There must be several ways in which drugs can stop the multitude of processes on which the brain depends for its normal functioning. It would be surprising indeed if there were only one susceptible point and that one involved only serotonin. Drugs directed at other points may cause interruption of those reactions of the brain which ensure the harmony of thought, emotion, and action which we call normal behavior. It would be asking too much to insist that all psychotomimetic drugs must be directed at serotonin directly. Nevertheless, so many of the known ones are, that the serotonin postulate has come into being.

Summary of the foregoing data and first suggestions of what they may mean. The primary evidence for the belief that schizophrenia is the reflection of a disturbance of the metabolism of serotonin in the brain is that a large variety of chemical compounds related structurally and functionally to this hormone cause in normal men mental changes resembling those of the natural disease. These analogs either act like serotonin, or they act against it, creating a deficiency of it.

Relationship of some tranquilizing drugs to serotonin. The most prominent drugs now in clinical use for the tranquilization of disturbed patients suffering from schizophrenia interfere with the actions of serotonin. It is conceivable that their tranquilizing effect on agitated mental patients is because of such interference. This deduction may not be justifiable, as critics have been quick to point out, but there is considerable evidence to entertain the idea that it is justifiable, and that the failure in the functioning of serotonin which these tranquilizers cause is connected with the mental effects. The chief reason for hesitancy in accepting such an idea is that the two principal tranquilizers, reserpine and chlorpromazine, also interfere in the functioning of other "neuromuscular" hormones such as norepinephrine and histamine. This relationship to hormones other than serotonin will be examined in Chapters 8 and 9. We shall see there that the interference with norepinephrine and histamine is not unrelated to the interference with serotonin.

The fact that tranquilizing drugs interfere in the functioning of serotonin was the second type of evidence to support the serotonin hypothesis about schizophrenia. The first was that normal minds could be disturbed (and made to function in many ways similar to those of schizophrenic patients) by giving analogs of serotonin. The second was that schizophrenic minds could be tranquilized (even though usually not cured) by giving drugs which interfered with the biological actions of serotonin. The serotonin hypothesis which had been formulated from the first kind of evidence found additional support from the second kind.

A. *Reserpine and serotonin.* When reserpine was discovered and identified and shown to calm certain mental patients, the findings had been made in the classical fashion, i.e., by accident and by careful observation (241). The chemical structure (shown in Figure 6 of Chapter 3) was established just after the enunciation of the hypothesis about schizophrenia and serotonin described in the preceding section. Reserpine was seen to be a relative of yohimbine and, distantly, of serotonin. The demonstration of the antiserotonin action of yohimbine 2 years before (35) suggested that reserpine, too, might be an antimetabolite of this hormone. The findings of the past few years suggest that it is. It is, however, not a reversible antagonist, and has other peculiarities.

When reserpine is given to experimental animals and to man, it displaces serotonin from the tissues. This displacement can be shown by direct analysis of the tissue, and also by the increased excretion of 5-hydroxyindoleacetic acid in the urine. These facts were first established by Pletscher, Shore, and Brodie (27 and 242), and they have been amply confirmed. The serotonin content of the intestines of a rabbit usually falls from about 1000 μg to about 350 μg after injection of 5 mg reserpine per kg (the maximal tolerated dose). The content of the brain may fall to 10 per cent of the control values. In platelets of the blood exposed to reserpine, either *in vivo* or *in vitro*, the serotonin falls markedly. In fact, very small concentrations of reserpine will inhibit the "active" transport of serotonin from blood plasma into platelets *in vitro* (243, 244). Several other alkaloids of *Rauwolfia serpentina* which, unlike reserpine, do not cause tranquilization, also do not cause the displacement of serotonin from tissues. Data to illustrate this point are given in Table 4, which has been reproduced from the paper of Shore et al. (243).

The displacement of serotonin is precisely what an antimetabolite of it would be expected to do. The analog combines with some of the serotonin receptors and displaces the hormone from them. This is the basic mechanism of action of antimetabolites, as we have already seen in Chapter 3. A synthetic and *bona fide* antimetabolite of serotonin —1-benzyl-2-methyl-5-methoxytryptamine, or BAS—also brings about such displacement (see Table 2, Chapter 3). The depletion is not as complete as it is with reserpine.

There is, however, something not quite orthodox about the biological properties of reserpine which causes hesitation in assigning to it the role of an antimetabolite of serotonin. To demonstrate its antiserotonin action in the usual tests with smooth muscles, special arrangements must be made. Thus, in the blood pressure test in the dog, Schneider and Rhinehart (245) found that it was necessary to cut the spinal cord and the vagus nerves before reserpine would act as an antimetabolite and inhibit the rise in pressure when serotonin was injected. If the

TABLE 4. *Serotonin concentration in the brain of rabbits 4 hours after intravenous administration of various* Rauwolfia *alkaloids*

Alkaloid	Dose, mg per kg	Sedative Action	Serotonin Concentration, μg per gram
None	—	—	0.57
Reserpine	2	Active	0.06
Deserpidine (recanescine)	2	Active	0.09
Rescinnamine	2	Active	0.10
Methyl reserpate syringate	3	Active	0.06
Raunescine	5	Active	0.07
Methyl reserpate acetoacetate	3	Slightly active	0.34
Isoreserpine	2	Inactive	0.48
Isoraunescine	5	Inactive	0.47
Methyl reserpate	2	Inactive	0.44
Reserpic acid	2	Inactive	0.52
Reserpinine	2	Inactive	0.49
Serpentine	2	Inactive	0.45
Ajmaline	2	Inactive	0.44
Ajmalicine	2	Inactive	0.55

nerves were left intact, reserpine enhanced, rather than reduced, the rise. This was probably because of the action of reserpine on the brain with consequent indirect effects through the cholinergic nerves to the blood vessels. The atypical behavior of reserpine has been seen in another way. When this drug is injected into a normal dog, or fed to it, the blood pressure falls. Synthetic analogs of serotonin, for which the antimetabolite character is never in doubt, do not cause a fall in normal blood pressure.

In like fashion, the assay of reserpine for antiserotonin properties in the isolated rat uterus showed only a partial inhibition of the serotonin-induced contraction, as Costa has indicated (36). In this *in vitro* test, however, the marked insolubility of reserpine made it difficult to add a sufficient concentration, and this may have accounted for the atypical response. In all of these assays, reserpine acted as an irreversible antagonist to serotonin. By contrast, its relative yohimbine is a competitively reversible one. All these properties, that is, antagonism to serotonin in tissues and the displacement of serotonin from tissues, suggest the conclusion that reserpine is probably an antimetabolite of serotonin, but an atypical one.[b] It is moreover one with unusual predilections for nerve tissues.

Reserpine not only displaces serotonin; it also displaces norepinephrine from brain and from nerve endings (246). This action is not surprising since reserpine is a structural analog of the epinephrines as well as of serotonin. The benzenoid rings fused to the harmine ring system give it the analogy to the epinephrines, and the harmine ring system gives it the analogy to serotonin. It has long been known that yohimbine is an antagonist of epinephrine, so that one would not be surprised to find that its relative reserpine also was. However, the direct demonstration of an anti-epinephrine or anti-norepinephrine effect on smooth muscle is more difficult than a similar demonstration of its anti-serotonin action. The principal evidence for the reaction of reserpine with norepinephrine receptors is the displacement of norepinephrine from tissues when the drug is administered to animals.

It is possible that reserpine acts on only certain kinds of receptors for either serotonin or norepinephrine, and not on all of them. The receptors for the storage particles (such as platelets) may have a special affinity for reserpine, so that when the drug reacts with these, much of the sequestered hormones is released. In keeping with this suggestion it is always noted that although reserpine may lower the serotonin and norepinephrine contents of a tissue very markedly, it never completely exhausts them. Much of the serotonin or norepinephrine which is displaced from a tissue is not bound in any chemical sense. It is merely physically sequestered in a membranous vesicle,

[b] Before this view of reserpine action gained acceptance, several papers by Brodie and his collaborators attempted to show that the action of reserpine was due to the serotonin which it displaced rather than to the drug itself. This postulate failed to take into account the fact that the displaced serotonin must exert a pharmacological effect by combination with a receptor. The serotonin receptors, however, were blocked by the reserpine which had displaced the hormone. They were consequently unavailable for reaction with serotonin. One of the experimental results which was used to support the contention that the displaced serotonin was really the active agent in the reserpine effect was that some reserpine-like reactions were observed in animals treated with massive doses of serotonin. The reason why this evidence was unacceptable was the following. Excessive amounts of serotonin can effectively inhibit or prevent the normal serotonin response as will be discussed later in this chapter. Consequently, the massive doses of serotonin probably exerted a reserpine-like action because they were acting as inhibitors of the hormone.

so that it remains pharmacologically inactive until the membrane is damaged. If the serotonin stored in the vesicles is displaced by reserpine more readily than is the rest of the hormone, one could understand why the drug does not readily displace all serotonin from tissues.

The findings of displacement of serotonin from tissues by reserpine lend support to the serotonin hypothesis about schizophrenia. This analog of serotonin causes a deficiency of it which can be demonstrated by direct chemical analysis. It also quiets or tranquilizes many excited schizophrenic patients. Relatives of reserpine which do not tranquilize the patients do not displace serotonin from tissues. The work with reserpine, thus, gives a clue, which suggests that the phase of excitement in the disease may be due to an excess of cerebral serotonin.

B. *Chlorpromazine (Thorazine) and serotonin.* Perhaps the most widely used tranquilizing drug for the control of agitated mental patients is chlorpromazine. Its chemical structure is shown in Figure 11. It calms psychotic excitement and makes the patient easier to manage. It can also relieve anxiety. Just as with reserpine, chlorpromazine does not seem to cure schizophrenia, but it has proved of much use in the management of agitated patients suffering from this disease, and has made it possible for many of them to return to society.

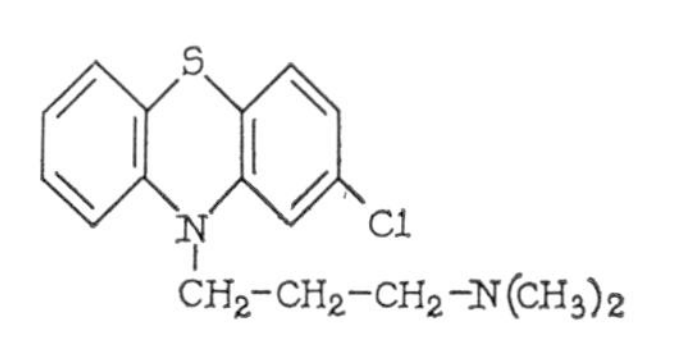

FIG. 11. *Structure of the tranquilizer chlorpromazine.*

Unlike reserpine, chlorpromazine is not a structural analog of serotonin, and is not an antimetabolite of it. Also unlike reserpine, chlorpromazine does not displace serotonin (or norepinephrine) from tissues, and consequently does not increase the urinary excretion of 5-hydroxyindoleacetic acid.[c] These are the biochemical signs which say that it is not acting as an antimetabolite of this hormone. It lacks both the structural resemblance and the functional aspects which an antimetabolite should show.

Nevertheless, chlorpromazine does interfere with the actions of serotonin on tissues. Most of the demonstrations have been made with smooth muscles. Thus, treatment of an isolated rat colon with

[c] In fact, chlorpromazine may actually decrease the urinary excretion of 5-hydroxylindoleacetic acid (247). This is probably a reflection of the fact that chlorpromazine depresses many oxidative enzymic reactions in the body. The oxidation of serotonin to 5-hydroxyindoleacetic acid is just one example of inhibited oxidations.

chlorpromazine renders it insensitive to the contracting action of serotonin (248). In such a test the effect is irreversible. Once the ability to respond to serotonin has been lost (either partially or totally) by exposure to the drug, it cannot be regained by washing, or by additions of small amounts of serotonin. In some way the chlorpromazine makes the tissue become unable to respond, in the normal fashion, to the hormone. In this type of test it shows rather high potency, because small amounts (in comparison to the dose required of an antimetabolite of serotonin) are sufficient to cause this loss of response to the hormone.

The reason for the serotonin-desensitizing action of chlorpromazine is not known. It would seem possible that the effect might be exerted at the cell membrane, and two postulates have been proposed to explain its action with this idea in mind. These may be summarized as follows:

a. Karreman et al. (249) found that chlorpromazine was a strong electron donor and would form charge transfer complexes. They emphasized the rarity of this property among chemical substances. The fact that chlorpromazine showed it, possibly meant that this drug owed some of its effects on tissues to this property. The electrical potentials generated at the membranes of cells of nerves and muscles, and the transport of metallic ions through these membranes might be disturbed by a drug like chlorpromazine which can form these charge transfer complexes. The drug might interfere with the ionic and electrical events at the membranes.

b. Harris et al. (250) found that chlorpromazine formed chemical complexes with gangliosides (strandin). It is now becoming clear that these complicated lipids (the gangliosides) are localized in the membranes of cells (251). In these membranes they may play a role in hormonal action. For example, they have shown considerable potency in the *in vitro* assay for the serotonin receptor substance (252). If it should turn out that they are more or less directly related to the hormonal receptors in cell membranes, then a drug which had the property of reacting with them chemically might be able to interfere with the actions of that hormone on cells.

These ideas represent only the starting points in the understanding of the mechanism of action of chlorpromazine. No detailed mechanism can yet be discussed. All that can be said is that chlorpromazine does interfere with the normal actions of serotonin on cells, and that this interference is not of the antimetabolite variety.

Chlorpromazine also interferes with the actions of certain other hormones which affect nerves and muscles. It was discovered in a routine screening program for the improvement of antihistamines. It is distantly related in chemical structure to histamine, and does show some potency as an antagonist of that hormone (248, 253). In addition, chlorpromazine has been found to prevent some of the actions of epinephrine and norepinephrine. It will, for example, antagonize the effects of one or the other of these hormones on blood pressure. If test systems are properly chosen one can thus show that chlorpromazine interferes with the biological actions of several hormones, a fact which is not unique to it, and which will be discussed at more length in Chapters 8 and 9.

With respect to serotonin, chlorpromazine exerts a net effect which in the end result is the same as that of reserpine. Either drug causes eventually a deficiency of this hormone. Reserpine does it by displacing serotonin from its receptors (as an antimetabolite should) so that the cell suffers from a lack of the hormone. Chlorpromazine does it by somehow preventing the response of the cell to serotonin. The mechanism is different but the net result is similar. Both drugs cause tranquilization of disturbed schizophrenic patients.

The foregoing summarizing paragraph is not to be interpreted to mean that the pharmacological effects of chlorpromazine and reserpine are identical, because they are not. Close observers can find that even the tranquilization which each causes is different in detail. The details of action in various smooth muscles likewise are different. The point which is being emphasized is that both drugs do interfere in the actions of serotonin and certain other hormones (for example, norepinephrine) which results in a net deficiency of these in cellular action. Both drugs subdue agitated minds. There may possibly be a cause and effect relationship between these similar properties of two chemically dissimilar drugs.

C. *Nicotinamide and serotonin.* Nicotinamide and nicotinic acid represent a kind of tranquilizing drug which has been used clinically, but has not been firmly established in the treatment of schizophrenia. Despite the uncertain clinical usefulness the situation deserves attention.

Hoffer et al. (254) claimed that massive doses of either nicotinic acid or nicotinamide would cure schizophrenic patients, provided that the use of the compound was started relatively early in the disease. A daily dose of 3 to 5 grams was recommended. The present author has seen no published reports to confirm or deny these claims of the tranquilizing and curative actions in schizophrenia.

Shortly after the publication of Hoffer's results, Woolley (255) undertook the study of massive doses of nicotinic acid and of nicotinamide in experimental animals. Large doses did bring about marked tranquilization in mice. Similar large doses could be shown to prevent the actions of serotonin on smooth muscles either in living animals or in isolated organs. For example, mice were completely protected against the diarrhea caused by injection of 5-hydroxytryptophan. The isolated uterus of a rat was protected against the contractions ordinarily induced with serotonin. The mouse diarrhea test required about 25 mg nicotinamide per mouse for complete protection against 0.4 mg 5-hydroxytryptophan. The rat uterus test required about 1.25 mg nicotinamide per ml to prevent the contractions induced by 0.01 μg serotonin. Nicotinic acid was unable to protect the isolated tissue, but either nicotinic acid or nicotinamide was effective in the living animals. Probably in the living animals the acid was converted to the amide which was the active substance in all cases.

Nicotinamide is not an antimetabolite of serotonin. The structural analogy is lacking. Furthermore, direct experimental evidence was found that the nicotinamide did not compete with serotonin for the hormonal receptors in the isolated rat uterus. Thus, nicotinamide did not prevent the transport of calcium ions into the cells of the muscle, whereas a *bona fide* antimetabolite of serotonin (BAS) did. Just as with chlorpromazine, nicotinamide owed its interference with the action of serotonin to some other causes. Nevertheless, the fact that it did interfere was readily demonstrated.

The tranquilizing and antiserotonin actions of nicotinamide on laboratory animals added to the evidence derived from the clinically effective tranquilizing drugs reserpine and chlorpromazine. Each of these dissimilar kinds of chemical compounds had the following points in common. They were tranquilizers, and they prevented the action of serotonin on tissues. Whether or not nicotinamide cures or even alleviates schizophrenia is not vital to the foregoing discussion. The fact remains that massive doses of it do tranquilize animals, and interfere with the actions of serotonin in them. Nevertheless, it would be most interesting to know if the findings of Hoffer et al. (254) about its effect on the human disease can be confirmed.

Summary of the relationship of tranquilizing drugs to serotonin. It was plain that three tranquilizing drugs of widely differing chemical structures could be found, each of which resulted in a deficiency of the tissue responses to serotonin. The mechanism of the interference with serotonin of each of these drugs was different. One (reserpine) was an antimetabolite of the hormone, and the other two were not, but each prevented responses of suitable tissues to serotonin. The diverse kinds of mechanism of these tranquilizers thus suggested that the deficiency of serotonin, which each caused in a different way, might point to a cerebral lack of serotonin as a major cause of tranquilized behavior.

Importance of the blood-brain barrier to serotonin. The existence of the blood-brain barrier to serotonin as described in Chapter 4 is of importance to the understanding of some of the evidence. Serotonin when injected into the periphery of an animal passes into the main part of the brain with difficulty if at all. Thus, it is possible for an animal to experience large changes of serotonin concentration in the body as a whole without suffering the debilitating mental changes. Large changes in peripheral serotonin concentrations do occur. After wounding, the liberation of this hormone from blood platelets can cause small increases. In cancers of the argentaffin cells of the intestines the increases may be very large as one sees in cases of human carcinoid. Nevertheless, marked mental changes do not take place in such circumstances, and the reason probably is that the excess serotonin in the periphery does not get into the brain. The author has analyzed the blood of a carcinoid patient which contained 25 μg serotonin per ml, but the spinal fluid of this patient showed only 0.02 μg. Finally, the peripheral injection of serotonin into normal human beings does not bring about mental changes similar to those of schizophrenia.

There are very powerful antimetabolites of serotonin which do not cause mental changes. These have been constructed so that they would not pass the blood-brain barrier. An example is 1-benzyl-2-methylserotonin (132). Such compounds possess the primary amino group and the phenolic group which seem to be the ones subject to attack by the enzymes which may constitute the barrier (113). The analogs fail to get through for the same reason that serotonin fails to get through. By contrast, the psychotomimetic analogs all have the ability to pass into the central nervous system. Two cases in point are bufotenine and psilocybin. In bufotenine the primary amino group has been protected from monoamine oxidase, and in psilocybin both primary amino group and phenolic group have been protected. These get into the brain, whereas serotonin does not readily.

As far as serotonin is concerned the body seems to be divided into two main compartments, the brain and the rest of the body. What the brain needs it makes for itself, and for this purpose it has the full complement of enzymes. What the periphery needs it also makes for itself. Between the two compartments there seems to be little exchange of serotonin. Of course, the idea of just two compartments is an oversimplification, because even within the brain there are great variations in the concentration of serotonin. How much interchange there is between various parts of the brain is unknown.

Antiserotonin actions of excess serotonin. In thinking about the interpretation of many experiments on the behavioral effects of injections of serotonin and its relatives, one must remember the following fact. Large excesses of serotonin can specifically erase the ability of a tissue to respond to this hormone. This was first demonstrated by Gaddum (135) who showed that doses of serotonin a hundred times greater than those needed to cause contraction of isolated rat uterus made this tissue insensitive to the usual serotonin-induced response. The excess could be washed away and the responsiveness was then restored. The same kind of effect was demonstrated in living animals by Shaw and Woolley (131). A dose of serotonin ten times the one required to cause maximal increases in the blood pressure of a dog not only failed to cause any rise in blood pressure, but also prevented the rise which should have followed injection of a smaller dose. The antiserotonin effect of the large dose was soon dissipated (probably because of destruction of the excess) and the normal responsiveness to the usual dose was restored.

In several experiments which have been done to test the actions of serotonin and its derivatives on the behavior of experimental animals and men, this antiserotonin action of large doses of hormone has been ignored. Consequently, some experimental results which may have been due to this inhibitory action have been said to represent a real hormonal effect of serotonin. If massive doses are to be used one must never forget the uncertainty which they introduce into interpretation.

Although the specific antiserotonin action of serotonin itself may seem fantastic, it is really not so. It is probably just a special case of the well known inhibition of an enzyme caused by an excess of its substrate. Ordinarily, one molecule of substrate combines with the active site of one molecule of enzyme. With the hormones one molecule ordinarily combines with one molecule of receptor. The hormone (or substrate) is attached to the active site at several points in the molecule. If a large excess of the hormone is present, several molecules of it may attach to the single active site, each by a different combining point. Because the active site is not occupied by a single molecule (but instead by several), the normal reaction does not take place.

Psychiatric changes in mental patients and normal people resulting from changes in the serotonin content of their brains. Increases in the serotonin content of the brains of schizophrenic patients seem to make their disease worse. By contrast, such increases in the brains of patients suffering from simple depressions seem to make them better. These summarizing statements require qualifications which will be made presently, but they represent the essence of the findings.

The increases in cerebral serotonin can be accomplished in one of several ways. The principal ones are (*a*) administration of 5-hydroxytryptophan and (*b*) administration of inhibitors of monoamine oxidase. The first method is specific for serotonin; the latter brings about increases of the epinephrines and certain other amines as well as of serotonin.

A. *5-Hydroxytryptophan administration to schizophrenic patients.* If one wishes to increase the serotonin content of the brain, it is of no use to inject serotonin itself into the peripheral tissues. As was pointed out in Chapter 4, Woolley and Shaw (78) and many others have shown that such injections do not cause a detectable increase in the brain. Bogdanski et al. (76), however, subsequently showed that the serotonin content could be increased by peripheral injection of 5-hydroxytryptophan. This precursor of the hormone can pass the barrier and enter the brain. In that organ it is converted by the decarboxylase into serotonin. Analyses of the brains of animals treated peripherally with 5-hydroxytryptophan do in fact reveal that an increase in serotonin occurs. At the same time, however, increases take place in most of the peripheral organs. The results there can be quite severe because various smooth muscles are caused to contract. Diarrhea, increases in blood pressure and visceral cramps ensue. These peripheral effects can be prevented by administration of an antimetabolite of serotonin such as BAS. BAS does not penetrate readily into the brain, and as was discussed earlier in this chapter, does not cause marked psychic effects. It does, however, prevent the peripheral actions of the excess serotonin formed from administered 5-hydroxytryptophan, and does not prevent the central effects (77). Data to illustrate this point are shown in Table 5.

Studies have been made with two schizophrenic patients given BAS and 5-hydroxytryptophan in an effort to determine what effect a specific increase in their cerebral serotonin might have on their mental disease.

TABLE 5. *Effects of 5-hydroxytryptophan and BAS on peripheral and central actions of serotonin and on cerebral serotonin content in mice; the peripheral actions are exemplified by diarrhea, and the central ones by changes in behavior*

Number of Mice	BAS, mg per mouse per day	5-Hydroxy-tryptophan, mg per mouse	Incidence of Diarrhea, per cent	Cerebral Serotonin,* μg per gram	Behavior
44	0	0	0	2.3	Normal
17	1.0	0	0	2.8	Normal or slightly subdued
3	0	0.5	100	—	Normal
10	0	2.5	100	—	Normal or slightly subdued
25	1.0	2.5	0	3.4	Slightly subdued
9	1.0	15.0	0	21.0	Marked excitement, convulsions, agitation

* Based on serotonin creatinine sulfate, not on the free base.

These studies were made in collaboration with Dr. P. O. Therman of Philadelphia (256). The subjects were selected to insure that they were not at the terminal stages of the disease, but rather were in a position to grow worse or better in a recognizable way. They were given 25 mg BAS four times each day for 3 weeks. During this time there was no noticeable change in their condition. The BAS was continued and 25 mg 5-hydroxytryptophan was injected intramuscularly four times each day for 2 weeks. The disease became worse. Cessation of the administration of 5-hydroxytryptophan relieved this downward trend. This strongly suggested that increases in the serotonin content of their brains enhanced their disease. A larger study of this kind would be desirable to make the conclusion stronger.

Two separate small studies have been made in which bufotenine was used instead of 5-hydroxytryptophan. Bufotenine was chosen because, as we have seen earlier, it is a compound with serotonin-like actions, but which can pass from the periphery into the brain. One of these studies involved only bufotenine (220), but the other used both BAS and bufotenine (257). Only one or two patients were used in each, but in each the disease was made worse during administration of the bufotenine. This suggested the same conclusion as did the experiments with 5-hydroxytryptophan.

B. *Tryptophan.* Another way of increasing serotonin in the body and one which is far less expensive, is to give tryptophan. This method has the disadvantage that it is less specific. Although tryptophan is hydroxylated in the body to give 5-hydroxytryptophan, and eventually serotonin, it also gives rise to a variety of other substances such as xanthurenic acid, nicotinamide, indole, skatole, etc. Because of these multiple functions, one must use quite large doses of tryptophan if one is to achieve effective increases in the production of serotonin.

Several studies have been made of the effects of feeding tryptophan to schizophrenic and to normal persons. Banerjee and Agarwal (266) gave 5 grams tryptophan to each of ten schizophrenic patients and found that the urinary excretion of 5-hydroxyindoleacetic acid was increased more than was the case in ten normal control subjects. Excretion of N-methylnicotinamide likewise was greater in the schizophrenic group. No marked change in the psychosis was reported, and the normal persons were not found to experience a model psychosis. Zeller (264) also fed tryptophan (50 mg per kg body weight) to twenty-four schizophrenic and sixteen normal people. He failed to find that the schizophrenic persons showed a greater increase in excretion of 5-hydroxyindoleacetic acid than did the controls, although of course all persons converted some of the tryptophan to this excretion product of serotonin. He did find a greater increase in xanthurenic acid excretion of the schizophrenics compared to the controls. Zeller went further, and increased the serotonin levels still more by giving iproniazid along with the tryptophan. The treatment was continued daily for 6 weeks and resulted in marked behavioral changes. The disease became worse just as Therman and Woolley had found when 5-hydroxytryptophan was administered. The greater increase in serotonin content (which resulted from a decreased rate of destruction in the presence of iproniazid) was reflected in a reduction in the urinary excretion of 5-hydroxyindoleacetic acid. Kety also fed large amounts of tryptophan to carefully controlled schizophrenic patients and found the psychosis to become worse during the treatment.

These studies suggest two main points. (*a*) They show that schizophrenia becomes worse when serotonin is increased. (*b*) They suggest that the metabolism of tryptophan differs in normal and schizophrenic people. One might conclude tentatively that the schizophrenic patients make or metabolize more serotonin than do normal people when loaded with tryptophan, and that the relative proportions of the various functions of tryptophan are not the same in normal and schizophrenic people. However, the conclusions are open to question because of the multiple functions of tryptophan.

C. ***Inhibitors of monoamine oxidase in schizophrenic subjects.*** As will be described below, a number of inhibitors of monoamine oxidase have been used in attempts to control mental diseases. The first of these was iproniazid (Marsilid). The rationale behind the use of these inhibitors is the serotonin hypothesis about mental diseases. These compounds inhibit one of the enzymes which destroys serotonin. Consequently, this hormone increases in the tissues when the inhibitors are administered. The increase in the brain and elsewhere can be demonstrated by analysis. It is, however, not a specific increase. Norepinephrine, epinephrine, and other amines, which are also destroyed by monoamine oxidase, also accumulate. It is therefore uncertain to what the psychic changes are to be attributed when they follow the administration of the inhibitors.

The consensus of opinion seems to be that schizophrenic patients are not helped by monoamine oxidase inhibitors (258). Many feel that they are made worse by such inhibitors. If this latter conclusion is correct it would be compatible with the idea that increases of serotonin in the brains of schizophrenic patients make the disease worse. The clinical experience with iproniazid has been very extensive. For this reason the conclusion that it is harmful to schizophrenic patients carries force. What is uncertain is the exact reason for the deterioration, whether serotonin or other amines.

D. ***Effects of inhibitors of monoamine oxidase on depressions.*** Many patients suffering from depression can be made well again by administration of inhibitors of monoamine oxidase (258 and 259). So-called simple depressions are said to be the oncs which respond best. The depression of schizophrenia does not respond. It is thus plain that these drugs do not relieve all kinds of depression. Nevertheless, the widespread clinical experience with them does seem to make it certain that the therapeutic effect is real.

The introduction of inhibitors of monoamine oxidase into psychiatry came about through a coincidence of chance and the serotonin hypothesis. Iproniazid, the structure of which is shown in Figure 12, had been synthesized in the course of a routine screening program for drugs which might control tuberculosis. When it was tried on a group of tuberculous human beings it was noted to produce a marked feeling of well being. This clinical observation was borne in mind by Loomer et al. (260) who several years later proposed the use of iproniazid for the treatment of depressions. They introduced it for this purpose under the name of psychic energizer.

While the original clinical observation regarding iproniazid was lying fallow in the literature, the serotonin postulate of the etiology of schizophrenia was put forward by Woolley and Shaw (78). At about the same time Barsky et al. (261) observed in studies *in vitro* that iproniazid was a potent inhibitor of monoamine oxidase. Several investigators were then able quite readily to postulate that the psychic effect might arise from an increase in the serotonin content of the brain which would be expected to follow the inhibition of this enzyme there. Determinations of the serotonin contents of the brains of laboratory animals which had been treated with iproniazid readily showed that the drug did in fact cause such increases. Furthermore, such measurements also showed, as one would expect, that epinephrine and norepinephrine were also increased.

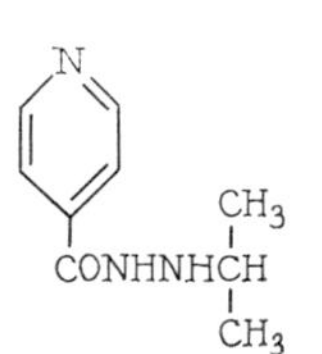

Iproniazid or Marsilid

FIG. 12. *An early clinically effective monoamine oxidase inhibitor.*

Routine screening programs were set up to find more potent and less toxic inhibitors of monoamine oxidase. These soon led to a group of such inhibitors. Most of them were substituted hydrazines. The best of these are now being used in clinical studies. Iproniazid itself proved to be too dangerous for clinical use, but in the enthusiasm before this was established approximately five hundred thousand mental patients were treated with it. The principal reason for toxicity seems to be that certain individuals develop damage to the liver when they are treated with it.

The inhibitors of monoamine oxidase have two kinds of disadvantages for use in attempts to understand the relationship of serotonin to schizophrenia and other mental diseases:

a. Inhibition of the enzyme causes increases of other neural hormones as well as of serotonin, as was discussed earlier.

b. They may inhibit other enzymes as well as monoamine oxidase. For example, iproniazid has been shown to inhibit the pyridoxal kinase of the brain (262). This and related observations raised the question as to whether or not the psychic effects of this drug were in any way related to serotonin. The uncertainty on this point was resolved, however, when it was found that the same kind of psychic effect was produced by monoamine oxidase inhibitors which did not interfere in these other kinds of reactions. For example, the serotonin analog α-methyltryptamine was such a compound which inhibits monoamine oxidase more specifically and still subdues depressions (263).

To summarize the findings with inhibitors of monamine oxidase and with 5-hydroxytryptophan one might say the following. Increases in serotonin brought about in the brain by these substances make many schizophrenic patients worse. By contrast these increases improve the condition of many depressed patients, especially those with so-called simple depressions. The increases brought about with inhibitors of monoamine oxidase are not specific for serotonin, whereas those with 5-hydroxytryptophan are more so. These observations are compatible with the idea that mental depressions can arise from a deficiency of serotonin in the brain. They might also be compatible with the idea that some of the manifestations of schizophrenia may be associated with excessive cerebral serotonin.

Evidence from serotonin analyses of schizophrenic tissues. The most direct method of obtaining evidence regarding the relationship of serotonin to schizophrenia would be to analyze various parts of the brain for this hormone, and to find that the amount present differed markedly from what it is in normal tissues. The reason why this has not yet been done is that it is so difficult to obtain fresh samples of those tissues. For an adequate study one would need samples of various parts of the brain, particularly hypothalamus and other regions of the mid-brain as well as of cortex. One would need samples from schizophrenic patients, preferably in the acute stage of the disease, and one would need corresponding parts from brains of normal human beings for comparison. Because of the labile nature of serotonin, the tissues would need to be taken as rapidly as possible, post mortem. Up to the present time it has not been possible even to approach these stipulations, and it may never be possible to do the crucial study. As a first approximation to the goal, some measurements of serotonin in cerebrospinal fluid have been conducted because this tissue can be obtained fresh. Even this has required much negotiating because most psychiatrists in big cities such as New York feel that the taking of samples of spinal fluid might adversely affect the patient.

Spinal fluids taken from 6 normal volunteers in good health physically and mentally and assayed without delay for serotonin by the rat stomach method have shown less than 0.001 μg per ml. Fluids from twenty-eight schizophrenic patients, some of recent onset and agitated, and some of long standing (catatonic, paranoid, or undifferentiated) have shown that these also lack detectable serotonin. Suitable rigorous tests were done in order to demonstrate that the fluids did not destroy added serotonin, and did not contain inhibitors of serotonin-action. All samples were tested immediately after withdrawal. It would therefore seem that neither normal nor schizophrenic spinal fluids contain detectable serotonin (61). If differences in the serotonin contents of normal and schizophrenic brains are to be found, one must look in the cellular parts of the brain. The spinal fluid is not a suitable tissue.

Earlier experiments in which the rat uterus method had been used had indicated that normal fluid contained about 0.015 μg per ml and that most fluids from schizophrenic patients had more (0.02 to 0.04 μg) (61). The reason why the rat uterus method gave higher values is not known, because care had been taken to show that the responses of the uterus to the fluids was overcome by a specific antimetabolite. The assays done with the rat stomach method, however, were so carefully controlled as to leave no doubt that, if serotonin had been present in the fluids, it would have been found.

An earlier study by Bulle and Konchegal (265) had indicated that spinal fluids from schizophrenic patients contained more serotonin than those from normal persons. The method of measurement of serotonin, however, was quite unorthodox. It involved the effect of serotonin on a pain response in dogs. No demonstration was made that the material detected in spinal fluid actually was serotonin, and no quantitative measurements were made.

Present evidence therefore indicates that there is no difference in the amount of serotonin in the spinal fluids of normal and schizophrenic persons. Nevetheless, one must take note of the unexplained contradictions.

Although differences in the serotonin content of spinal fluids from normal and schizophrenic persons have thus not been found, such differences do occur in certain organic psychoses. Thus, in many brain tumor cases, the fluid may contain as much as 1 μg per ml (61). In tubercular meningitis of children serotonin contents of 0.2 to 3.0 μg per ml have been reported (267). These are diseases in which marked disturbances of consciousness are prominent features, but there is no way to decide whether the elevated serotonin of spinal fluid contributes to the psychosis. In other non-schizophrenic mental deficiencies there is yet no information about serotonin content, but there is information about one of its degradation products, 5-hydroxyindoleacetic acid. In hydrocephalus the values in spinal fluid were particularly high and in manic depressive psychosis they were unusually low (268).

When peripheral tissues such as blood of schizophrenic patients are analyzed for serotonin, no difference from normal has yet been found. This is not surprising when one remembers that the disease is in the central nervous system and not in the periphery. Nevertheless, the accessibility of peripheral tissues constantly invites a study of them rather than of the brain.

Several examinations of the urines of schizophrenic patients have been made in an effort to determine whether they differ from normals with respect to 5-hydroxyindoleacetic acid or other indoles. No clear picture has emerged from these investigations. There is a general agreement that urinary 5-hydroxyindoleacetic acid in unselected schizophrenic patients is either normal or slightly below normal (264, 266, 269, 270). Leyton (269), however, distinguished a group of schizophrenic persons amounting to 20 per cent of those studied, in which urinary excretion was markedly subnormal. He suggested that schizophrenia might not represent a single disease and that the 20 per cent of his patients who had deficient excretion might represent a kind of schizophrenia in which insufficient serotonin was an important factor. Their disease might be basically different from that of the other 80 per cent. There have been prior examples of this sort of thing as witnessed by the fact that many patients diagnosed as childhood schizophrenia have proved to have phenylketonuria when urinary tests for phenylpyruvic acid were conducted.

In many of these studies of urinary excretion of indole derivatives by schizophrenic patients there has also been agreement that two or more indoles not yet identified chemically are present in much greater than normal amount (269 and 270). There has also been a recent finding that indoles with hydroxyl groups in the 6-position of the indole ring are more abundant in schizophrenic urine (271).

The studies of urinary excretion of indole derivatives have been criticized from several standpoints. In some of the studies no attempt was made to control dietary intake. It is well known that schizophrenic patients may resort to quite bizarre dietary habits. It is also known that foods such as bananas and pineapples contain enough serotonin to cause change in urinary 5-hydroxyindoleacetic acid. Another factor which can lead to equivocal results is that indole derivatives can be formed by bacterial action in the intestinal tract and that the amounts formed increase in constipation. Chronic schizophrenic patients tend to be constipated. It would not be correct to assume that all investigators have been unaware of these pitfalls. Some, though not all, have taken pains to guard against them.

It is possible that the urine and other peripheral tissues are not the ones to examine. The disease is in the brain, and it may be that the differences with respect to serotonin content will be found there, if anywhere. Nevertheless, it is not beyond the range of possibility that if a defect in the metabolism of serotonin does exist, it can be detected in the body as a whole as well as in the brain. The accessibility of the peripheral tissues as compared to those of the brain is of course the reason which prompts people to study them instead of the brain.

To summarize, analysis of tissues for serotonin has not given clear evidence. This is most likely because the right tissues have not been analyzed, but the problem of getting the right ones is formidable. Several studies suggest that in some organic psychoses there may be excessive serotonin in the central nervous system. There has been clear evidence that in schizophrenia the metabolic pattern of tryptophan and serotonin is altered. There is also suggestive evidence that these metabolic reactions are related to the mental state.

Effect of shock treatment on the serotonin content of the brains of experimental animals. Because shock therapy (induced either electrically or by chemical agents such as Metrazol) has been a favorite way to attempt to control schizophrenia and various kinds of depression, several studies have been made in experimental animals to determine whether such shocks change the serotonin content of the brain. The results of such experiments are not in agreement. Some find that electroshock increases brain serotonin (272), but others find that Metrazol induced shock does not change the concentration (274). All are agreed that the serotonin content of peripheral organs is not changed by electrical or chemical shock either in rats or in men (272, 273, and 274).

Ceruloplasmin in schizophrenia. Ceruloplasmin is a blue copper containing protein present in blood plasma. It can act as an enzyme which will oxidize and destroy the biological activity of serotonin and various aminophenols and phenylenediamines. In fact ceruloplasmin seems to be the previously misnamed soluble amine oxidase of blood (279). The amount of this protein in the blood is not constant. It rises sharply in the third trimester of pregnancy and in infections. Furthermore, the oxidative activity of it can be altered by dietary changes in such nutrients as ascorbic acid. Against this background one must view results which have been obtained by measurement of the ceruloplasmin in the blood of schizophrenic patients. Akerfeldt (278) reported that the oxidative activity of ceruloplasmin was higher in the bloods of schizophrenic patients than it was in normal people. This report incited much study of ceruloplasmin. Conflicting statements appeared, some of them quite heated, as to whether or not elevated ceruloplasmin was a diagnostic test for schizophrenia (275, 276, and 277). The question of whether the dietary intake of ascorbic acid rather than the mental disease was the cause of the original observations loomed large in these debates. When this variable was controlled (275) the most recent finding was that ceruloplasmin was elevated in the blood of schizophrenic patients. Nevertheless, the value of ceruloplasmin determinations for the diagnosis of schizophrenia is not yet established. Furthermore, all of the measurements of ceruloplasmin have been indirect. Instead of measuring the protein itself, the oxidase activity of serum or even its copper content has been used to indicate the amount of ceruloplasmin.

If ceruloplasmin actually is more abundant in the blood of schizophrenic persons there would be an interesting connection with the serotonin hypothesis about this disease. Serotonin is destroyed by ceruloplasmin. If this protein were elevated in tissues the destruction of serotonin would be expected to be enhanced. It is possible that a deficiency of serotonin could arise from an excess of ceruloplasmin. As we have already seen, deficiencies of serotonin induced by antagonists of it can lead to psychic changes, especially depression. The supposed deficiency would need to be localized rather than general throughout the body because no marked deficiency of serotonin has been detected in the blood of schizophrenic patients.

Relation of oligodendrogliocytes to schizophrenia and manic depressive psychosis. The oligodendrogliocytes are brain cells of especial interest, because, as was described in Chapter 4, they can be seen to contract tetanically when serotonin is applied to them. Normally, these cells are in a state of slow pulsation, but excess serotonin intensifies and prolongs the phase of contraction and eliminates the relaxation. The appearance of some of these cells before and after application of the hormone is shown in Figure 13. Their motions in the absence of the hormone were illustrated in Figure 5 of Chapter 4.

According to Elvidge and Reed (280), the oligodendroglia are histologically abnormal in persons with schizophrenia and manic depressive psychosis. They anesthetized thirteen schizophrenic patients and six having manic depressive psychosis, drilled a small hole in the skull in the occipitoparietal region, or occasionally in the frontal region, and removed a small plug of brain tissue. Both cortex and

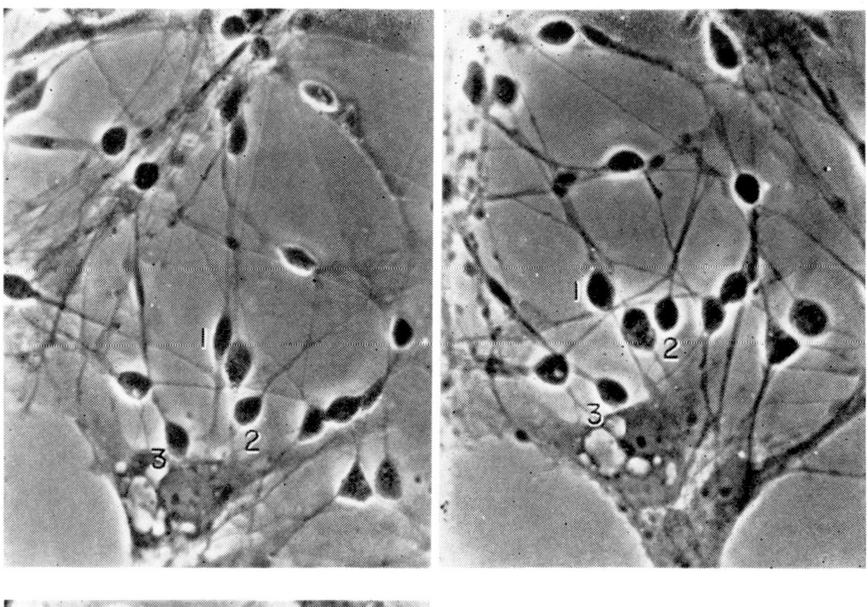

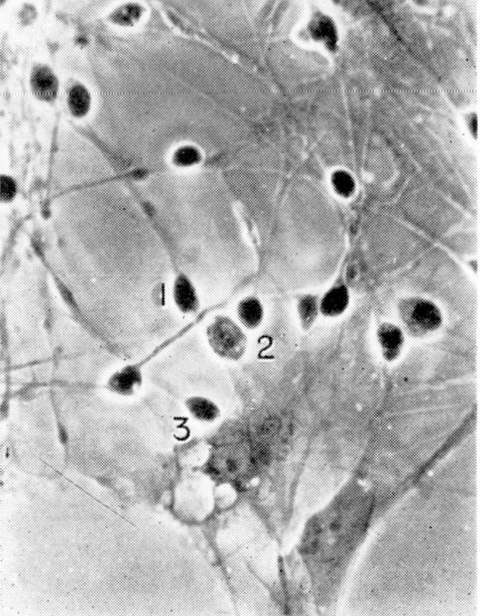

FIG. 13. *Action of serotonin on human oligodendroglia. The cells in the top left plate are shown before application of serotonin. Those in the top right are shown 7 minutes after application of serotonin, 5 μg per ml. Contraction is marked in cells 1, 2, and 3. On some other cells serotonin has not yet exerted its full effect. The lower plate shows cells in general contraction 30 minutes after application of serotonin.*

underlying white matter were taken. These pieces of tissue were sectioned, stained and examined for oligodendroglia. In each case abnormalities of these cells were found, primarily in the white matter. These consisted of swelling of the cell bodies, and frequently pyknosis of the nuclei. In a few of the patients the histologic abnormality was less marked, but the numbers of these cells were much below normal. A second examination of this kind was made after periods ranging up to two years. This showed that the abnormality had endured because the general abnormal features were still visible. It was not possible to have adequate controls in such a study because normal people cannot be subjected to such procedures on any pretext. However, non-schizophrenic patients undergoing surgical operations for neurological reasons were examined. These included five persons with epilepsy. Of these, two, who were mentally confused in the periods between seizures, had the same kinds of abnormalities in their oligodendroglia, whereas others had normal cells. A more adequate control was the case of a mentally normal man who had suffered severe trauma such that the brain substance was exuding from a wound in the head. Despite the severe trauma, the oligodendroglia of this man were normal.

In commenting on the paper of Elvidge and Reed, W. G. Penfield (in whose laboratory the work had originated) pointed out that he had always found histological abnormalities of oligodendroglia in diseases marked by clouding of consciousness.

It is surprising indeed that more work has not been done to confirm or deny the findings of Elvidge and Reed. The present author has been unable to locate any other report on histological changes in the oligodendroglia of patients with schizophrenia and manic depressive psychosis, despite the fact that 25 years have elapsed since the original paper appeared. It is of first importance to know with certainty whether in these mental diseases an abnormality of these particular cells is characteristic. If it should prove to be so, a reappraisal would be required by followers of the idea that schizophrenia must arise from psychological trauma rather than physical change. The lack of a characteristic histological abnormality in schizophrenia has been one of the main reasons why the Freudian view has been followed.

If, in the natural diseases (schizophrenia and manic depressive psychosis), there really is a characteristic abnormality of the oligodendroglia, this fact will coincide nicely with the serotonin hypothesis about these diseases. Serotonin is known to affect these brain cells. Furthermore, the changes caused by application to them in tissue culture of serotonin and psychotomimetic drugs such as LSD were quite similar to those found in schizophrenia. Coincidently, the paper of Elvidge and Reed was unknown to Benitez et al. (107) when they studied the actions of serotonin and its antimetabolites on oligodendroglia *in vitro*. When considered together the two sets of findings complemented each other. Furthermore, Cazzullo and his associates have recently observed that mescaline, LSD, and other drugs which affect the mind caused these same abnormalities histologically visible in the oligodendroglia of animals treated with large doses of these drugs. Thus, different kinds of evidence all point to these cells as being of importance in mental diseases.

The findings with the oligodendroglia suggest one explanation for the actions of serotonin and its analogs on the mind. It is well known that interference with the supply of oxygen or of glucose to the brain can lead to marked neurological changes. The convulsions of anoxia are an example. It is less well known, but true, that interference with the glucose supply can lead not only to convulsions (as in insulin shock), but also to some psychic changes which resemble what is experienced in schizophrenia. The author has had personal acquaintance with these.

In order to experience the psychic changes of glucose deprivation of the brain, insulin is injected, and the subject is allowed to go to sleep. As the blood sugar slowly falls towards the convulsive level, the subject usually begins to arouse. In this condition he is then quite disoriented. He can walk about, and even respond to questions, but sometimes with irrational answers. These answers have a real connection with the visual hallucinations which he is experiencing. The most prominent feature of the episode, however, is the awesome and terrifying anxiety which these hallucinations engender. The memory of this anxiety remains after the episode is terminated by administration of glucose. Curiously enough, when an insulin shock is developed while the patient is awake, the psychic phenomena are much less prominent, although the incoherence of speech produced is well known.

We see thus that lack of glucose in the brain can call forth temporarily many of the signs of schizophrenia. If the stoppage of the motions of the oligodendroglia by serotonin or its analogs also resulted in a deprivation of glucose in some brain cells, because of a sluggish transfer from capillaries to neurons, we might expect similar results. The oligodendroglia are found in the brain in the spaces between blood capillaries and neurons. The brain is poorly vascularized when compared to several other organs and it may be that one of the functions of oligodendroglia with their pulsating movement is to act as little stirring devices to facilitate diffusion of oxygen, glucose, etc., from capillaries to neurons. Interference with the action of these cells would thus disrupt the supply of these nutrients. We have just seen that disruption of the supply of glucose by injection of insulin can call forth psychic changes, resembling those of schizophrenia. If it is really true that schizophrenic people lack normal oligodendroglia one could imagine that they also might be in the same sort of difficulty.

The objection has been raised that if the idea outlined above were applicable to schizophrenia, then one should be able to find differences from normal in the uptake of oxygen or of glucose by the brain. Such differences have not been found. This objection, however, does not take account of one fact. The entire glucose and oxygen consumption of the whole brain is measured, not that of small portions of it. The changes in these small portions could be sufficient to account for the psychic manifestations.

It is not intended that the idea outlined in this section should be taken as the whole explanation of the action of serotonin on the brain. There is evidence to support the belief that serotonin can act on nerves in which oligodendroglia have not been found. It is quite possible that this hormone serves several purposes. Nevertheless, the factual findings about oligodendroglia cannot be forgotten.

The question of too much or too little serotonin. If it be granted that the foregoing evidence suggests that something is wrong with the metabolism of serotonin in the brains of schizophrenic patients. the problem remains of deciding just what is wrong. Is it an excess, or is it a deficiency brought about by too-rapid production, too-slow destruction, or a defect in the receptor mechanism? Some evidence suggests that the difficulty is an excess and other data point to a deficiency. Information now at hand is compatible with the following view. The agitation or frenzy, or excitement which is often seen early in the disease in the acute phase, and which may remain into the chronic period is associated with an excess of cerebral serotonin. The depression familiar in the disease (or the withdrawal into catatonia) may be associated with a deficiency. The evidence for such a postulate may be summarized as follows:

a. The analogs of serotonin which cause hallucinations and other forms of excitement in normal men exhibit serotonin-like actions on several tissues including some brain cells. The mental changes may be the result of this serotonin-like action on the brain. If this is the correct interpretation, the excitement phase of schizophrenia might be the result of an excess of cerebral serotonin.

b. The analogs of serotonin which induce depression in normal men usually act on tissues as antagonists of the hormone, bringing about deficiency of it. This is true of reserpine, BOL, and the nitro analog of serotonin shown in Figure 5.

c. Increases in the serotonin content of the brain brought about with 5-hydroxytryptophan, or by an inhibitor of monoamine oxidase usually make labile schizophrenic patients worse.

We must not forget that there are some discordant findings which are sufficient to make one cautious about drawing a final conclusion. Thus, the excitement-producing analogs of serotonin do act as antagonists of the hormone in some test systems, even though they are serotonin-like in other tests, and the ones which cause depression in normal men can be found to act like serotonin if one searches long enough for a suitable test object. The nitro analog, for example, acts like serotonin on the clam's heart. Also, although the monoamine oxidase inhibitors will relieve simple depressions they will not do so for the depressions of schizophrenia. Finally, evidence such as that of Leyton (269) that some schizophrenic patients excrete in their urines less 5-hydroxyindoleacetic acid than do normal people might suggest a serotonin deficiency (although not necessarily in the brain). The evidence about increased ceruloplasmin in the blood in schizophrenia might also suggest deficiency of serotonin. Nevertheless, several other explanations can be made to fit these findings so that they are not crucial. We must view the question of excess or deficiency as an open question in which the evidence favors slightly the association of excitement with excess, and of depression with deficiency of serotonin in the brain.

Summary of the serotonin hypothesis. According to the serotonin hypothesis schizophrenia is the result of an abnormality in the metabolism of serotonin in the brain. The abnormality can result from a failure to synthesize the proper amount of the hormone there, or from a failure to destroy it at the normal rate, or from a defect in the receptor mechanism. The evidence favors the view that hallucinations, agitation, and other manifestations of excitement are associated with an excess of cerebral serotonin, and that depression is associated with a deficiency of it. Enough evidence, however, is not available to decide these matters. It may well be that the mechanism which controls the concentration of the hormone has become defective so that sometimes too much is present and sometimes not enough. The swings from depression to excitement which can frequently be seen in early schizophrenia might mirror this loss of control. Even though most psychiatrists teach that schizophrenia is quite different from manic depressive psychosis in which the swings from depression to excitement are very prominent, the fact is that some students of psychoses have remarked on the idea that when a mental disease strikes down an individual, perhaps as the result of emotional stress, the introvert develops schizophrenia and the extrovert, manic depressive psychosis (227). This may indicate that the two diseases are not as far apart in etiology as is taught in the textbooks.

The serotonin hypothesis regards the mental abnormality as being the result of changes in the functions of cells in the central nervous system which are brought about by the abnormal serotonin levels. The oligodendroglial cells particularly are involved, but there is insufficient reason to think that they are the only ones concerned. There are experiments to suggest that inhibition of nerve impulses (the so-called inhibitory processes) may be the ones affected.

The serotonin hypothesis pictures the aberration in serotonin to be located in the brain. Aberrations in other parts of the body need not also occur, nor must they be excluded.

The hypothesis takes into account the fact that serotonin both in its formation and its functioning is intimately intertwined with some other hormones of the nervous system, namely, epinephrine, norepinephrine, histamine, acetylcholine, melatonin, and possibly others. The interrelationships of these will be the subject of Chapter 9. The hypothesis also maintains that several mental diseases in addition to schizophrenia may result from abnormalities in the metabolism of serotonin, and are demarcated from schizophrenia on a symptomatic basis because of the nature of the abnormality with respect to serotonin metabolism, to the time in life of the onset of the difficulty, or to the anatomical localization of the defective biochemical reactions. These aspects will be dealt with in succeeding chapters.

The serotonin hypothesis regards schizophrenia in a light similar to that in which students of diabetes mellitus view that disease. The error in metabolism of serotonin is pictured as arising early in adulthood, just as the error in metabolism of insulin develops usually in adult life. Just as diabetes can occasionally appear in childhood, so also can schizophrenia, but the metabolic error is probably not full-blown at birth. There is probably an error in metabolism of serotonin which is full-blown at birth, but this will be dealt with in the chapter on phenylketonuria. In schizophrenia, the tendency to succumb to the disease may be inborn, but the actual metabolic disturbance probably develops mainly after many years of life. Schizophrenia is regarded as starting with a failure to form enough serotonin in the brain, and this is seen as the shyness and depression which are usually the forerunners of the disease. With sharply increased emotional strain, the control mechanism which governs the level of serotonin in the brain begins to fail. The production of serotonin may increase sharply (or its rate of destruction may decrease), and this probably coincides with the agitated phase. Subsequently, decreased production may again take place. Even more, the reverberations in the form of changes in the concentrations of other neurohormones may intervene and accentuate the disease. This is the working hypothesis which is proposed in this book and which will be developed further in succeeding chapters.

Criticisms of the serotonin hypothesis. Many criticisms have been directed at the serotonin hypothesis of mental diseases since its enunciation in 1954, and there is every reason to believe that more will be. Some of these are valid, but others which have received wide currency seem to disregard clearly established facts. Most certainly the hypothesis lacks sufficient experimental support to establish it as a sound theory. It is just an hypothesis which has arisen to make understandable a mass of information, and to give direction to future experimental work.

Criticism of the serotonin hypothesis about schizophrenia is in order because the evidence which supports it is indirect. The data always require some interpretation to give them meaning. Perhaps the nearest thing to direct evidence yet obtained has been the deterioration of schizophrenic patients which is found to take place when the serotonin contents of their brains are increased with 5-hydroxytryptophan, but even this is far from being above reproach.

A. ***Do psychotomimetic drugs really mimic schizophrenia in their effects on normal people?*** The changes caused in normal people by a psychotomimetic drug are not identical with schizophrenia, but they can be quite similar to it. All psychotomimetic analogs of serotonin do not bring about identical psychic effects. The one which has received the most varied study is undoubtedly LSD. It will serve to illustrate some of the points of criticism.

To show that the psychic changes caused by LSD were not identical to schizophrenia, Hollister (281) made tape recordings of question and answer interviews with normal people shortly after they had taken LSD. Similar interviews were recorded from schizophrenic patients. The recordings of these interviews were then given to a number of well-trained psychiatrists, who did not know which were the patients and which the experimental subjects. The psychiatrists then determined from the responses which were the schizophrenic persons. They were usually able to do so accurately.

This experiment had the following shortcoming. The normal person who has just taken LSD (or any other drug) is under an acute and transient disturbance. It is to be expected that his reactions will differ in some details from those of a schizophrenic person who has been under the influence of his disturbance for a period of months or years. If one wishes to have data on this point one must only recall the clinical experiences with the natural disease ergotism (214). The psychosis which a person may develop after a long period of eating of ergot is rather far removed from the acute LSD-induced changes. In ergotism (as was described earlier in this chapter) a condition similar to catatonia is found, and not the agitation and hallucinations of LSD administration even though the psychotomimetic agents involved are very close relatives.

Other examples of the influence of time can be found among psychotomimetic drugs not related to serotonin. The psychosis associated with long use of bromides is so like that of schizophrenia that most psychiatrists cannot distinguish it without the aid of a chemical analysis of the blood for bromide. Amphetamine when taken for long periods can induce changes in a few normal people which seem not to be distinguishable from paranoid schizophrenia (282). However, because amphetamine does not invariably induce such a psychosis in every normal person, one can argue that the paranoid symptoms developed in the group studied were a reflection of the social background and the innate tendencies of those who succumbed. More important, however, it is to be noted that it was the long-continued use of amphetamine which brought on the psychosis. A single experience did not. It is possibly for this reason that the analogs of serotonin have failed to mimic all of the features of the natural disease. They have not been used for prolonged periods. When they have, as in ergotism, they call forth a response somewhat modified from that of acute administration.

When one deals with psychotomimetic drugs and attempts to understand their relationship to the origins of schizophrenia it is well to understand what schizophrenia is as a disease. It is not just visual hallucinations, nor is it just auditory hallucinations. It is not just hysteria and agitation, because those who study it clinically know that depression is a large feature in it. Many believe that it begins with excessive shyness and depression over social failures or imagined social failures. Finally, it is not just anxiety, although anxiety may be a contributing cause of the agitated breakdowns which often begin the acute stage of the disease. If we take the judgment of a student of the disease such as Strecker (227), we might say that schizophrenia is a disunion of thinking and emotions. The disharmony is visible in the form of many kinds of inappropriate behavior. As mentioned earlier it is often preceded by excessive shyness, introspection, and depression. Very often when the disease has progressed for some time, and often some time after an agitated phase of excitement or hysteria, the withdrawal from reality begins to grow. The distortion of the body image in the patient's own mind is a frequent finding.

All of these features of the disease must be kept in mind when one treats with psychotomimetic drugs and tries to understand the relationship of the changes they induce in normal subjects to those found in natural schizophrenia. Perhaps too much attention has been given to hallucinations. They are a feature of the natural disease, but they are not the only one and may be not even a primary one. If one looks only for hallucinations he may miss a great deal that is relevant.

B. *Why do not all analogs of serotonin induce the same psychic change?* This has been the basis of the criticism raised by Cerletti and Rothlin (142 and 205) and which carried much weight in some minds when it was first raised. Their question was why did BOL fail to cause the same kind of mental change as did LSD, since both drugs were analogs and antimetabolites of serotonin, and both drugs seemed to reach the brain? As indicated earlier in this chapter, the most probable explanation in the light of current knowledge is that with LSD the serotonin-like component of biological activity is much more prominent than with BOL. There are more kinds of tissue for which LSD is serotonin-like. In fact, in mammalian tissues BOL has never shown serotonin-like actions, but instead only antiserotonin effects. In some invertebrate tissues (clam heart), however, BOL does act like serotonin. It is probably only a question of time until someone finds a mammalian tissue in which BOL is serotonin-like. Past experience has shown that this is the usual course of events. The fact remains, nevertheless, that it is not serotonin-like on as many kinds of tissue as LSD is.

It is curious that the criticism arising from the case of BOL exerted such influence. In their original paper, Woolley and Shaw had pointed out that all antimetabolites of serotonin were not psychotomimetic and had indicated reasons why this should be understandable. Before one criticizes a postulate too severely one must take care to understand it, and this has not always been done.

Each analog of serotonin does not induce an identical psychic change. The reasons for this are several. They include differences in mode of absorption and distribution of the drugs in the body, differences in rate of elimination, and differences in the pro- and antiserotonin effect of each analog on various tissues.

C. ***The lack of specificity of some of the drugs.*** This is a valid criticism. Several of the psychotomimetic drugs not only interfere in the actions of serotonin, they likewise can interfere with the actions of the epinephrines, and sometimes of histamine, acetylcholine, substance P, etc. These facts have been mentioned for several drugs earlier in this chapter—for example, for reserpine, yohimbine, and the ergot alkaloids. It does not seem to be such an important feature in the actions of such drugs as bufotenine, psilocybin, and 2-methyl-3-ethyl-5-nitroindole, but that is probably only because less study has been made of these. In view of the facts to be discussed in Chapter 9, that the hormones themselves (acetylcholine, serotonin, the epinephrines, etc.) can influence the actions of each other, he would be rash indeed who would maintain that an analog could ever be obtained which would be perfectly specific for acting against any of these hormones in all kinds of tissues.

To add to the instances of lack of specificity which have been given earlier in this chapter, one need only say that choline esterase has been found to be inhibited by LSD, harmine, and even by serotonin. The same thing is true for monoamine oxidase. The inhibition of these enymes in differing degrees with consequent changes in the rate of destruction of the hormones concerned must contribute to the effects which the psychotomimetic drugs show in normal people.

All of these points could be raised with equal force when one comes to consider the mechanism of action of the inhibitors of monoamine oxidase. However, this problem was discussed in the section concerned with those drugs.

One must not be too frightened by the problems of lack of specificity. There are varying degrees of it among all the drugs. The fact that many of the basic psychiatric features remain when drugs of greater and greater specificity are tried is one of the reasons for entertaining the serotonin hypothesis. One would never have ventured into the hypothesis if he had had only one or two drugs for evidence.

D. ***The lack of information about differences in serotonin content of the brain.*** This is a serious criticism. Before the serotonin postulate can be established it will be necessary to demonstrate by analysis that schizophrenic patients actually do have more or less serotonin than normal people in certain parts of their brains. However, before insisting too strongly on this point one must remember the facts in an analogous case. In diabetes mellitus many patients can be found (but certainly not all) who have normal production of insulin in their pancreas, but who, nevertheless, have the disease which is held to be an insulin deficiency, and which is adequately controlled clinically by the use of insulin.

E. *The use of experiments with smooth muscles.* Many of the deductions about the relationship of psychotomimetic and psychotherapeutic drugs to serotonin have been made through the use of smooth muscles. It is objected that such experiments have no relevance to psychiatry.

It is true that one must be cautious in bridging this gap. Nevertheless, in those cases where the experiments in smooth muscles have been checked by experiments with brain cells (such as those with oligodendroglia) the agreement in the results has been most striking. The cases of LSD and of medmain and 1-methylmedmain may be cited. Whenever such correlations are attempted it is necessary to know the complexities involved in the test systems. If these are disregarded (as, for example, the blood-brain barrier or the pro- and antieffects), difficulties can be anticipated.

Suggestions from animal experimentation. One reason why progress is slow in the study of mental diseases is that the maladies cannot be reproduced in animals. One can cause all sorts of behavioral changes in animals. One can induce neuroses as Pavlov did by changing the requirements for conditioned reflexes. One can produce anxiety (or so it is thought) by subjecting the animals to conditioned avoidance behavior in a Skinner box as is now fashionable for the testing of tranquilizers. But one can never be sure that one has induced a condition related to schizophrenia in man. The animals have difficulty in telling the experimenter what they are thinking about, or whether there is discord between thought and emotion.

Despite this inherent shortcoming of animal experimentation in the study of mental disease one can learn some things from it. The real answers must come from studies on human patients, but some clues can be found in animals. The extrapolation from animals to man, however, is fraught with peculiar difficulties when it comes to mental diseases, and these cannot be forgotten with impunity.

One problem in addition to the major one just discussed is the difference in response of various species. A classical example of this is the fact that morphine excites cats and anesthetizes human beings. Another is that 2-methyl-3-ethyl-5-nitroindole, as we have seen earlier in this chapter, depresses human beings, but excites mice to savage behavior. The brain and the nervous system are complicated mechanisms. If one alters a given circuit by means of a given drug in one species the result may not always be the same when one goes to another. The wonder of it is that very often the results in one species can be applied with validity to several others.

Historical footnotes about the origins of the serotonin hypothesis. So much misinformation has appeared in the literature about the discovery of the serotonin hypothesis about mental diseases that it may be right to set down here the events which took place. If the importance of the idea is to be measured by the number of contenders for the distinction of the discovery, one can only conclude that this idea has considerable attractions. Documentary proofs of the course of events are not lacking, but the flood of papers and the passage of time tend to obscure them.

The first published statement primarily concerned with the relation of serotonin to mental disease appeared in *Science,* on April 30, 1954 (286). This was an abstract of a paper read at the meeting of the National Academy of Sciences on April 27 of that year. The paper was read, and the full manuscript was published a month later in *Proceedings of the National Academy of Sciences* (78) entitled "A biochemical and pharmacological suggestion about certain mental disorders."

This paper had had a stormy career before publication. It had been written early in the summer of 1953 and submitted for publication to *The Lancet.* After a considerable time the paper was summarily rejected with the comment that it might be considered only if the authors were able to cure schizophrenia as a result of application of their deductions about causation of that disease. The manuscript was next sent to the *British Medical Journal,* from which no acknowledgement came. After several months had elapsed without any word, it was recalled and sent to *Proceedings of the National Academy of Sciences,* where it was printed in April 1954 (78). Soon a letter was received from the *British Medical Journal,* saying that the editor had been ill, and that correspondence had consequently piled up. The editor was unhappy that the manuscript had been recalled, because he felt that he would like to publish it. He suggested that a somewhat more extended paper should be prepared which would cover the same evidence. This was done and the manuscript was published without delay in July of 1954 (112). This is the reason why two papers instead of one appeared in 1954.

Woolley and Shaw had started work aimed at the production of antimetabolites of serotonin in December 1951 at the time when the structure of serotonin became settled. Their paper describing the first known antimetabolite of this hormone was published in July 1952 (119). They were thinking then of application to hypertension and of the idea that antimetabolites might reveal some physiological roles for serotonin previously not suspected. During the progress of this work the recognition of yohimbine and the ergot alkaloids as antimetabolites of serotonin occurred. An effort was made to publish the results in June 1952, but because of editorial rejection of the manuscript it was delayed in publication, and the results did not actually appear in print until the spring of 1953 (35 and 288). Even despite the delays this was the first demonstration that the ergot alkaloids and yohimbine were antimetabolites of serotonin. The thinking about the ergot derivative LSD was begun in November 1952 at a dinner party, where there was some discussion of the psychotomimetic properties of this relatively new drug. Because one of the guests at this party had been pursuing for several months the idea that ergot alkaloids owed much of their pharmacological action to interference with serotonin, and because he had been observing marked behavioral changes in animals given synthetic antimetabolites of this hormone, the striking psychic effects of LSD suggested the relationship of serotonin to schizophrenia.[d]

While these developments were taking place in New York, Gaddum, in Edinburgh, became interested in the newly discovered serotonin and wished to find drugs which would protect tissues from it. In April of 1953 Fingl and Gaddum (287) published a short abstract of their experiment which showed that ergotamine was able to do so. They made no mention of any idea that ergotamine was in fact an antimetabolite of serotonin. Their abstract appeared at about the same time as the complete paper of Shaw and Woolley (35) mentioned above, which demonstrated that the ergot alkaloids and yohimbine were antimetabolites of serotonin. In the summer of that same year (1953) Gaddum published another abstract in which the ergot derivative LSD was shown to be more active than ergotamine as an antagonist to the action of serotonin on isolated rat uterus (289). No mention was made

[d] The experimental proof that LSD was an antimetabolite of serotonin was not appended to the main manuscript on the antiserotonin activity of other ergot derivatives. That manuscript was already in press, and it was considered not surprising that LSD should be like the other ergot derivatives with respect to serotonin. The actual data about LSD were consequently not published until 1955, although the case of LSD was used in the original arguments for serotonin in mental processes.

in this abstract of any concept that serotonin was concerned with mental diseases.

In that same summer (1953), a small, closed meeting was held in London to discuss hypertension. The reports of this meeting were not made public until the summer of 1954, when the papers presented were published (290). In 1952 Woolley and Shaw had published a paper (119) proposing that hypertension was probably the result of excess serotonin in the circulation, and that it might be controlled by an antimetabolite of this hormone. Because this idea was attracting some attention the London meeting included a short paper by Dr. Gaddum on drugs antagonistic to serotonin. The chief concern of this communication was with hypertension, but at the end it was pointed out that the most active drug examined, LSD, was known to cause mental disturbances in man, and that such side effects might be a serious drawback to any use of antiserotonins in hypertension. The chairman (Dr. Pickering), according to the published report, concluded the discussion with the statement that a relationship of serotonin to hypertension probably did not exist and that useful therapeutic agents related to serotonin were unpromising.[e] In Dr. Gaddum's presentation there was no postulate that serotonin was concerned in mental diseases such as schizophrenia. By the time of publication of the papers of this closed meeting, however, the serotonin hypothesis of mental diseases had already been put forward at length in the two papers of Woolley and Shaw, mentioned earlier in this section.

Dr. Gaddum was rather hesitant to conclude that serotonin did in fact have anything to do with schizophrenia. He had only the example of LSD, whereas Woolley and Shaw had a variety of psychotomimetic drugs, including the ergot derivatives. The publication of the criticism of Cerletti and Rothlin based on the first findings with BOL made him lean to the idea that the serotonin hypothesis was a mistake. During 1956 and 1957 he published two full papers in which he rejected the idea of a relationship of serotonin to schizophrenia based on the evidence from LSD (204 and 211). The criticism of Cerletti and Rothlin, however, did not take into account the serotonin-like actions of LSD. When these were emphasized in 1956 by Shaw and Woolley (9), the criticism lost much of its force.

The findings relating the tranquilizing drug reserpine to serotonin came considerably later. The serotonin hypothesis had been published for more than a year before the first preliminary note of Pletscher,

[e] This conclusion soon proved to be questionable when it was shown that a suitable antimetabolite of serotonin, BAS, was able to control hypertension in a considerable number of human patients (109).

Shore, and Brodie (27) described the displacement of serotonin from animal tissues by reserpine. This finding, which is often stated to be the origin of the serotonin hypothesis came only after the hypothesis had been widely discussed. In fact, Pletscher et al. acknowledged that the serotonin hypothesis of mental diseases had stimulated their own thinking about reserpine.

The details of the emergence of the ergot alkaloids, especially of LSD, as antimetabolites of serotonin have been given because it seems to be a general impression that the serotonin hypothesis about mental diseases started with LSD alone. Actually this was not the case. The synthetic antimetabolites of serotonin had been found as early as 1952 to cause mental changes in men and laboratory animals. It was these observations which gave direction to the thinking and allowed interpretation of the results with LSD and other alkaloids. A major point in the paper of Woolley and Shaw was not just that LSD induced psychic changes, but rather that a variety of antimetabolites of serotonin, including LSD, did.

The original interpretation favored by Woolley and Shaw was that the psychotomimetic effects of antimetabolites of serotonin probably meant that schizophrenia was the result of a serotonin deficiency in the brain. However, the idea was also entertained (but given a less prominent position) that it could be the result of serotonin excess. As more experiments were done, the results suggested more and more that the acute excitement and hallucinations might be due to excess of serotonin rather than to deficiency. The thinking, thus, evolved to the point represented in this chapter.

chapter 7

Comments about manic depressive psychosis and epilepsy

Possible relationship of serotonin to manic depressive psychosis. The classical teaching of psychiatry is that schizophrenia can readily be distinguished from manic depressive psychosis. It is said that in schizophrenia thinking is usually not impaired. It is more the connection with reality, and the coordination of thought and emotion (as expressed in behavior) which are at fault. In the depressed phase of manic depressive psychosis on the other hand, thinking is believed to be minimal or absent. By contrast, in the manic phase ideas seem to come in great profusion. It must remembered, however, that even though there may be this flight of ideas, the distortions of reality which they portray are often striking indeed. The loss of contact with reality is thus not confined to schizophrenia.

All psychiatrists do not seem to be satisfied that there is a clear distinction between schizophrenia and manic depressive psychosis. The idea (based on careful observation) has been in existence for quite some time that whether a mentally ill person exhibits schizophrenia or manic depressive psychosis may be greatly influenced by the type of personality he has. Thus, an introvert is quite likely to express his mental illness as schizophrenia, and an extrovert will probably express his as manic depressive psychosis. This matter is discussed at some length by Strecker in his *Fundamentals of Psychiatry* (227), although the original concept goes back much further.

The striking feature of manic depressive psychosis is the regular alternation between periods of mania and of depression. This, however, is not only to be seen in this disease, as any careful observer can readily perceive. In schizophrenia there are depressions and there are times of great agitation. The disease is usually preceded by shyness and long depression. This may flare into agitation or hysteria, and may eventually subside again into prolonged depression or catatonia.[a] The periods of excitement and depression may not be regularly spaced, but they can usually be found if one looks for them. In fact, even in normal people one can observe these alternations which have been muted so as to pass unnoticed by most of society.

One cannot do otherwise than ask whether manic depressive psychosis may not be just a modified form of schizophrenia. Could it be that the manic phase is the result of an excess of serotonin in the brain, and that the depressed phase is the result of a deficiency of it there? The control mechanism which ordinarily keeps production and destruction at normal levels may have been deranged. Feedback mechanisms which control the steady state may not then be sufficient to maintain this same steady state, and wide swings in the functioning amount of serotonin could result. These would appear in behavior as mania and depression.

According to this view there would be no fundamental difference between schizophrenia and manic depressive psychosis. Both would be pictured as errors in the metabolism of serotonin in the brain. The differences of thought and behavior, which have been used in the past to distinguish the two diseases, would be regarded as arising from secondary modification of the basic fault.

There is yet scarcely any experimental evidence to support such a view. The observations of Elvidge and Reed (280) on the oligodendroglia in the brains of patients with manic depressive psychosis showed that they had an histologic abnormality of these cells quite similar to that found in schizophrenia. These changes were described in Chapter 6. Thus, the cells of the brain which can be shown to respond to serotonin were abnormal in patients with manic depressive psychosis. The argument used in Chapter 6 about this fact with respect to schizophrenia would apply with equal force to manic depressive psychosis.

Although measurements of the amount of serotonin have not been reported for any part of the central nervous system in manic depressive psychosis, there has been a determination of the amount of 5-hydroxyindoles (presumably 5-hydroxyindoleacetic acid) in the spinal fluids of 9 cases of depressive psychosis (268). These show the amount to be considerably below that in control specimens. The controls were not from normal people but rather from patients with various neurological

[a] The author is well aware that there is a school of thought which maintains that catatonia represents excitement. Catatonia does seem to involve extreme withdrawal from the environment, but why this should be considered as excitement is not clear. It has more of the aspect of grieving and of depression.

disorders. Consequently, the evidence is not secure that in depressive psychosis the 5-hydroxyindole content of spinal fluid is subnormal.

The findings with analogs of serotonin discussed in Chapter 6 might also apply to manic depressive psychosis. Some of these analogs cause excitement in normal people and some even induce what might be called a flight of ideas. Others bring about depression, sometimes with melancholia. The kinds of excitement and the kinds of depression vary with the individual analogs and with the length of the period of administration. The analogs which cause depression may do so by creating a deficiency of serotonin in certain parts of the brain by acting as antimetabolites. Those which bring about excitement may be expressing their serotonin-like actions there, more than their antagonistic ones. In any event all of the findings with the analogs would not distinguish between schizophrenia and manic depressive psychosis. They would be compatible with the idea that both diseases represent a difficulty in the serotonin mechanism of the brain.

Patients with manic depressive psychosis would be more useful for study of the serotonin hypothesis of mental diseases than those with schizophrenia. It should be possible to change a patient from the depressed to the manic phase at will by manipulation of the serotonin content of the brain. Means for doing this are now known, as, for example, the administration of 5-hydroxytryptophan or even of tryptophan. The manic depressive psychosis would have the great advantage for study that it is easier to decide than in schizophrenia whether a given manipulation has in fact affected the disease in a given direction. It might also be that the swings in cerebral serotonin levels might be greater in manic depressive psychosis than in schizophrenia, and hence more readily detectable by chemical analysis of tissues from the central nervous system. Furthermore, each patient would serve as his own control in such a study of serotonin content, because it should be high in mania and low in depression. The almost impossible task of getting control tissues from normal people would, thus, be obviated. It would seem that the study of patients with manic depressive psychosis might, thus, have several advantages for the understanding of mental diseases.

The one disadvantage of the study of these patients is that they have become quite uncommon. Either the disease has been dying out since the writing of many of the classical textbooks, or (more probably) the patients with the disease are now being classified as schizophrenic.

Possible relationship of serotonin to epilepsy. Two kinds of experimental findings suggest that an excess of serotonin in some part of the brain may be related to the seizures of grand mal epilepsy. These may be summarized as follows:

a. Large amounts of serotonin injected into the brains of mice or rabbits cause convulsions which resemble those of grand mal seizures of man. The principal uncertainty about interpretation of this finding is that the dose required is large. The analog of serotonin known as medmain (Figure 5, Chapter 6) which shows serotonin-like action in some tests will cause similar seizures when fed or injected peripherally (29). Its very close relative 1-methylmedmain, which lacks the serotonin-like component of action either on smooth muscles or on oligodendroglia, does not cause the seizures. This was the first evidence which suggested that serotonin might have something to do with epilepsy. The finding of the induction of seizures with serotonin injected into the brain, came later. The serotonin must be injected into the brain since peripheral administration causes no convulsions. Medmain probably owes its convulsant activity to the fact that it is a substance with serotonin-like action and one which is able to penetrate into the brain.

The convulsions induced in mice by medmain can be prevented by those drugs which control the grand mal seizures of epileptic human beings. For example, prior treatment of the animals with diphenyl hydantoin (Dilantin) protects them from the effects of medmain.

b. An antimetabolite of serotonin has been claimed to reduce the frequency and severity of seizures in human epilepsy (291). Sicuteri reported that 1-methyllysergic acid butanolamide showed this effect in 5 patients, although it did not prevent electrically induced seizures in experimental animals. This derivative of lysergic acid is one for which the antiserotonin effects have been demonstrated in smooth muscles. These findings with epilepsy are quite preliminary and will require confirmation, but if they are real, and particularly if other suitably designed antimetabolites of serotonin can be shown to have similar action, they may be important.

If the idea that serotonin is casually related to epilepsy is valid, one might expect to find increased amounts of this hormone in the cortex of the brain at foci where the seizures are thought to originate. Through the collaboration of Dr. M. Rayport, neurosurgeon of the Albert Einstein School of Medicine, measurements have been made of the serotonin content of these diseased foci. The foci were located by exploration of the cortex with microelectrodes, and the samples of diseased cortex removed in the type of surgical operation taught by Penfield for the relief of epilepsy. The specimens were analyzed by the rat stomach method immediately after removal. The amount of serotonin present in the three cases studied was the same as that found in normal cortex removed from the same location in cadavers of non-epileptic persons within a few hours post mortem. In all of the specimens, correction was made for the serotonin contained in the blood which remained in the cortex. This correction was small.

These preliminary findings thus failed to show that the serotonin content of the foci of seizures in the cortex was abnormal. One might object that it might be necessary to take the specimen for analysis during the actual seizure, or just before it, if an increased amount of serotonin were to be demonstrated. This may be true. At the moment, however, there has been no demonstration of an excess of serotonin at the foci of seizures in the cortex. The evidence linking serotonin to the seizures is indirect.

Because epilepsy is not schizophrenia, it is right to ask how it is possible even to consider an excess of serotonin as being involved in both diseases. One way to rationalize this would be to invoke the idea that the epileptic seizures might be the result of an error in the production of this hormone, which is highly localized anatomically. The first guess as to where this might most probably occur is at the foci in the cortex where abnormal electrical activity can be demonstrated. The partial success in the suppression of the seizures by surgical removal of these foci argues for their importance in the seizures. It is, however, not certain that the seizures arise there *de novo*. Some neurologists believe that they are initiated elsewhere, possibly in the hippocampus, and that the cortical foci are only relay stations.

In view of the suggestive indirect evidence that elevated serotonin may play some role in grand mal seizures, it may be advisable to explore various regions of the brain to find out whether in some of them there may be either increased serotonin or increased enzymic ability to make this hormone. The difficulties of getting the tissues needed for analysis are the reasons why this has not been done either in epilepsy or in manic depressive psychosis or in schizophrenia. The indirect evidence leaves much to be desired. For example, large doses of serotonin will produce a convulsion, but the largeness of the dose makes interpretation uncertain. As discussed in Chapter 6, excess serotonin can act as an inhibitor of the usual response. The excess required to induce a convulsion may do so by inhibition of some action of serotonin. The evidence obtained with medmain helps us with this very difficult question, but it does not settle the matter. Medmain induces convulsions whereas 1-methylmedmain which has the same antiserotonin potency does not. This suggests that it is the serotonin-like property of medmain (which 1-methylmedmain lacks) which is responsible for the convulsion. It cannot be forgotten, however, that medmain does act on certain tissues as an antiserotonin. Its action on the brain in causing convulsions may only be because it reaches certain parts which 1-methylmedmain fails to reach. The meager evidence available at the present leans in the direction of excess serotonin rather than deficiency.

chapter 8

Relationships of other neurohormones to schizophrenia

Following the introduction of the serotonin hypothesis about mental diseases, ideas began to appear to the effect that not serotonin, but norepinephrine or epinephrine or acetylcholine were at fault. It was proposed that abnormalities in the metabolism of one or more of these neurohormones might be the cause of the mental disease. The evidence which connected these other hormones with conditions such as schizophrenia was of the same kind as that which suggested the serotonin hypothesis. This evidence was, however, somewhat less than for the serotonin hypothesis. Actually, what this additional information suggests is that abnormalities in the functioning of several neurohormones may lead to some of the signs of schizophrenia. In Chapter 9 we shall explore the interrelations of serotonin, the epinephrines, acetlycholine, and histamine, and we shall be able to see that changes in the concentration of one can change the functioning of others of these hormones. In this way one might then suspect that the norepinephrine hypothesis or the acetylcholine hypothesis is merely a corollary of the serotonin hypothesis, and not in opposition to it. The present chapter will summarize the evidence which connects these other hormones with psychiatric phenomena.

Norepinephrine (noradrenaline). The first and most cogent evidence which suggested that norepinephrine might be connected with psychic disturbances was that certain drugs which affect the mind can be shown to interfere in the functioning of this hormone. Without this the fact that norepinephrine occurs in the brain, and that it is released from nerves when they are stimulated electrically would show only that this hormone is important in the functioning of nerves, but not that it is necessarily related to psychiatric phenomena.

Both stimulating and tranquilizing drugs are known which can be linked in their actions to norepinephrine. In general, the stimulants in question act like the hormone in suitable pharmacological tests; the tranquilizers in question act antagonistically. This simplification of the findings is only the first approximation to the whole truth, but it is a useful one.

Among tranquilizing drugs, both chlorpromazine and reserpine can interfere in the functioning of norepinephrine. Thus, chlorpromazine when given to an animal such as a morphinized dog will prevent the rise in blood pressure which follows intravenous injection of norepinephrine (292). Its antagonism to epinephrine in this blood pressure test is even more marked.

With respect to the tranquilizing drug reserpine there is a different kind of evidence for interference with the action of norepinephrine. Reserpine causes displacement (loss) of norepinephrine from the midbrain (especially the hypothalamus) and from peripheral nerve endings (246). Yohimbine, a relative of reserpine, has long been known to counteract the contracting effects of the epinephrines on certain smooth muscles. Whether reserpine itself acts in this way is not yet known. Norepinephrine occurs in the endings of peripheral nerves from which it is liberated by electrical stimulation. It is displaced from these endings by treatment of the animal with reserpine. After such treatment with reserpine, electrical stimulation of the nerves no longer liberates the hormone, because the supply of it has been exhausted by the drug.

It is argued that these interferences with the actions of norepinephrine may be the reason why such drugs cause tranquilization. The actions on smooth muscles, for example, might be taken as models of what these drugs do in the brain. The direct actions of reserpine on the brain in bringing about displacement of norepinephrine from the hypothalamus indicate that this postulate has merit. One must not forget, however, that the same drugs do the same things with respect to serotonin, as was described in Chapter 6.

Another reason which has been advanced for relating norepinephrine to mental processes is that it occurs in the brain. In fact, it occurs in those parts of the brain (the hypothalamus, for example) which can be shown by suitable electrical stimulations to be the parts concerned with emotions such as pleasure, rage, and appetite (293). Nevertheless, as mentioned at the start of this section, the mere occurrence there is not enough to justify belief in a direct role in the maintenance of normal mental processes.

Inhibitors of monoamine oxidase such as iproniazid, which cause euphoria, and which will relieve simple depressions, bring about an increase in the norepinephrine content of the brain. This they do at the same time that they increase the serotonin content, and the content of other amines, such as epinephrine.

Several stimulating drugs are known which are structural analogs of the epinephrines and which exhibit norepinephrine-like action in some pharmacological tests. These drugs have psychotomimetic action on normal human beings. Perhaps the best example is amphetamine, the structure of which is shown in Figure 1. This compound, which has been widely tested in clinical medicine, causes wakefulness and excitement when taken as a single dose by a normal person. If the administration is continued for long periods, many individuals show only the original symptoms of a single dose. Some, however, develop a psychosis. According to Hampton (282), this psychosis may be a typical paranoid schizophrenia with the delusions of persecution and other signs found in that disease. Discontinuance of the drug sometimes, but not always, stops the symptoms. The production of paranoid symptoms is noteworthy because most other psychotomimetic drugs have not been found to cause such changes. However, most of them have not been given to normal people for long periods.

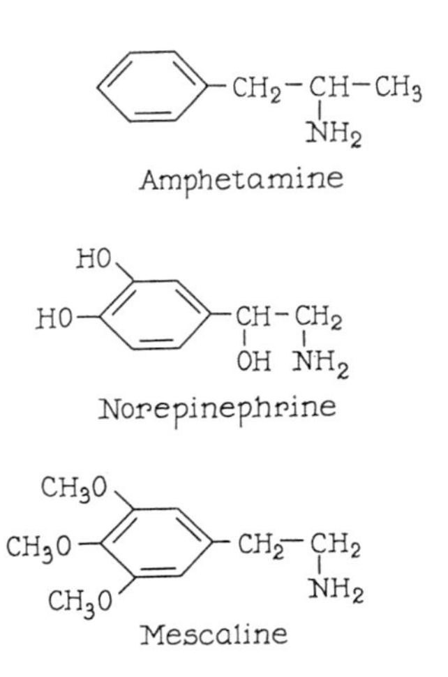

FIG. 1. *Some psychotomimetic drugs related to norepinephrine.*

Amphetamine acts like norepinephrine in some pharmacological tests. However, because it is not subject to ready attack by monoamine oxidase and by the enzymes which methylate and inactivate norepinephrine, it can enter the brain easily and exert actions there. Likewise, it may exert actions on nerves, where norepinephrine fails to do so, possibly because of failure to penetrate. Chronic administration of amphetamine to rats brings about a reduction of the norepinephrine content of their brains and an increase in the serotonin content (294). Presumably, the drug takes the place of some of the norepinephrine and fulfills its function. For this reason, the norepinephrine is low. The reason why the serotonin is high may be understandable after reading Chapter 9.

Another psychotomimetic drug which has a formal relationship to norepinephrine is mescaline. The structural resemblance is clear from Figure 1. Unfortunately, however, a functional relationship has not yet been established. The ability of mescaline in relatively large doses to cause visual hallucinations in normal people has been much studied. In these hallucinations vivid colors frequently occur just as they do in the LSD psychosis.

To summarize the evidence up to this point, the reasons why norepinephrine is believed by some investigators to have a role to play in schizophrenia are the following:

a. Some drugs which interfere with the actions of this hormone cause tranquilization of schizophrenic patients or of normal individuals.

b. Some drugs which can cause normal people to develop a schizophrenia-like condition seem to act like norepinephrine in some pharmacological tests.

These reasons are quite reminiscent of some of those which caused the formulation of the serotonin hypothesis. In fact, a few of the drugs are the very same ones which, among others, were used to support that hypothesis. The question naturally arises as to which one to believe. The involvement of several psychotomimetic drugs with the functioning of both serotonin and norepinephrine makes difficult any decision about which is the most affected, and consequently, which is to be assigned the role of participation in conditions such as schizophrenia. As was stated at the outset of this chapter, a decision of this sort seems rather meaningless, or at best consists of splitting hairs, because the actions of these two hormones are so interrelated. These interrelations will be explored in Chapter 9.

Nevertheless, proponents of the norepinephrine hypothesis to the exclusion of the serotonin one like to cite the following experiment of Carlsson et al. (295). This was designed to determine whether the tranquilizing action of reserpine was to be attributed to interference with norepinephrine or with serotonin in the brain. Mice were reserpinized, and, when they were exhibiting prominently the behavioral effects of this drug, the serotonin content of their brains was increased specifically by injection of 5-hydroxytryptophan, the precursor of the hormone. The tranquilization was not overcome. However, when the precursor of norepinephrine, viz. 3,4,-dihydroxyphenylalanine (dopa), was injected peripherally, the effects of reserpine were removed. A combination of both precursors was better than dopa alone. The doses required were reduced and there was more complete cancellation of the reserpine effect.

Proponents of the serotonin hypothesis like to counter by quoting the following experiment of Brodie et al. (296) which they believe indicates that the tranquilizing action of reserpine is due more to its interference with serotonin than with norepinephrine. Experimental animals kept in the cold (like those at room temperature) lose much of their cerebral norepinephrine when treated with reserpine, but unlike similar animals kept at room temperature, they lose little serotonin. The animals kept in the cold are not tranquilized by reserpine despite their loss of norepinephrine. However, experiments of this sort are not conclusive even though they are suggestive.

It will take more than experiments with reserpine in laboratory animals to decide between the relative importance of serotonin and norepinephrine in schizophrenia. This disease is not to be represented merely by the opposite of tranquilization in laboratory animals. Probably the most which the experiments with reserpine show is that both serotonin and norepinephrine play some role in normal behavior.

There are many drugs which affect the mind and which have little demonstrable relationship to norepinephrine, but which do have such relationship to serotonin. Examples are psilocybin, bufotenine, 2-methyl-3-ethyl-5-nitroindole, and Apresoline. Those who would wish to replace the serotonin hypothesis by a norepinephrine one would be faced with the difficulty of explaining the actions of such substances.

To the present author there is no reason for insisting upon a norepinephrine hypothesis or a serotonin hypothesis, or for that matter an acetylcholine hypothesis. Rather, the truth may be represented more by the idea that interference with the metabolism or functioning of any one of a group of neurohormones in the brain can be expected to lead to mental disturbances resembling those seen in schizophrenia.

Acetylcholine. The idea that acetylcholine might play a role in mental processes arose first from the discovery that acetylcholine was a hormone of the nervous system released from the endings of many parasympathetic nerves when they were stimulated electrically. This by itself was no evidence for its participation in psychic changes, but such participation was an intuitive hunch difficult to prove or deny. A similar kind of hunch also fathered the ideas that norepinephrine and epinephrine as well might be of importance to normal mental processes.

The strongest evidence which suggests a role for acetlycholine in mental processes has come from some recent experiments with some new analogs of this hormone (299 and 300). The new psychotomimetic compounds are esters of substituted acetic acids with alkylated piperidine alcohols. Two of the most potent are shown in Figure 2.

When either of these compounds is given to normal people psychic changes are produced. The changes include visual and auditory hallucinations, paranoid delusions, and other losses of contact with reality.

Ditran and its relatives are strong antagonists to the action of acetylcholine on smooth muscles. This and the structural resemblance to that hormone make them antimetabolites of it. Probably the mental changes produced by these drugs are the result of an interference with acetylcholine, which they may bring about in some parts of the brain. However, there has been reluctance to accept such interpretation. Even the inventors of these psychotomimetic drugs have stated that their actions on the mind are probably not the result of any interference with acetylcholine (310). The reason for this has been that small changes in the chemical structure of the drugs can lead to psychically inactive compounds which are still good antagonists to acetylcholine in smooth muscle. For example, the removal of the —OH group, or the addition of a $-CH_3$ group to the N atom erases the ability to affect the mind. Such objections have been met before in connection with analogs of serotonin. They do not take into account such problems as penetration of the drugs into the brain and the ability to act like the hormone in some tissues. Consequently, they are not crucial criticisms. Another reason for believing that the psychotomimetic effects of Ditran may not be related to the functioning of acetylcholine has been the following finding. Either piperidine or acetylcholine antagonized the effect of Ditran on some tissues. Because piperidine was detected as a constituent of brain it was argued that the psychic effects of Ditran may have been the result of interference in a supposed physiological function of piperidine. Future work may be able to substantiate this suggestion, but at the present time the acetylcholine hypothesis seems to be a reasonable one.

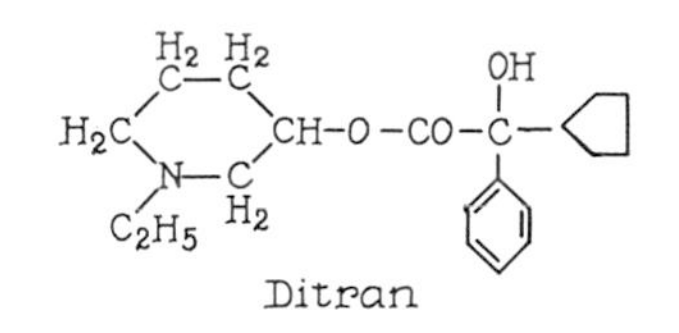

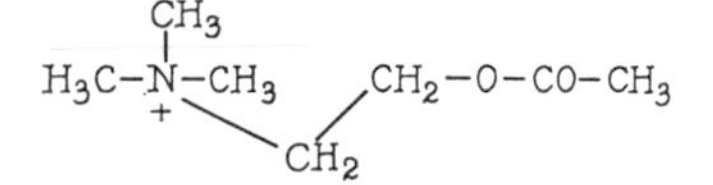

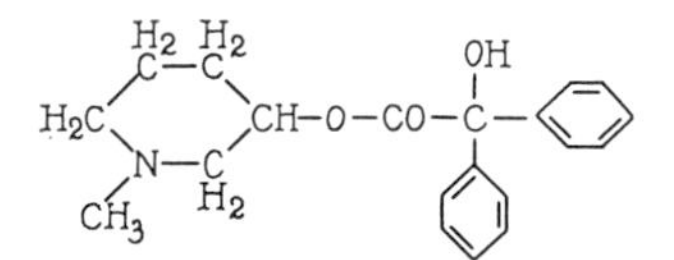

FIG. 2. *Psychotomimetic analogs of acetylcholine.*

One could dismiss the psychotomimetic actions of the aforementioned compounds as mere examples of toxic psychoses. This they undoubtedly are. But could it be that the signs of mental disease which they cause give us a clue about the so-called functional psychoses, the mental diseases of unknown cause? The effects of these drugs might suggest that a defect of metabolism which leads to distortion of the concentration and functioning of acetylcholine in the brain might also bring about directly the symptoms of some mental diseases.

Some older evidence relating cerebral acetylcholine to mental processes also exists. This had been obtained by the use of other drugs which interfered with the action of acetylcholine or which increased the amount of it by inhibition of the cholinesterases.

Several drugs which inhibit the cholinesterases are known. Most of these do not cause mental changes in man, but some do. Thus, lysergic acid diethylamide (LSD) has been shown to inhibit pseudocholinesterase (297, 298), and to a lesser extent the true cholinesterase. Of course, it is not clear whether the psychotomimetic effects of LSD are to be attributed to this action which would increase acetylcholine, and more particularly propionylcholine, in the brain. In Chapter 6, the hallucinogenic action of LSD was ascribed to its serotonin-like and antiserotonin properties, but the possible effect on acetylcholine cannot be ignored. Poisons to the cholinesterases such as diisopropylfluorophosphate (DFP or diisopropylphosphofluoridate) can bring about marked behavioral changes with neurological signs in man and laboratory animals. This is probably due to an increase in cerebral acetylcholine and related esters. Such increases can be demonstrated by chemical analysis. The excess can also be nullified by use of atropine or other brain-penetrating antimetabolites of the hormone. Nevertheless, the disorders called forth by these poisons do not resemble schizophrenia closely.

It is not without interest that several of the inhibitors of cholinesterases are indoles. They include physostigmine (eserine) as well as serotonin and LSD. This might tend to suggest that the active site of the enzyme may be rich in tryptophan or some such indole so that it specifically attracts these indolic inhibitors. Serotonin itself by inhibition of these esterases may play a physiological role in the control of the acetylcholine level. There is no actual proof yet of such ideas aside from the demonstrated inhibitions of the enzymes *in vitro*.

Several of the older inhibitors of the action of acetylcholine with its receptors (antimetabolites of acetylcholine) are known to produce effects on the mind. Many others, however, do not show this property. It is possible that all would do so if they could reach the proper locations in the brain, but this is difficult to prove. Scopolamine, and to a lesser extent atropine, do cause actions on the mind. Scopolamine, for example, is a central nervous system depressant, but in large doses may cause excitement, delirium, and weird effects on memory in some people. These two drugs are classical antagonists of the action of acetylcholine.

It is plain from experiments of this kind that alterations in the amount of acetylcholine or changes in the functioning of it in the brain can lead to behavioral disorders. With some of the drugs used for this purpose the changes may be rather dissimilar from those of schizophrenia, but with others such as Ditran they may be rather similar to the symptoms of that mental disease.

Epinephrine (Adrenaline). The reasons which some investigators have for an idea that changes in the functioning of epinephrine may be the cause of certain mental diseases such as schizophrenia are of the same kind as have been described for norepinephrine and for acetylcholine. These are that it occurs in nerves and the brain. It is one of the mediators of nerve action. More important, some drugs which affect the mind act like epinephrine and others act as antagonists to it. There has, however, been less enthusiasm for invoking epinephrine in the causation of mental disease than has been the case with norepinephrine. The reasons have been that there is more norepinephrine than epinephrine in the brain, and that excitor activity in contrast to inhibitor activity is more marked with norepinephrine than it is with epinephrine. These are, of course, very poor reasons, but they have commanded attention. The relationships of the two epinephrines are so close, and the evidence linking both of them to mental disease is so indirect, that it would be surprising indeed if at this stage one could distinguish them in relation to psychiatry.

Hoffer et al. (301, 302), however, have advanced an hypothesis for the causation of schizophrenia which is based on a postulated defect in the metabolism of epinephrine alone. They suggested that in schizophrenia more epinephrine was changed to adrenochrome or adrenolutin than was the case in normal people. The adrenochrome or adrenolutin was believed to be a toxin which caused the signs of the mental disease.

The basis of this belief was that injection of adrenochrome or adrenolutin into normal human subjects caused mental changes characteristic of schizophrenia. Others have attempted to confirm the psychotomimetic action of adrenochrome, and to demonstrate the presence of this substance in the tissues of schizophrenic patients, but have failed to do so. The hypothesis must therefore be taken with reserve until more definitive evidence to support it can be collected.

Histamine. There are a few reasons for entertaining the idea that histamine may play a role in normal mental processes. As mentioned in Chapter 5, there is some suggestive evidence that this compound functions in the activities of some sensory nerve fibers. The only direct link with mental disturbance is the fact that a few special antihistamines such as chlorpromazine or 1-benzyl-2-(2-dimethylaminoethyl) isoindoline (309) do affect the mind by causing tranquilization. This is offset by the fact that these same drugs, although they may be strong antihistamines, are even more powerful antiserotonins, and antiepinephrines. The isoindoline compound, for example, is even a structural analog of serotonin as well as an antagonist to it. The case for histamine is thus almost non-existent. It is, however, one to keep in mind.

chapter 9

Interrelationships of serotonin, the epinephrines, and acetylcholine

Evidence exists which shows interconnections of the biological activities of the neuromusclar hormones we have been considering. The effects of one, such as serotonin, may be closely related to the effects of another, such as norepinephrine or acetylcholine. It is the purpose of this chapter to enumerate some of these interrelations in function, because it is believed that they help us to understand why drugs which influence the actions of one of these hormones may not be without effects on the functions of the others. Thus, we may come to see that a certain mental change can arise from direct interference with serotonin, or by indirect interference with it by way of a direct action against norepinephrine or acetylcholine. The evidence cited in Chapter 8, then, may appear as no deviation from the main concept of this book. Furthermore, we may thus be able to penetrate more deeply into the factors which maintain normal mental equilibrium.

It must be emphasized that all of the actions of acetylcholine or of the epinephrines are not mediated through indirect effects on the action of serotonin. These hormones each have independent actions of their own. Nevertheless, they do have interrelationships and these are the subject of this chapter.

The epinephrines. The interrelationships of norepinephrine and epinephrine are abundantly clear. In the first place, epinephrine is made biochemically from norepinephrine. If there is no norepinephrine there can be no epinephrine made from it. This fact is, however, somewhat offset by the storage of epinephrine inside of subcellular particles. These can provide a source of one of the hormones for a limited time. When the epinephrine stored in the adrenal glands is depleted, as, for example, by the injection of insulin, more can arise only by way of norepinephrine, which then begins to accumulate in those glands.

In the second place, the pathways for destruction of these two hormones are quite similar. Enzymes such as monoamine oxidase can attack either, although not at the same rate. The rate of removal of either hormone from its site of action is thus influenced by the amount of the other which may be present because both compete for the attention of the destroying enzyme.

Finally, in many tissues either epinephrine or norepinephrine can call forth the same sort of biological response. Thus, either hormone can cause the blood pressure to rise or can inhibit the contraction of uterine muscles, or can inhibit the passage of a nerve impulse in the transcolossal pathway of the optic nerve tract. They differ quantitatively in their potencies in each of these tests, but qualitatively they are quite similar. All of such evidence suggests that the receptors for these hormones must be quite similar, and that to set apart their separate functions may be most difficult. One could not, therefore, make a case for an epinephrine theory of mental disorders without giving much room for the participation of norepinephrine as well.

Serotonin and norepinephrine. The interactions of serotonin and norepinephrine can be seen in several ways. They both depend on the same enzyme for their formation. They both can be destroyed by a single enzyme for which they probably compete. They can exert their actions independently on some tissues, but on others norepinephrine can act as a powerful antagonist to serotonin. The first two points suggest that the amount of each hormone present in a given tissue may in part depend on the amount of the other. The last point suggests that the biological functioning of serotonin can be prevented in some tissues by norepinephrine. How important these kinds of hormonal interplay are in normal physiology and in disease remains to be explored.

The first place at which one can find evidence for the interrelationship of serotonin and norepinephrine is in their formation biochemically. Serotonin is formed by decarboxylation of 5-hydroxytryptophan, and norepinephrine is formed by decarboxylation of dopa and subsequent hydroxylation of dopamine. The same enzyme carries out both decarboxylations. For some time this point of view was denied by one school of thought, and maintained by another, but finally both schools agreed that the same enzyme was concerned (74). When this single enzyme is presented with both substrates at once, both must compete for it. The amount of serotonin formed as well as the amount of norepinephrine is thus influenced by the relative concentrations of 5-hydroxytryptophan and dopa. In living animals, this fact is in part counterbalanced by the storage of the two hormones in separate subcellular particles from which they can be released individually to exert their biological effects without participation of the decarboxylase. Nevertheless, it is conceivable that situations might arise in which the particles are exhausted, and the supply of serotonin and norepinephrine would then depend on the activity of the decarboxylase.

One of the main ways of destruction of both serotonin and norepinephrine, the monoamine oxidase way, uses the same enzyme for both hormones. Thus, in their removal from the site of biological action, as well as in their generation, both of these hormones are dependent on the same enzymes. Unless these enzymes are present in great excess, situations could arise in which one or the other of the hormones must wait its turn to be destroyed and thus to cease biological activity.

Inhibition of the action of monoamine oxidase with drugs such as iproniazid (Marsilid) which cause mental changes thus influences more than just the amount of serotonin in the brain and other tissues. These drugs influence the amounts of norepinephrine, as well as of epinephrine and several other amines. In Chapter 6, this point has already been discussed, and its bearing on hypotheses about mental diseases has been mentioned.

In the biological functioning of serotonin and of norepinephrine one finds evidence of interaction of these two hormones. In some tissues each hormone produces a similar response. In others, norepinephrine acts as a potent inhibitor of serotonin (303, 304, 305, 306, and 307). If one examines the contractions of blood vessels, either as isolated strips of muscle, or as judged by rises in blood pressure in the intact animal, one finds that either serotonin or norepinephrine causes contraction with resultant rise in pressure. Similarly, in the transcolossal passage of nerve impulses in the optic tract of the brain, either hormone causes suppression of passage of the impulse. In this case serotonin is the more active, but in the blood pressure test norepinephrine is the more potent. The important fact for the moment is that either hormone causes the same kind of action. In these tests they function independently.

They are antagonists, however, in the isolated rat uterus, and in some other tissues. In these tissues norepinephrine by itself causes no contraction, whereas serotonin by itself does. We may say that uterus lacks norepinephrine receptors. Norepinephrine, however, is a very potent inhibitor of the action of serotonin (303 and 304). It acts as an antimetabolite of serotonin.

The inhibition of the biological action of serotonin by norepinephrine is very similar to that of an antimetabolite (303). It will be remembered from Chapter 4 that the action of serotonin on the smooth muscles of uterus is to bring about the active transport of calcium ions through the cell membranes. An antimetabolite of the hormone such as 1-benzyl-2-methyl-5-methoxytryptamine (or BAS) prevents this active transport (see Table 1, Chapter 3, and reference 255). Although the active transport of calcium ions is blocked by the antimetabolite, the passive "leakage" of these and other ions through the membrane into the cells is not blocked. Consequently, large increases in the concentration of calcium ions in the external fluid will still cause contraction of the muscle even in the presence of the antimetabolite. This shows that the contractile machinery and the source of energy are still unimpaired in the presence of the antimetabolite. Once the calcium ions get through the membrane they can cause the muscle to contract. This is despite the fact that the active transport of calcium ions (brought about by serotonin) has been blocked by the antimetabolite.

To summarize this complicated point, an antimetabolite of serotonin blocks the active transport of calcium ions, but not the passive "leakage" of them into the cells, so that in the presence of the antimetabolite, large concentrations of calcium ions still cause contraction. The specificity of this kind of test can be shown by use of inhibitors of serotonin which are not antimetabolites of it. Such compounds are nicotinamide (255) and histamine (303). They interfere with the contraction of rat uterus induced by serotonin, but they also interfere with those induced by large concentrations of calcium ions. The site of their poisonous actions probably differs from that of an antimetabolite of serotonin.

When norepinephrine is used instead of BAS the findings are the same as with the antimetabolite (see Table 1). With norepinephrine serotonin will not cause contraction, but large amounts of calcium ions will. The norepinephrine has stopped the active transport of calcium ions by serotonin, but has not interfered with other parts of the contraction process. This is evident because, by forcing calcium into the cells by high external concentrations they still respond.

Possibly the norepinephrine combines with the serotonin receptors in rat uterus, and blocks them just as BAS seems to do. There is thus actual functional evidence which points to an action of norepinephrine similar to that of an antimetabolite of serotonin.

When epinephrine was tested in the same way it also was found to show the same kind of effect. It behaved as did the antimetabolite of serotonin.

TABLE 1. *Antagonism to serotonin of epinephrine, norepinephrine, and the antimetabolite BAS and its reversal with calcium chloride*

Serotonin, μg per ml	$CaCl_2$,* μg per ml	Epinephrine, μg per ml	Norepinephrine, μg per ml	BAS,† μg per ml	Contraction, cm
0.005	0	0	0.00	0	2.7
0	0	0	0.10	0	0.0
0.005	0	0	0.01	0	1.6
0.005	0	0	0.03	0	1.0
0.005	0	0	0.10	0	0.2
0.005	0	0	0.00	0	0.9 ‡
0.020	0	0	0.00	0	3.5 ‡
0	200	0	0.00	0	2.5
0	200	0	0.10	0	2.3
		New Uterus			
0.01	0	0	0	0	3.5
0.01	0	0.001	0	0	0.2
0.01	0	0	0	0	1.1
0.02	0	0	0	0	4.5 ‡
0.02	0	0.001	0	0	5.0
0.02	0	0.003	0	0	4.2
0.02	0	0.010	0	0	0.2
0.02	0	0	0	0	0.4 ‡
0.04	0	0	0	0	3.7 ‡
0	400	0	0	0	2.5
0	400	0.01	0	0	2.2
		New Uterus			
0.01	0	0	0	0	4.1
0	200	0	0	0	4.3
0.01	0	0	0	1	1.0
0	200	0	0	1	4.5

* $CaCl_2$ in addition to that in the Ringer's solution which supplied 20 μg per ml.

† BAS: 1-benzyl-2-methyl-5-methoxytryptamine hydrochloride.

‡ Contractions elicited on retesting the tissue after the treatments preceding in the table.

One can now ask whether these laboratory demonstrations of the various kinds of interplay of serotonin and norepinephrine have any physiological significance or any importance in disease. One might object that since many enzymes are usually in excess of their substrates in tissues, there must be plenty for the formation and destruction of both serotonin and norepinephrine. For example, there must be plenty of the 5-hydroxytryptophan decarboxylase in the brain. Consequently, it would be unlikely that the decarboxylase could ever be so occupied with forming norepinephrine that it would not form serotonin in sufficient amounts. Likewise the monoamine oxidase might not ever be so tied up in the destruction of norepinephrine that it would fail to destroy readily any physiological amount of serotonin. The merits of these arguments await actual measurements of the amounts of substrates in relation to the quantities of enzymes in these particular cases.

It may be that even though the same enzymes participate in formation and destruction of these two hormones, there is enough of each enzyme to insure maximal production and destruction under all conditions, but this has not been demonstrated. With respect to the antagonism between the epinephrines and serotonin, so little norepinephrine is required for a tissue such as uterus to render it insensitive to serotonin that the requisite amounts for such inhibition could be found normally in the tissues. In the brain, however, the importance of this antagonism is yet to be demonstrated experimentally.

The only experimental suggestion that the amount of functional norepinephrine in the brain can influence the amount of serotonin comes from a recent experiment with rats. This one was mentioned in Chapter 8 (294). When rats are treated with amphetamine (a drug which can cause in man the symptoms of paranoid schizophrenia) for several days, the amount of serotonin in their brains increases, and the amount of norepinephrine decreases. The decrease in norepinephrine probably is related to the fact that amphetamine takes its place and functions like it. The feedback mechanisms at work in several enzyme systems probably are also at work here and send back the message to the enzymes concerned in the synthesis of norepinephrine that there is plenty, and that they should slow down. It may not be the decarboxylase which is thus slowed down, but rather the next step in the biosynthesis of norepinephrine, the hydroxylation of dopamine (see Chapter 5). If the decarboxylase were not affected it would continue to form serotonin and dopamine, but not norepinephrine. We might thus understand why serotonin increases in the presence of amphetamine. The reduced amounts of norepinephrine may then induce formation of less monoamine oxidase for destruction of that hormone. This would tend to increase the amount of serotonin present, since monoamine oxidase also plays a role in its disappearance as well. This would make understandable the increase in serotonin above the normal amount. There has not yet been detailed experimental proof that this is the mechanism. Rather, these possibilities are being mentioned only to indicate that a frame of reference exists in which the known facts can be understood. The whole idea of the existence of interplays between these hormones is so new that detailed explorations of mechanisms have not yet been made.

If we are to understand the inhibitory action of the epinephrines as being due to blocking of the serotonin receptors, how are we to view the effects on blood pressure and nerve impulse transmission in which either serotonin or norepinephrine causes the same kind of response? It would seem that in the tissues concerned with these responses both serotonin receptors and norepinephrine receptors exist, and that for the serotonin receptors there, norepinephrine does not combine and block as in the case of those of uterus. An antimetabolite of serotonin such as BAS still combines with the serotonin receptors in blood vessels, and blocks them for use by serotonin. The antimetabolite does not combine with and block the norepinephrine receptors. This is why, as shown in Table 5 of Chapter 4, a dog treated with BAS phenol is protected against the pressor effects of serotonin, but not against those of norepinephrine or epinephrine.

What we can deduce from all of this is that there may be serotonin receptors in certain tissues which combine with the epinephrines and suffer blockade such that these tissues are now insensitive to serotonin. In other tissues this does not take place because they have their own norepinephrine receptors. We can thus begin to see a direct interrelationship in the actions of these hormones on certain tissues. Such direct interactions may well exist in some parts of the brain, although they have not yet been demonstrated or even searched for. If they did we might have some insight into how the liberation of, let us say, norepinephrine could result in inhibition of a process being activated by serotonin. The norepinephrine hypothesis of certain mental disorders might then not be more than part of the serotonin hypothesis, or vice versa. These are speculations only, but the facts established up to the present time in tissues other than the brain may point to what may come.

Serotonin and acetylcholine. In several situations in animals serotonin and acetylcholine bring about opposing responses. For example, acetylcholine when applied to a heart slows the beat. Serotonin increases it, either in rate or (more generally) in amplitude of the beat. The net result is that cardiac output is diminished by acetylcholine and increased by serotonin. So also, in effects on blood pressure, one sees the opposing actions of these two hormones. Intravenous injection of serotonin increases blood pressure in dogs or men by causing constriction of the blood vessels.

This effect seems to be opposed by acetylcholine. The evidence for this is, however, indirect. It consists of the demonstration that antagonists of acetylcholine such as atropine erase the ceiling which seems to exist on the rise in blood pressure. As explained in Chapter 4, injections of serotonin cause rises in blood pressure, but not of more than about 50 mm mercury. An antagonist of acetylcholine removes this ceiling so that after such a drug, the rise following injection of serotonin may exceed 100 mm mercury. The same effect can be achieved by cutting the spinal cord, which presumably carries a reflex message to expand blood vessels which is expressed at nerve endings by liberation of acetylcholine (90).

These antagonistic actions of serotonin and acetylcholine are most probably not direct interactions such as have been pictured in the preceding section for serotonin and the epinephrines. Rather, they are brought about by indirect means. Acetylcholine is one of the chemical mediators of parasympathetic nerves. Serotonin seems to be involved more in sympathetic nerves.[a] Equilibrium or homeostasis is maintained in large measure in an animal by the counterbalancing of effects, for example, those of the sympathetic and parasympathetic nervous systems. It would seem that in many situations, serotonin is on one side of the balance and acetylcholine on the other.

To pursue the matter further, the opposing or counterbalancing actions of serotonin and acetylcholine are probably not exerted on a single cell. Rather, serotonin stimulates one kind of cell to do one thing, and acetylcholine stimulates another cell to do something else which is, however, in opposition to the end result of the serotonin-stimulated cell. In other words, the antagonism in indirect. It is the resultant of the activities of opposing tissues. This is in contrast to the direct kind of antagonism discussed earlier for serotonin and

[a] Some investigators will consider this statement unjustifiable because the evidence is still quite meager. Most of the evidence which does exist has come from invertebrates.

norepinephrine in which the effect was ascribable to competition of the two hormones for a single receptor in an individual cell.

Such a point of view is in agreement with the biochemical understanding of the mechanism of action of serotonin and acetylcholine. In Chapters 4 and 5 each of these hormones was pictured as providing a way of entry for calcium ions into a cell through the membrane. If each brought about calcium entry the result should be the same in any given cell. However, calcium entry into cell A may cause it to contract, whereas in cell B of different internal composition, the entry may result in some other kind of change. If this other kind of change is in opposition to the effect of contraction in cell A the opposing action would result.

There are physiological responses, however, in which these two hormones are on the same side. Thus, in smooth muscles of intestines or uterus either serotonin or acetylcholine will cause contraction. This is probably because receptors for both hormones exist in these tissues, probably even in single cells, and activation of either kind of receptor causes contraction. Calcium ions can be carried into the single cell either by way of the serotonin mechanism or the acetylcholine mechanism. The end result is the same. Such a situation gives no evidence of interaction. Rather, it speaks in favor of independent actions.

In addition to such independent actions some evidence for synergism also exists. When mice are injected with lysergic acid diethylamide (LSD) they undergo the marked changes in behavior described in Chapter 6. These can be prevented if the animals are given intracerebral injections of large amounts of serotonin and acetylcholine (210). Neither hormone alone will prevent the behavioral changes. In fact, acetylcholine because of its rapid destruction is not very effective even in combination, but more stable derivatives of it such as carbamylcholine (which have pharmacological actions like acetylcholine) are effective. The carbamylcholine must be used in combination with serotonin for the effect on behavior. There is thus synergism.

Additional and important reasons for suspecting some interrelationship in the actions of serotonin and acetylcholine are the findings with antimetabolites. Herxheimer (110) showed that when guinea pigs inhaled aerosols of serotonin they developed an anaphylactoid shock, just as they did from injection of histamine. This shock could be prevented with an antimetabolite of serotonin (LSD), but it could also be prevented by an antagonist of acetylcholine (atropine). In other words, interference with the action of acetylcholine also interfered with this action of serotonin. In many tissues, especially smooth muscles, atropine has been shown not to antagonize the actions of serotonin. One wonders whether the anaphylactic action of serotonin is mediated through acetylcholine. Of course, one could be seeing in this case an indirect interaction such as that described in the control of blood pressure at the start of this section.

The preceding examples probably represent only indirect interactions of acetylcholine and serotonin, i.e., those not involving the same active site or receptor. If one thinks of the possibility of direct interplay of these two hormones, the effects of certain indoles on cholinesterase come to mind. The classical inhibitor of these enzymes is physostigmine (eserine), which is an indole. Another indole, viz., indoxylacetate, has been found to be a substrate for pseudocholinesterase (298). Other indole derivatives such as LSD and bufotenine can inhibit the action of pseudocholinesterase. Even serotonin, another indole, can inhibit this enzyme.

Could it be (as mentioned in Chapter 8) that this enzyme, so intimately associated with the biological actions of acetylcholine, has an active center which is either derived from serotonin or hydroxytryptophan or even tryptophan as a residue in the peptide chain? Such a situation might give the enzymes the specific power to attract serotonin and its analogs, which would then act as inhibitors because they cling to the enzymatically active site. If serotonin actually behaves in the living animal as an inhibitor of pseudocholinesterase an increase of serotonin might result in an increase of acetylcholine in a suitably situated tissue. If the two hormones were pitted against each other as they frequently seem to be, in their indirect interrelations the net result of increasing both might be to cancel out each other, but if each hormone were acting independently in a given tissue, increases in both would augment the end result.

If we think only of the indirect interplay of these two hormones in which they cause conflicting responses then we see that an antimetabolite of acetylcholine might serve to reinforce the actions of serotonin. The antiacetylcholine prevents the biological action of acetylcholine and thus brings about deficiency of that hormone. Such a deficiency may take the brake off a function which is being pushed in one direction by serotonin and in the other by acetylcholine. The end result might be that the antiacetylcholine would exert an effect similar to an excess of serotonin. This is one way to consider the induction of schizophrenia-like conditions in normal people through administration of antimetabolites of acetylcholine such as Ditran. The end result of the antiacetylcholine may be the same as an increase in serotonin. However, it should not be inferred that this is the only possibility. Acetylcholine has independent actions in addition to those which are under the influence of serotonin.

Serotonin and histamine. The action of serotonin on smooth muscles such as those of uterus can be prevented by histamine (303). The amounts of histamine required are rather large. For this reason it may be questioned whether the antagonism has physiological significance, but it is at least an experimental model to show what can happen. In the case of the antiserotonin action of the epinephrines, which was described earlier, the amounts of the latter (which were very small) were of the order to make quite possible that the physiological actions of serotonin may be under the influence of the epinephrines. With histamine it is plain that the antagonism is of no physiological importance, at least in the uterus of rats. What is not plain, however, is whether in other tissues, e.g., the brain, the potency of histamine might be greater, and thus might be of much importance. Furthermore, the only demonstration of the antagonism of histamine to the action of serotonin has been made with rat uterus, and rat tissues are well known to be rather insensitive to histamine when compared to tissues of guinea pigs or human beings. For these reasons then, the possibility remains that the antagonism may have considerable significance for the human.

The antagonism of histamine to serotonin is not of the same kind as that of norepinephrine. This was readily shown by use of the test with calcium ions which was described earlier in the section on serotonin and noreipnephrine. Histamine rendered rat uterus unresponsive either to calcium ions in excess or to serotonin. Norepinephrine interfered only with serotonin, but not with calcium ions (303). This was interpreted to mean that histamine was acting not to block the serotonin receptors but rather to interfere at some other step in the sequence of events in muscular contraction. For example, it may have inhibited the processes which energize contraction or at some other point.

Some interdependence of these two hormones is also indicated by the results obtained with antimetabolites. Erspamer showed (308) that the action of serotonin in guinea pig uterus was antagonized by antimetabolites of histamine such as Pyribenzamine and Phenergan. A discussion of the possible meanings of such drug effects will be found in the last section of this chapter.

Epinephrine and acetylcholine. When a tissue such as a rat uterus is rendered insensitive to the action of serotonin by application of epinephrine, it is also rendered insensitive to the action of acetylcholine. It seems as if the epinephrine blocks some reaction which is essential to the functioning of both hormones. No postulate to account for these facts has been advanced with any supporting evidence.

Evidence from the multiple actions of drugs against the hormones. When sufficient testing is done it usually turns out that a drug which was originally thought to interfere with the actions of just one of the hormones we have been discussing does in fact interfere with several of them. Frequently it is necessary to search for a suitable test object before such a demonstration can be made, because in some tissues the specificity for one hormone, which is exhibited by a given drug, is rather striking. What is most surprising is that a given drug which is a structural analog of, let us say, acetylcholine may act as a specific antagonist of acetylcholine on some tissues, but on others it may act not only as an antiacetylcholine, but also as an antihistamine and even as an antiepinephrine and antiserotonin. Similarly, a structural analog of serotonin may prove to be a specific antagonist of serotonin in some tissues, but in others it may antagonize the action not only of serotonin, but of acetylcholine and histamine also. Many instances of this sort of behavior are known. A case in point is chlorpromazine, which was invented as an antihistamine. It is that, but it is also able to prevent the actions of norepinephrine in some test systems, and of epinephrine (but not of norepinephrine) in others. In still others it can prevent the action of serotonin. Earlier in this chapter the cases of atropine, Pyribenzamine, and Phenergan acting as antagonists to serotonin were cited. It is thus quite plain that a drug may be a specific anatagonist for one of the hormones in some tests, but not in all.

What interpretation is to be placed on the non-specific cases? One might say, as some have said, that the drugs are just general poisons which damage tissues in such a way that they can no longer respond to normal stimuli. The fact is, however, that other functions of the tissues in question may not be affected. The present author prefers to believe that the lack of specificity is in some way connected with the interplay of these hormones which act on nerves and smooth muscles.

Epilogue. Very little experimentation has yet been done to understand the interrelationships of these hormones. The idea that such interrelationships exist at all has only very recently appeared. It would seem now that there are enough solid facts and enough clues to begin the exploration of these interrelationships. The existing evidence seems almost sufficient to make one wonder why there must be a serotonin hypothesis and a norepinephrine hypothesis and an acetylcholine hypothesis of mental diseases. They all may be parts of the same hypothesis.

chapter 10

Genetic aspects

Several kinds of mental disease run in families. This has been known for centuries, and the present-day statistical analysis does not deny it. There may be psychoses which have no familial predisposition, such as some of the mental changes induced by ingestion of certain toxic chemicals, but, for phenylketonuria and galactosemia, the genetic part of causation has been proved to the satisfaction of all. For diseases such as schizophrenia there is little doubt that family background contributes markedly to predisposition to the disease, even though inheritance of the disease has not been established as it has been for phenylketonuria and galactosemia.

In schizophrenia and in manic depressive psychosis the familial predisposition to the disease is clear, but whether or not the predisposition is inherited (that is, whether it is genetic) is not so clear. There are those who maintain that the predisposition is an environmental one brought about by unhealthful mental attitudes inculcated into children by parents who are themselves schizoid. These students of the disease feel that a mother with leanings towards schizophrenia exposes her children to the mental attitudes which encourage the development of the disease. They feel that it is environment rather than inheritance of any biochemical abnormality which is the familial contribution to the disease. This point of view seems inadequate to the present author. He feels that there is probably an inherited chemical abnormality which predisposes certain individuals to schizophrenia just as there has been shown to be a more severe inherited chemical defect which results in the idiocy of phenylketonuria. The environmental factor in the family is an added stress which contributes to the disease. It can be a very real factor in schizophrenia.

If one examines only diseases such as phenylketonuria or galactosemia the genetic factor is found to be the deciding one, as we shall see in Chapters 11, 12, and 13. It is true that, in these diseases, a drastic and highly specific environmental change, such as the elimination of phenylalanine or of galactose from the diet of the infant with the genetic defect, will prevent the mental disease, but less specific environmental changes, such as a revision of mental attitudes in the home, and otherwise lightening the mental strain will do nothing to prevent the onset of the disease. There is a genetic inevitability which can only be circumvented by highly specific chemical changes in the environment of the newborn. With schizophrenia or manic depressive psychosis on the other hand this genetic inevitability is lacking. The diseases develop almost always in adult life,[a] and the genetic background which predisposes to the disorder is by no means mathematically precise as it is in phenylketonuria. Nevertheless, statistical study of numerous cases of schizophrenia have indicated to some a genetic predisposition to that disease.

In mental diseases in which the inevitable inheritance is not well established, a simple equation has often been used to show the relative parts played by genetics and environment (227). This equation states that

$$\mathrm{MB} = \frac{P + S}{R}$$

where MB is mental breakdown, P is predisposition, S is stress, and R is resistance. Predisposition and resistance probably are factors determined by genetics and mediated by enzymic reactions. Stress is an environmental factor represented by the effects of social customs, education, and individual emotional events. Of course it is not possible to make predisposition entirely chemical and stress entirely psychological because, as is well known, stress is mediated through changes in specific chemical substances in the body (311). Nevertheless, this simple equation has considerable value. It emphasizes the well-known fact that many people can undergo emotional and physical stresses which are said to be causally related to mental diseases and yet remain normal.

Basic laws of genetics. Readers of this book will be well aware of the Mendelian laws of inheritance. They will know that many particular differences in individuals are the results of inheritance, and that the expressions of differences such as the color of the hair or the eyes or

[a] The development of the disease after the attainment of maturity is by itself no argument against a genetic basis. There are well-known mental diseases which have an inherited inevitability but which do not usually appear until middle age. Such a disease is Huntington's chorea.

the skin and numerous other traits are the expressions of the actions of genes. They will also know that there are dominant and recessive traits. They will know that genes are to be found localized at particular points along chromosomes, and that the close proximity of two genes on a chromosome can lead to certain modifications in the inheritance of the traits related to these genes. They will have heard of the postulates which relate genes to nucleic acids, particularly desoxyribonucleic acids, and that possibly the genes may be composed of desoxyribonucleic acids. They will also have heard of the postulate of one gene, one enzyme. Most of these matters are discussed fully in textbooks of genetics (312).

The basic idea of Mendelian genetics is that most single traits are inherited as individual particles which are passed from one generation to the next at the time of mating. For example, the color of the subcutaneous fat of a rabbit is an inherited trait governed by the Mendelian laws of genetics. In wild rabbits the fat is colorless, whereas in certain domesticated breeds it is yellow. The reproductive cells of wild rabbits are a pure strain with respect to this trait of colorless fat. Similarly, the reproductive cells of the domestic breed are a pure strain with respect to yellow color of the fat. If wild rabbits are mated, the offspring will all have white fat, and if the domestic breed is mated, all of the offspring will have yellow fat. If a wild rabbit is mated with one of the domestic strain, all of the first generation offspring will have white fat. Their hybrid character will appear only in the second generation.

If these hybrids are now mated with other hybrids of the same genetic constitution, the result is found to be the following. One-fourth of the offspring will have yellow fat and will behave in future matings as a pure strain with respect to yellow fat. This one-fourth of the second generation are no longer hybrids. The other three-fourths of the second generation will have white fat, but they will not be identical with respect to this trait. One out of three of them will be a pure strain with respect to the white fat trait. The other two out of three will still have white fat but will be hybrids with respect to this trait. This can be shown readily if they are mated with hybrids or with pure strain animals and the color of the fat in the offspring is noted.

The gene for white fat is expressed as an enzyme which destroys the xanthophyll pigments of the green plants which the rabbits eat as food. If the enzyme is present in a rabbit, it destroys the xanthophylls. If it is not present, the xanthophylls are not destroyed but are deposited in the fat depots, which are consequently colored yellow by these pigments. The presence of the enzyme (the white-fat trait) is a dominant trait. Thus it may be that the hybrids have only half as much of this enzyme as the pure strain white fat rabbits, but half as much enzyme is enough still to destroy all of the xanthophylls from the food. Consequently, the hybrids have white fat.

In the mating process, which involves the fusion of two reproductive cells, one from each partner, we may picture the transfer and segregation of genetic information about this enzyme as follows. If two hybrids are mated, the male cell contributes what we may call a dominant particle (allele) and a recessive particle. Similarly, the female cell contributes a dominant and a recessive particle for this trait. These may be called w and W. The male is wW and the female is wW. The progeny are ww, wW, wW, and WW in equal numbers. In this random distribution of particles one-fourth of the offspring turn out to be pure strain with respect to having the enzyme, one-fourth turn out to be pure strain with respect to not having the enzyme, and one-half are hybrids with approximately half the normal amount of enzyme. In this fashion one can visualize why it is that in the second generation one gets the precise 1:1:2 ratio of pure strains of each original trait and hybrids.

Relationships of genes to enzymes and their products. According to the work which began with the discoveries of Beadle and Tatum, genes control the formation of the various individual enzymes in a living thing. These enzymes in turn control the chemical constituents of an individual, and consequently his physical traits. We have seen this in the example of rabbits in the preceding section. If gene A is required to be present before enzyme B can be formed in the body, then if the gene is absent as the result of inheritance, or if it is slightly changed as the result of mutation, enzyme B will not be formed, and the chemical substances which are the products of the action of this enzyme also will not be formed. The substrates for the enzyme, which are being produced by other enzymes, will not be metabolized in the normal way since their special enzyme is not there, and these substrates may accumulate. In this way the chemical constitution of the individual is changed even more.

If, for example, the gene were lacking which controls the formation of the enzyme which hydroxylates tryptophan, the following consequences would be expected. 5-Hydroxytryptophan would not be synthesized from tryptophan, at least not in the normal amount. The excess tryptophan would thus be diverted into other metabolic reactions such as the formation of kynurenine and of indoleacetic acid which might consequently increase both in the tissues and in the urine. Furthermore, the substrate for the synthesis of serotonin (5-hydroxytryptophan) would be lacking. The activities dependent on serotonin would be depressed because there would be a serotonin deficiency. One of the substrates of monoamine oxidase would be lacking, and the result of this would be the finding that the urinary excretion of 5-hydroxyindoleacetic acid would be greatly diminished. Actually, there are mental diseases in which the urinary excretion of this acid is greatly diminished and some in which the excretion of indoleacetic acid is increased (313).

Recently it has been found (313, 314) that this is the case in phenylketonuric idiots. Similarly, in a small percentage (8 per cent) of patients in a mental hospital diagnosed as schizophrenics this also was the situation (269). In the patients diagnosed as schizophrenics, the exact enzymic defect has not been established, but in the case of the phenylketonuric subjects the enzymic defect is not the failure to hydroxylate tryptophan. Rather, it is an indirect effect of the failure to hydroxylate phenylalanine. Because of the lack of the enzyme which hydroxylates this amino acid, phenylalanine accumulates in the tissues. It and its immediate metabolic products cause inhibition of the decarboxylase which forms serotonin and dopamine (315 through 322). The failure to form enough serotonin and epinephrines is thus an indirect result of the lack of an enzyme for metabolizing phenylalanine (322 and 323). In Chapter 11, the metabolic defects of phenylketonuria will be described at greater length, but for the present discussion the repercussions of the genetic defect in this disease illustrate the point. This point is that an inheritance of the lack of a particular gene can lead to the failure to form a particular enzyme. The lack of this enzyme can, by accumulation of its substrate and deficiency of its products, lead to profound changes in the body and mind.

Summary. A few kinds of mental disease have been proved to be inherited according to Mendelian laws. These include phenylketonuria and galactosemia, which will be examined in more detail in the next chapters. They are diseases which are present at birth, and which usually result in idiocy early in life. In these diseases one enzyme is lacking, and this is probably the result of the failure of a single gene.

Although just one enzyme is lacking the metabolic abnormalities which ensue from this deficiency can be multiple. Thus, in phenylketonuria the lack of an hydroxylase leads to the accumulation of phenylalanine in the tissues. This causes inhibition of the decarboxylase which forms serotonin and dopamine and its derivatives the epinephrines. The deficiency of serotonin is reflected by diminished excretion of 5-hydroxyindoleacetic acid in the urine. Thus, a train of metabolic abnormalities follows the failure to form a single kind of enzyme.

The mental diseases which have been shown to be inherited are rather rare. They are drastic diseases which mentally incapacitate the individual in infancy, and thus represent the full expression of the genetic aspect of psychoses.

In the more common types of mental diseases such as schizophrenia and manic depressive psychosis there is widespread experience of familial predisposition. There is no clear demonstration of genetic inevitability. An individual with genetic predisposition to the disease may escape it completely. Almost always he escapes it until adult life. If there is a genetic factor represented by the lack of a certain enzyme, the deficiency may not be complete. It may be so slight that the individual can escape difficulty unless subjected to unusual stresses. An experiment by Cannon et al. (324), in which the peripheral sources of the epinephrines were removed surgically from a cat, showed that under unexciting conditions the animal could function normally. When stress was applied failure of normal behavior ensued. It may be the same with these mental diseases. Thus, an inherited defect in the enzyme which makes serotonin in the brain, especially if it were only a quantitative difficulty, in which the incorrect amount of the hormone but still some of it was made, might be tolerated for years. A particular increase in stress might then bring about failure to react normally. It thus is of particular importance to measure the enzymes concerned with serotonin metabolism in the brains of patients with these diseases.

This chapter will serve as introduction to Chapters 11, 12, and 13, in which severe mental diseases of undoubted genetic causation will be explored with relation to the biochemical defects which characterize them.

chapter 11

Phenylketonuria or phenylpyruvicoligophrenia

Although phenylketonuria is somewhat rare, it is one of the best understood of mental diseases. Both biochemically and genetically, the factors which give rise to it have been recognized. Very recently, as a result of this understanding, it has become possible to avoid the idiocy which would otherwise develop in infants recognized as having been born with the disease. It has even been possible to predict something about the probable occurrence of it in the children from the marriage of normal individuals suspected of being heterozygous for this trait.

Phenylketonuria is an inborn error of metabolism which leads almost invariably to the development of idiocy early in childhood, if not in infancy. Biochemically it is characterized by the occurrence in the urine of phenylpyruvic acid. This acid arises from the excessive amounts of phenylalanine which are in the blood and other tissues.

Discovery. In 1934, Fölling (325) reported that, when the urines of inmates of a mental hospital were each tested with a few drops of acidified ferric chloride solution, some of them turned green. The substance responsible for the production of this green color was isolated and identified as phenylpyruvic acid (Figure 1). The isolation can be accomplished easily as the 2,4-dinitrophenylhydrazone. Because certain other substances which give a green color with ferric chloride can occasionally be found in otherwise normal urine, the actual isolation of the hydrazone and determination of its melting point serve to minimize errors in diagnosis which might otherwise be made if sole reliance were placed on the ferric chloride test.

The patients who excreted phenylpyruvic acid were of such low mental powers as to be considered idiots. They had been in this condition since infancy. About 1 per cent of some forty-eight thousand inmates of various mental institutions have been found to be phenyl-

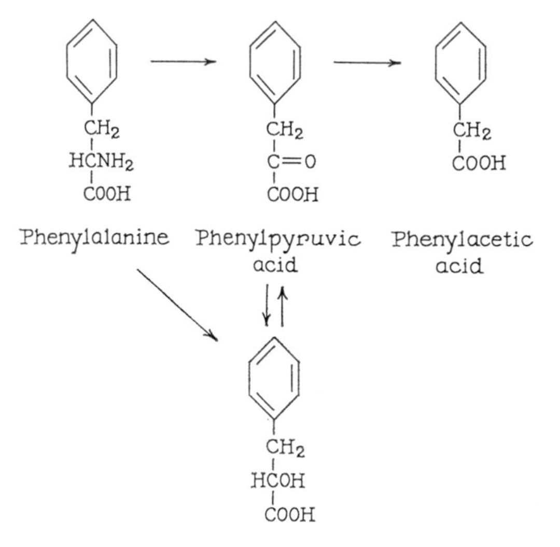

FIG. 1. *Immediate metabolic products of phenylalanine which accumulate in the urine of phenylketonuric patients.*

ketonurics (326). No normal person was found to excrete phenylpyruvic acid, although more than ten thousand have been tested.

Many of the biochemical and genetic findings about this disease have been made by G. A. Jervis. Fortunately he has reviewed the principal points in two recent publications (326 and 327). His contribution and that of many others to the understanding and control of this disorder will appear in the following sections. In addition, an original suggestion will be made that the mental disease may be the result of a serotonin deficiency induced by the metabolic error with respect to phenylalanine. The peculiar force of the deficiency will be suggested to arise from the fact that it has been present ever since birth in the patient.

The mental defect. As mentioned earlier, persons suffering from phenylketonuria are mentally defective and frequently are classified as idiots. They are often slow and morose (328). The degree of mental retardation varies considerably from individual to individual. The intelligence quotient is usually below 20 (see Table 1), but it can be as high as 90. These data have been taken from the paper of Jervis (326). Aside from these generalizations, a more precise psychometric description cannot be given. The morose tendency will

TABLE 1. *Distribution of IQ in three hundred thirty phenylketonurics*

	IQ							
	Below 10	11 to 20	21 to 30	31 to 40	41 to 50	51 to 60	61 to 70	Above 70
Number	122	88	41	34	31	7	4	3
Per Cent	37	26	12	10	9	2	1	0.9

be of some interest when we come to consider the possible relationship of serotonin to this mental disorder.

Physical characteristics. In addition to the mental defect, phenylketonuric patients usually exhibit some common traits. They tend to be of fair complexion. This is a reflection of their biochemical defect which is the lack of the enzyme which converts phenylalanine to tyrosine. The pigments of skin and hair are usually melanins which are made from tyrosine by way of dihydroxyphenylalanine. Some investigators have reported demyelination of nerves in histological sections taken from these patients, but there is no agreement on this point. Jervis (326) did not observe such demyelination in his extensive series of cases. There is, however, agreement that phenylketonurics frequently have epilepsy. Aside from these characteristics, the patients seem not to differ from normal people.

The philosophical implications of the lack of an anatomical defect. The lack of a distinctive anatomical defect in phenylketonuric patients is an important point to bear in mind when one considers the argument advanced by many students of psychiatry with respect to functional mental diseases. Because no distinctive anatomical defect has been demonstrated always to be present in schizophrenic patients,[a] the conclusion has been promulgated that there is no physical basis for the disease, and that it must arise from psychological stresses. This has been the position taken by most of the adherents of the Freudian point of view.

In phenylketonuria, just as in schizophrenia, one fails to find uniformly a characteristic anatomical lesion, and yet we now know that

[a] An exception is the swelling of oligodendrogliocytes described in Chapter 6, but the fact that this observation of swelling has not been searched for in large numbers of patients makes one hesitate. Certainly it has not entered into the thinking of psychiatrists with respect to the philosophical question under discussion.

the cause of the idiocy which develops in patients with phenylketonuria is the lack of one enzyme. This lack results in the accumulation of phenylalanine in the tissues. When this accumulation is prevented the idiocy does not develop. These patients thus suffer from a biochemical lesion which cannot be found by the usual histological examinations. To find the lesion one needs a specific chemical test—that is, one for accumulation of phenylalanine or its metabolic product, phenylpyruvic acid. It is not without interest that, now that a specific test for phenylketonuria (the ferric chloride test coupled with the isolation of the hydrazone) is known, it is found on examination of the records of admission to mental institutions that many phenylketonurics were admitted with a diagnosis of childhood schizophrenia (Jervis, personal communication).

Biochemical characteristics. The central biochemical defect in phenylketonuria is the lack of the enzyme which converts phenylalanine to tyrosine. This oxidative enzyme, which is called the phenylalanine hydroxylase, is normally found in the liver. It is absent from the livers of phenylketonurics (329 and 330). When these livers are incubated with phenylalanine either *in vitro* or *in vivo,* no tyrosine is formed. Because of this defect, the phenylalanine which is eaten in the food is not metabolized normally, and accumulates in the tissues. Analysis of blood for example shows that a phenylketonuric patient may have 100 to 350 μg phenylalanine per ml, whereas the normal person shows about 5 to 15 μg per ml (331, 332, and 333). In normal urine there is about 160 mg phenylalanine per 24 hours, but for phenylketonuric urine, there may be as much as 1 gram per 24 hours (326, 331, and 334). Phenylalanine is an essential amino acid which the body cannot make for itself. It is required for the formation of all of the proteins in the body and for other reactions such as the synthesis of tyrosine, melanin pigments, etc. It is still incorporated into proteins of the phenylketonuric patient in the same way as in the normal. A hypothesis of Linus Pauling that the mental defect arose from incorporation of extra phenylalanine into proteins did not prove to be correct, at least not in so far as the protein of hemoglobin is concerned. Normal hemoglobin is formed in phenylketonuric patients (327).

The excess phenylalanine which circulates in the blood is deaminated. The product of this deamination is phenylpyruvic acid, which is excreted in the urine, and forms, as we have already seen, the basis of a simple colorimetric test for the detection of the disease (the ferric chloride test). Phenyllactic acid and phenylacetic acid also accumulate in the urine of patients with this disease as do smaller amounts of *p*-hydroxyphenyllactic acid, *p*-hydroxyphenylacetic acid and *o*-hydroxyphenylacetic acid. These are compounds which arise from simple transformations of phenylalanine or phenylpyruvic acid. The probable reactions involved for the major ones are outlined in Figure 1.

Indoleacetic acid excretion in the urine of patients with phenylketonuria is greater than normal (313 and 314). The probable reason for this is more involved than for the other acids just mentioned. As discussed in Chapter 10, phenylalanine and its immediate metabolic products inhibit the decarboxylation of 5-hydroxytryptophan to serotonin. Consequently, the serotonin pathway of tryptophan utilization via 5-hydroxytryptophan is suppressed. More tryptophan is available to participate in other metabolic pathways. One of these is the conversion of tryptophan to indoleacetic acid by decarboxylation, deamination and oxidation. One would therefore expect to find increased excretion of indoleacetic acid. However, because the indoleacetic acid way of metabolism of tryptophan is a minor pathway (because most of the tryptophan is used for other purposes) one would not expect to find a very large increase in indoleacetic acid excretion. Actually, the observed increase is small. In contrast to indoleacetic acid the urinary excretion of 5-hydroxyindoleacetic acid is decreased in phenylketonuria. The reason for this will be discussed in the next section.

Serotonin and the epinephrines in phenylketonuria. Why does the excess of phenylalanine in the tissues cause idiocy? This question cannot be answered at the present time, but there are some fascinating clues. When the concentration of serotonin and of epinephrine in the blood of phenylketonurics was measured both hormones were found to be lower than normal (315 through 323). As might then be expected, the urinary excretion of 5-hydroxyindoleacetic acid was subnormal. This is a reflection of the deficiency of serotonin throughout the body. The reason for these deficiencies of serotonin and epinephrine seems to be that the excessive phenylalanine and its immediate metabolic products in the tissues inhibit the decarboxylase for 5-hydroxytryptophan and dopa (315 and 316). This is the enzyme which normally forms serotonin and the precursor of the epinephrines (see Chapters 4 and 5). The inhibition of the enzyme can readily be demonstrated by tests with the decarboxylase *in vitro*.

Could it be that the deficiencies of serotonin and the epinephrines which are present from birth in phenylketonurics are the cause of the idiocy? If one or both of these hormones exerted an effect on the development of the brain in the newborn such that a deficiency of the hormone might lead to some disorganization of some part of the brain, one might have an explanation for the development of the idiocy. The defect could not be large in an anatomical sense, otherwise it would have been detected in the extensive histological examinations which have been conducted on the brains of these patients. Still, if it amounted to no more than a failure to form some special enzyme the defect probably would not be detected by the routine histology.

One must remember that the excess of phenylalanine, and consequently the deficiency of serotonin and the epinephrines, has been present since birth. It is thus operating at a time in development when the central nervous system is still in a state of rapid change. A deficiency of, let us say, serotonin at that time might be expected to be of much greater consequence then than it would be in the adult brain. In light of this one could then understand how a deficiency of serotonin in the adult brain, which we have pictured to be a cause of psychotic depressions of schizophrenia, might result only in the altered mental processes of that disease, and not in total idiocy such as one finds in phenylketonuria. In schizophrenia, the deficiency has been imposed in adult life when the brain is mature.

We may ask if there is any evidence to support an idea that a serotonin or epinephrine deficiency does in fact harm an infant brain more than that of an adult. The evidence on this point is not clear, but there is some. Preliminary results suggest that phenylketonuric infants who have been saved from idiocy by the introduction of a phenylalanine-deficient diet very early in life can return to a normal diet containing phenylalanine after a few years. When this is done the idiocy seems not to develop.[b] These results are of necessity of a preliminary nature, and one does not know whether in adult life these patients will in fact develop schizophrenia or complete idiocy. The understanding of phenylketonuria has been of such recent discovery that the final outcome of the use of phenylalanine-deficient diets is

[b] If the ideas discussed in Chapter 6 are valid, we might expect a high incidence of schizophrenia among phenylketonuric children when they become adults. The children are now being treated with the phenylalanine-low diet during infancy, but practical considerations make it quite probable that the diet will be used only during early childhood. They will then return to normal food containing phenylalanine. As a result the deficiencies of serotonin and the epinephrines will again be established in their tissues. We might expect these deficiencies imposed in adult life to contribute to the appearance of schizophrenia in such individuals unless steps are taken to avoid this.

not clear, aside from the fact that they do prevent the development of idiocy in the young children. Nevertheless the findings as they are known today suggest that the infant brain cannot stand the metabolic defect which the more mature brain may be able to tolerate later in childhood. The mental defect of the untreated patients may be the result of a deficiency of serotonin or the epinephrines very early in development.

Finally, one may ask whether there is any evidence to suggest that changes in, let us say, the serotonin content of an individual can in fact lead to an error of development. There is positive evidence that such changes can, although the evidence deals not with the central nervous system, and involves an excess rather than a deficiency of serotonin. Thus, if young rats are fed for long periods a constant intake of 5-hydroxytryptophan, which maintains a high level of serotonin in their tissues, frank anatomical lesions of the stomach develop (335 and 336). Furthermore, in the carcinoid syndrome of human beings, in which serotonin levels of the peripheral tissues are maintained high for many months or years, a frank anatomical lesion of the heart develops. These findings indicate that some structures in the body are susceptible to gross change when serotonin levels are altered. A submicroscopic change which leads to the idiocy of phenylketonuria might therefore conceivably arise from a deficiency of this hormone, especially since this deficiency is known to be imposed very early in life. These points are all easily tested in experimental animals, and will probably be so tested now that the problem is clearly in view.

The moroseness of most phenylketonuric persons is in keeping with the deficiency of serotonin which they exhibit. In Chapter 6, evidence was presented which suggested that mental depression is probably a direct result of a lack of serotonin in the brain. The phenylketonuric person is afflicted with a serotonin deficiency not only in his brain, but in peripheral organs as well. He has grown up from infancy with this deficiency. His attitude of depression thus fits well with the findings in other mental disorders.

Experimental production of phenylketonuria in laboratory animals. If human phenylketonuria is the result of excess phenylalanine in the body it should be possible to cause such an excess in laboratory animals. It might then be possible to demonstrate a defect in the mental powers of such animals, especially if the excess of phenylalanine were to be established at birth and maintained. Recently, in rats, it has been possible to cause an increase in phenylalanine in the tissues and excretion of phenylpyruvic acid in the urine. This was done by feeding a normal diet to which had been added large amounts (2.5 to 3.75 per cent each) of phenylalanine and tyrosine (322 and 337). The feeding of phenylalanine alone did not cause urinary excretion of phenylpyruvic acid[c] because the phenylalanine hydroxylase in the normal animals was abundant enough to destroy large amounts of the amino acid. The inclusion of tyrosine suppressed the hydroxylase somewhat so that the heavy load of phenylalanine was then able to cause increases of that amino acid in the tissues and consequent excretion of phenylpyruvic acid in the urine.

When normal rats were made phenylketonuric by this technique the serotonin content of their blood and the 5-hydroxyindoleacetic acid content of their urine fell below normal (322). The biochemical changes in the animals were thus similar to those in the human patients.

The intelligence of rats made phenylketonuric in this way for several months was tested (337). The time required for the animals to learn to discriminate between fixed time intervals was measured in a Skinner box and compared to the result obtained with normal rats. Admittedly, it is very difficult to measure adequately the intelligence of laboratory animals, and many objections can be raised about any method. Nevertheless, the phenylketonuric rats required a longer time to learn their lesson. This may suggest that they had experienced some mental difficulty. Quite probably much more work will be required to improve these techniques, but they offer a beginning in the ability to use controlled laboratory experiments to explore this human disease.

Dietary management of phenylketonuria. Because it is known that the biochemical defect in the disease is the accumulation of excessive phenylalanine in the tissues, with the consequent metabolic repercussions just discussed, the control of the disease might be expected if the phenylalanine intake were to be restricted. Trial of a phenylalanine-deficient diet for phenylketonuric infants would be useful in two ways. First and foremost, it might prevent the mental deterioration, and secondly, if it were to succeed there would be direct proof that the idiocy was in fact due to the excessive concentrations of phenylalanine in the patients.

[c] In human beings, however, large amounts of phenylalanine alone will cause excretion of phenylpyruvic acid. Thus when normal persons are treated with very large amounts of phenylalanine, they excrete this keto acid, as can be seen in Table 2 of this chapter, in the section on detection of the heterozygous (carrier) state.

During the 1950's and early 1960's the use of a phenylalanine-deficient diet for newborn infants found by the ferric chloride test to be phenylketonurics was successful. The development of the idiocy, which is otherwise almost inevitable, has been prevented (327). The first preliminary trials of this diet were made by Bickel et al. (338) and by Armstrong et al. (339).

Because phenylalanine is an essential amino acid which must be taken in the food if life is to be maintained, the diet is not free of it. The quantity is reduced by adsorption of some of it from a protein hydrolysate. This phenylalanine-low amino acid mixture is used as the source of amino acids in the diet. It is necessary to start the infants on this diet early in life. Once the mental defect has been established, the withholding of phenylalanine from the diet accomplishes nothing beneficial. As indicated above, there is some suggestion that the special diet is not required for a lifetime, and that after a few years the patient can be returned to a normal diet. The data are, however, too scanty and the time interval of the testing too short to be sure of this.

Because the use of the phenylalanine deficient diet was begun only in 1953, it is too early to say whether it will be a complete success. It has prevented the appearance of idiocy, but one cannot say whether it has prevented any mental defect. It will take a lifetime of study to determine whether mental difficulties may arise eventually. The results so far have been most encouraging.

Genetic aspects. From the time of the first recognition of the disease, phenylketonuria has been known to have a genetic background. Two of the first cases recognized were brothers (325). The inheritance of the biochemical defect has now been explored in a large enough group of individuals that it can be plainly seen to obey the established Mendelian law of genetics. The trait is inherited as a simple recessive allele.

The general population contains individuals whom we might call carriers or hybrids or heterozygotes with respect to this trait. They are normal people and show no mental defect. In fact some of them have exhibited extraordinary intellectual accomplishments. Let us say that they have only half as much of the phenylalanine hydroxylase as do normals. If two of these individuals mate, phenylketonurics will be found among the children. If phenylketonuria is a recessive trait involving just one gene one-fourth of the children of such a marriage would be expected to be phenylketonuric idiots. One-half would be hybrids or carriers, and one-fourth should be pure strain normal. Actual experience with the disease has shown that on the average one-fourth of the children actually are phenylketonuric idiots. Jervis (326) and others have applied the approved statistical calculations used in population genetics to this question. For example, a total of 1094 children from 266 families in which phenylketonuria had occurred were used for one of the calculations. The percentage of phenylketonuric children was 27.4 by the "sib method" and 22.4 by the "proband method." The deviation from the expected 25 per cent was calculated to be within the standard error. The percentage incidence of frank disease in cases of consanguineous marriages was very much greater than in marriages of unrelated partners based on the assumption that the incidence of phenylketonuria in the country at large is 0.004 per cent.

The number of children who are hybrids cannot be determined so readily because of the difficulty (to be discussed below) of making a precise biochemical test for such hybrids. If such a test becomes feasible it will be possible to prove whether or not exactly 50 per cent of all the children from marriages of carriers (heterozygotes) actually are hybrids with respect to this trait.

There have been a very few cases of the mating of two phenylketonuric people. The offspring of these unions have all been phenylketonurics. This result is to be expected from the Mendelian laws of inheritance because those individuals who exhibit the idiocy would be expected to be a pure strain with respect to the inheritance of this disease. Matings of two pure strain individuals should give only pure strain offspring. The actual experience has confirmed this even though the number of individuals involved has been very small.

Detection of the heterozygous (carrier) state. The carriers do not excrete phenylpyruvic acid in the urine. They presumably differ from normals in having less of the hydroxylase in their livers, but this tissue is not readily accessible for the making of measurements of the amount of enzyme. In galactosemia, as we shall see in the next chapter, the enzyme in question is found in the blood so that it is quite possible to detect carriers by measurement of the amount of enzyme *in vitro* in this readily available tissue, but this is not true for phenylketonuria where the enzyme is in the liver.

Because of the public health aspects of the inheritance of phenylketonuria it would be advantageous to have a practical method for the detection of carriers so that marriages between heterozygotes could be minimized. One recently proposed method of detection of carriers is to conduct a phenylalanine loading experiment *in vivo*

TABLE 2. *Changes in tyrosine production and urinary excretion of relevant compounds by normal, heterozygous, and phenylketonuric persons 4 hours after ingestion of a load of phenylalanine (330 mg per kg)*

Kind of Person	Number of Persons	Blood Tyrosine Increase, mg per 100 ml	Urinary Phenyl-pyruvic acid, mg per mg creatine	Urinary Indole-acetic acid, mg per mg creatine
Normal	20	2.9	0.86	12.9
Heterozygous	21	0.8	0.88	10.8
Phenylketonuric	14	0.0	—	—

(340). A large amount of phenylalanine is given orally to a subject and his ability to convert it to tyrosine is measured. As shown by the data in Table 2, which have been condensed from the paper of Jervis (340), the phenylketonuric individual shows no increase in tyrosine in the blood after such a load of phenylalanine. The normal individual shows a considerable increase in tyrosine. A person who is a carrier shows a rise in blood tyrosine only about half as great as that given by normal people. Among the persons studied there was no overlapping of the three categories so that the test appeared to be capable of distinguishing heterozygotes from normal persons. Whether it will be reliable for public health purposes remains to be seen.

A less clear cut test was made by measurement of the increase in phenylalanine content of the blood following an oral load of phenylalanine. Phenylketonuric persons gave a rise in blood phenylalanine which lasted for a long time. This reflected their inability to metabolize this amino acid. Normal persons cleared the administered phenylalanine more rapidly. Carriers were intermediate in this respect. However, the test based on phenylalanine determinations was not as clear cut as that based on increases in blood tyrosine.

The urinary excretion of phenylpyruvic acid, indoleacetic acid and other degradation products of phenylalanine following a load of phenylalanine gave no differentiation between normal and heterozygous persons. Note that even normal human beings will excrete some phenylpyruvic acid if the load of phenylalanine has been great enough.

Although the ferric chloride test of the urine is not given by carriers, it is of course given by infants with phenylketonuria. Simple sticks of wood are available which have been soaked in ferric chloride, and which turn green when placed in phenylketonuric urine. It is thus very easy to detect an infant with this disease. If idiocy of such an infant is to be avoided, remedial measures (dietary restriction of phenylalanine) must be taken soon after birth.

The carriers of phenylketonuria are not people of low intelligence. In fact, they may be people of outstanding mental powers, for they include winners of Nobel prizes.

Epilogue. The discoveries in phenylketonuria constitute a model of what can be done biochemically in psychiatry. They have shown that a visible anatomical lesion need not be identified in the brain before it is possible to conceive of a severe mental disease as arising from organic causes, not psychological ones. They have shown that with a suitable chemical test the biochemical defect lying at the base of a mental disease can be found. Once the crucial clue has been noted, the biochemical defect can be traced to its source. An understanding of the chemical cause of the mental disease allows the instigation of specific chemical measures for the control of it, as the introduction of phenylalanine deficient diets for phenylketonuric infants has shown. Such measures not only give means of controlling the disease but give convincing proof of the biochemical causation of it. The heritable nature of the disease allows an understanding of etiology and opens the possibility of prevention by the detection of carriers of the genetic defect. Intermarriage of such carriers can be discouraged. The fact that phenylketonuria was singled out as affecting less than 1 per cent of the population of mental institutions may be of much significance. The fact that the disease can be readily detected by a simple and specific chemical test allowed the study of it to be removed from the uncertainties of the statistical approach. Consider what would have been the interpretation if someone had determined phenylalanine in the bloods of a thousand inmates of a mental institution and had reported that six of them were much above normal. These six would have been the phenylketonuric patients, but the report would have been judged to be below the required level of significance by statistical means. It may be that the chronic mental patients represent a very heterogenous group of diseases even though all of them are recorded in the admission books of mental hospitals as one of the four types of schizophrenia. The principal single factor which brought order out of all of the chaos with respect to this single disease entity known now as phenylketonuria was the introduction of a specific chemical test. The biochemical clues arising from this test have unfolded much about the origin of the disease, and have provided a way of controlling it.

chapter 12

Galactosemia

Galactosemia is a disease marked by physical abnormalities as well as by mental failure. It thus differs sharply from phenylketonuria in which the patient is physically normal but mentally undeveloped to the state of idiocy. Both diseases represent inborn errors of metabolism, but each of a different kind. The inheritance of both diseases as single recessive traits has been established. Thus, phenylketonuria is characterized by an inherited lack of the enzyme phenylalanine hydroxylase which shows itself by accumulation of excess phenylalanine in the tissues, and of phenylpyruvic acid in the urine. Galactosemia is characterized by an inherited lack of the enzyme galactose-1-phosphate uridyl transferase, which shows itself by accumulation of galactose-1-phosphate in the tissues and of galactose in the urine. Galactosemia is a very rare disease. Since it was first recognized (344 and 345) in 1917, only about seventy-five cases have been described, but there is reason to believe that the actual number of patients is greater.

Signs of the disease. The present author has had little personal experience with galactosemic patients. The clinical and biochemical descriptions presented here have been taken from the writings of those who have had more experience: Kalckar (341, 342) and Isselbacher (343). The suggestions about the possible relationship of the mental symptoms in the disease to serotonin are, however, original.

Galactosemic patients are first recognized as infants who have failed to develop normally either physically or mentally. They are underweight for their age, dull, and usually with markedly enlarged livers and spleens. The underweight is probably the result of inanition, because these infants tolerate milk poorly and often regurgitate after feeding. The enlargement of the liver progresses to cirrhosis if treatment is not instituted. Usually cataracts develop in the eyes.

If treatment, in the form of withdrawal of foods which contain galactose, is not given to these individuals many will die in infancy, and many of those who survive will be idiots. However, it is noteworthy that a few have been known to grow to adulthood with possession of normal, or at least adequate, mental abilities. This may be because they have avoided milk but possibly also because they have been able to expand a minor pathway of metabolism of galactose-1-phosphate which avoids the biochemical defect characteristic of the disease.

Biochemical examination of the patients shows that the urines contain a reducing sugar, which is not glucose. This sugar has been identified as galactose (344 and 345). The identification of this sugar was the feature which first led to recognition of the separateness of the disease and to its naming. Galactose is also found in relatively large amounts in the blood. On the other hand, glucose in the blood is below normal (346). The galactose which accumulates in many tissues, as for example in red blood cells, is not free, but is largely present as galactose-1-phosphate (347). The free galactose arises from enzymatic hydrolysis of this ester.

The fact that galactose metabolism is at fault in the disease is shown not only by the accumulation of this sugar and its phosphate in the tissues, but also by the results of loading experiments. When galactose is fed to or injected intravenously into a normal human subject its concentration in the blood rises sharply, but soon returns to normal. When similar administration is made to a galactosemic patient, the rise in blood galactose occurs and persists for many hours (343).

Biochemical functions and transformations of galactose. Galactose occurs in the body as a part of several carbohydrates, lipids, and proteins. In milk it is principally present as the disaccharide, lactose. In several glycoproteins it may be present as one portion of the carbohydrate part of the molecule. Among lipids those of the brain are outstanding because they contain more galactose derivatives than do those from other tissues. These are the cerebrosides, cerebron

$$CH_3(CH_2)_{12}CH{=}CH{-}\underset{\displaystyle OH}{\underset{|}{CH}}{-}\underset{\displaystyle \underset{\displaystyle R}{\underset{|}{NH}}}{\underset{|}{CH}}{-}CH_2{-}O{-}\text{sugar}$$

FIG. 1. *Type structure of galactose containing lipids. R = fatty acid such as stearic, lignoceric, or cerebronic. When sugar is galactose, lipid is cerebroside. When sugar is galactose-6-sulfate, lipid is cerebron sulfate. When sugar is polysaccharide containing acetylneuraminic acid united with galactose or other mono- or polysaccharide, lipid is a ganglioside.*

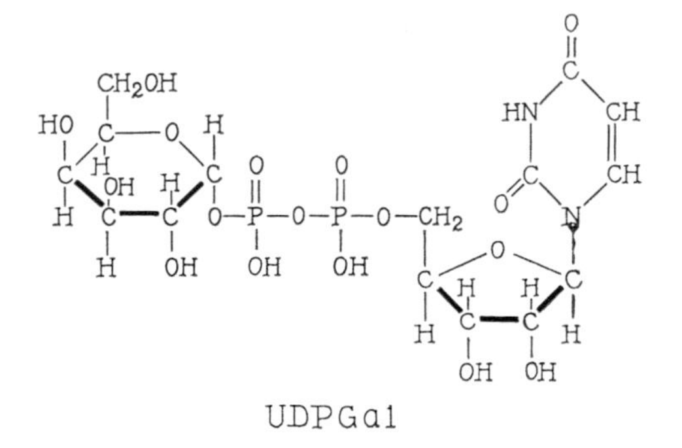

Fig. 2. *Structure of uridine diphosphate galactose (UDPGal), the active form of galactose for synthesis of many galactose-containing compounds.*

sulfate, and the gangliosides. The chemical structures of these substances are shown in Figure 1.

The galactose-containing lipids as well as other galactose derivatives are believed to be made in living tissues from an activated form of galactose, viz., uridine diphosphate galactose or UDPGal, the structure of which is shown in Figure 2. For example, one way in which lactose is synthesized in the mammary gland is from UDPGal and glucose (G) as illustrated in the following equation (348).

$$\text{UDPGal} + \text{G} \rightarrow \text{UDP} + \text{lactose}$$

The biosynthesis of the galactose-containing lipids of the brain has not been thoroughly explored, but there is experimental evidence (350) to indicate that the galactose portion is introduced by way of UDPGal. The reaction involved would be analogous to that of lactose synthesis except that the place of G would be taken by a more complicated alcohol such as the sugar-free portion shown in Figure 1. It is of much interest that these lipids are formed in the brain after birth and only slightly in the prenatal period.

Ways for the biosynthesis of UDPGal. It is known to be made in three different ways, and one of them, the principal pathway, is lacking in galactosemic individuals.

The first and principal way of making it is the reaction shown in the following equation:

$$\text{UDPG} + \text{Gal-1-P} \rightleftharpoons \text{UDPGal} + \text{G-1-P}$$

UDPGlucose reacts with galactose-1-phosphate to give UDPGal and glucose-1-phosphate. The enzyme which catalyzes this reaction is called galactose-1-phosphate uridyl transferase which we shall call the transferase for simplicity. This enzyme is found in liver, brain, and, most importantly for practical psychiatry, in red blood cells. We shall see why this is important shortly.

The second way of making UDPGal, the 4-epimerase way, also starts with UDPG. By means of an oxidation and reduction UDPGal is formed from it. The enzyme responsible for this reaction is not affected in galactosemia. This enzyme is called uridine diphosphate galactose 4-epimerase (349), or more simply just the 4-epimerase. It was originally called galactowaldenase by Leloir, who discovered it and many of the UDP compounds. It changes the relative position of the hydroxyl group in the 4-position of glucose. Inversion of this hydroxyl group is all that is required to pass from glucose to galactose (and, of course, back again). The epimerase acts on UDPG to yield UDPGal. The fact that the enzyme requires diphosphopyridine nucleotide suggests that the reaction is an oxidation followed by a reduction. Presumably the hydroxyl group in position 4 is oxidized to a ketone, which is then reduced back to an hydroxyl group, but on the opposite side of the carbon chain from the original one.

This enzyme (the epimerase) is present in normal amounts in the tissues of galactosemic individuals. It can serve as a means of making UDPGal, but is of no use in disposing of galactose-1-phosphate, the harmful metabolite of galactosemia.

The third way of making UDPGal is a reaction between Gal-1-P and uridine triphosphate which yields inorganic pyrophosphate and UDPGal (351). The enzyme which catalyzes this reaction also has a long name which can be shortened to the pyrophosphorylase. It is present in normal amounts in galactosemic individuals. It is, however, not abundant enough to metabolize all of the galactose in an infant's diet and thus fails to prevent the accumulation of Gal-1-P in the tissues when the transferase is absent. Preliminary studies on a limited number of human beings have indicated that the amount of this enzyme may increase as the individual grows older. The increase in this enzyme with age may be the reason why a galactosemic person once past the period of childhood can tolerate galactose somewhat better than the infant can. Abnormally high amounts of this enzyme may also be the reason why a few galactosemic individuals survive, although untreated, and do not become imbeciles (343).

To recapitulate, the normal person changes the galactose he eats in his food into glucose, which can then be metabolized. He does this principally by means of the transferase which converts galactose-1-phosphate into UDPGal. To a lesser extent he does it by means of the enzyme which reacts galactose-1-phosphate with uridine triphosphate which also gives UDPGal. The UDPGal made by either process can then be converted to UDPG by means of the epimerase. The UDPG is then utilized as one of the kinds of activated glucose from which glycogen is made. The UDPGal serves not only as a way of transforming galactose to glucose. It is the activated form of galactose which is needed for the synthesis of the lipids and other galactose derivatives in the body.

The biochemical defect in galactosemia. Galactosemic people lack the transferase enzyme. The 4-epimerase is normal as is also the pyrophosphorylase (352). This discovery of Kalckar and his students is the base for much important work, both practical as well as theoretical. Galactose-1-phosphate and galactose accumulate in the tissues and urine because this transferase enzyme is not present to form UDPGal. The alternative pathway for conversion of galactose-1-phosphate to UDPGal, the pyrophosphorylase way, is not present in large enough amounts, even in normal individuals apparently, to metabolize the dietary galactose.

The problem now arises of how to understand the changes both mental and physical which occur in galactosemia in relation to this enzymic defect, and the consequent accumulation of galactose-1-phosphate in the tissues. The principal difficulty is the accumulation of Gal-1-P and not the failure to make UDPGal in adequate amounts. This is proved by withholding galactose from the food of galactosemic infants. When this is done the idiocy does not develop. Why is Gal-1-P poisonous? The answer is not known. Some clues and several speculations are nevertheless available.

In galactosemia the glucose in the blood is subnormal. One explanation of why this should be so is that the galactose-1-phosphate has been found to inhibit the enzyme which converts glucose-1-phosphate to glucose-6-phosphate (343). The inhibition of this enzyme should reduce glucose production from glycogen.

The low blood glucose of galactosemics has been suggested as a possible reason for the mental defect (343). It is true (as described in Chapter 6) that low blood glucose can cause mental and neurological disturbances, but whether the permanent idiocy which is usual in untreated galactosemic infants can be the direct result of a minor hypoglycemia is questionable. Severe hypoglycemia can cause permanent damage (e.g., in the brain and in the testes) but the hypoglycemia in galactosemia is not severe. However, the possibility remains that mild but persistent hypoglycemia early in infancy might be more damaging to the brain than it is later in life. The glucose deficiency hypothesis, however, does not seem adequate to explain the mental failure in galactosemia.

The possible relation to serotonin and other neurohormones. The fact that UDPGal is the activated form of galactose from which the galactose-containing lipids of the brain are formed may be of great importance to an understanding of the mental defect. These galactolipids may be part of the receptors for serotonin and for the epinephrines, and Gal-1-P may inhibit their formation. There is no proof of this, but there are some interesting observations which bear on this point. Gangliosides and cerebrosides, especially cerebron sulfate, have high potency in the cell-free, *in vitro* assay for the serotonin receptor as described in Chapter 4 (353). In other words, gangliosides or cerebron sulfate cause serotonin to pass from an aqueous solution into a lipid phase. Furthermore, in one of the bioassays for serotonin (that involving increase in amplitude of the beat of the clam's heart) brain gangliosides had serotonin-like action (354). One might say that these lipids had rendered the heart more susceptible to serotonin just as an increase in receptor might be expected to do. Such a finding would be compatible with the idea that these lipids are part of the serotonin receptor. A failure to form serotonin receptors in the brain and elsewhere would be the equivalent of a serotonin deficiency in the cells which normally respond to this hormone. Similar considerations would apply to epinephrine and norepinephrine. Could it be that the mental defect of galactosemia is to be understood in this fashion, namely that there has been a lack of synthesis of galactolipids which are the receptors for serotonin or one of the other neurohormones? Possibly Gal-1-P inhibits one of the enzymes which introduces galactose into one of these lipids. Such a lack of receptors would be the same as a deficiency of the hormone.

It must be pointed out that a failure to form galactolipids in the brains of galactosemic patients has not been demonstrated. It would be necessary to measure the quantities of these substances in various parts of the brains of many individual cases, and to compile information on the variation from case to case. A similar series of normal brains would be needed for comparison. Such measurements have not been made. If the tissues could be obtained the measurements might give valuable information about the disease.

If the mental defect of galactosemia is the result of a deficiency in receptors for serotonin or other neurohormones, there are some simple and direct experiments which should reveal such a deficiency. These are experiments which could be done readily on galactosemic patients. For example, intravenous injection of serotonin or of norepinephrine into a galactosemic patient might fail to cause the changes in blood pressure which these hormones bring forth in normal people. One might argue that since the hormonal receptors seem to differ somewhat in various tissues, the ones concerned with changes in blood pressure might be normal in galactosemia but that others in other organs might be the ones not formed. There are other ways of testing for responses to serotonin or to norepinephrine, and these could be tried. Thus, it could be determined whether galactosemic blood platelets are able to concentrate serotonin in the way in which normal platelets do. All of these experiments are safe and simple ones which should be done on untreated galactosemic persons in an effort to understand the reason for the mental failure.

Some very preliminary studies of this kind have been made very recently with two adolescent galactosemic morons. These studies were conducted by the author of this book at the Louisiana State Colony and Training School with the collaboration of Drs. R. Lampert, B. Shaver, and R. Heath. Results indicated that both of these patients were supersensitive to epinephrine and relatively insensitive to serotonin. Large increases in blood pressure were produced by as little as 0.2 μg epinephrine per kg, but no detectable rise was caused by serotonin below 50 μg per kg. The responsiveness to norepinephrine was normal.

Genetic aspects. Galactosemia is inherited. The situation is similar to that with phenylketonuria. The mutant gene which is responsible for the disease is thought to be a single recessive one, although the number of cases studied is not great enough to be certain. If two individuals mate who are both heterozygous for this trait, one-fourth of the offspring should be galactosemic. One-half of the offspring should be heterozygous, or carriers of the trait, and one-fourth should be normal. The heterozygous individuals should appear to be normal until they are examined for the amount of the transferase enzyme. They should possess this enzyme, but in reduced amount.

Theoretically the carriers, because of their heterozygous state, should have half the amount of transferase as normals have, whereas the galactosemics, who are homozygous for the mutated gene, should have none. Actual measurement of the amount of this enzyme in the red blood cells of human beings have borne out these predictions rather well (355). In the beginning there were methodological problems of quantitative determination of the enzyme. When these difficulties were overcome it appeared that the galactosemic individuals did in fact have no transferase, or at least less than 10 per cent of the normal amount (343 and 349). In the liver the enzyme was less than one per cent of the normal amount.

As to the carriers, the situation was not entirely clear. Some estimates have shown a content of transferase about half that of normal (355) although the amount of enzyme approached normal values in some individuals (343). The variation among normal people was great enough that their range overlapped that of the carriers. In view of the methodological problems the agreement with theoretical predictions seems good. However, just as in the case of phenylketonuria the biochemical (enzymic) test for the carrier state does not seem to be precise enough in its present form to make it satisfactory for public health purposes. It is not good enough to be the basis of an infallible warning against parenthood.

The occurrence of the transferase enzyme in the red blood cells is of considerable importance for the easy detection of carriers. Blood samples are readily obtainable. By contrast, in carriers of phenylketonuria the enzyme involved (the phenylalanine hydroxylase) is not present in blood. It is found in the liver. Samples of liver are so difficult to obtain that it is not possible to consider as a public health measure the determination of carrier state by means of direct assay of the amount of enzyme. In galactosemia, because the required tissue is readily available, the reverse is true.

Detection. The most reliable method for the detection of a case of galactosemia is to measure the amount of the transferase in red blood cells or in a specimen of liver. Since specimens of liver are usually not obtainable, the assay for the enzyme is almost always done on red blood cells. The enzyme is absent in cases of the disease. As explained in the preceding section, it is present in reduced amount in carriers of the trait.

A simpler method of detection is to test the urine for galactose. Relatively easy procedures are available for this purpose. A simple test for reducing sugar is not adequate because of the inability of such a test to distinguish galactose from glucose. Glucose can occur in the urine in diseases which have no relationship to galactosemia. In some of the tests for galactose in urine, any possible glucose is destroyed by treatment with a glucose oxidase before making the test for galactose. Galactose can occur in the urine of non-galactosemic persons but usually not in that of infants, and for this reason the de-

TABLE 1. *Clinical experiences of Slack et al. (355) with thirteen galactosemic patients reared on galactose-free food*

		Galactose-free diet		Intelligence		
Patient	Clinical Manifestations	Age at Introduction	Nature of Diet	IQ Score	Age When Tested	Comment
CK	diarrhea, wasting, hepatomegaly	4 months	strict	109	12½ years	
AK	jaundice, hepatomegaly	7th day	occasionally took milk	110	8½ years	Brother of CK.
TJ	vomiting, cataract, headaches, shivering, fainting	9 years, 2 months	strict	121	10 years, 2 months	Milk intake restricted from infancy. Probably had hypoglycemic attacks.
SJ	vomiting, chills, headaches, cataracts	5 years	strict	116	6 years	Milk intake restricted from late infancy. Sister of TJ.
JM	jaundice, cataracts, edema	4 months	had some milk products	119	10 years, 11 months	
RM	jaundice, cataracts	1 month	had some milk products	110	5 years	Brother of JM.
DP[1]	vomiting, diarrhea, poor weight gain, jaundice	1st week of life	probably strict	102	9 years, 4 months	
DP[2]	jaundice, vomiting, diarrhea, poor weight gain	10th day	strict	81	7 years, 7 months	Brother of DP[1].
MM	reluctance to feed, loss of weight, hepatomegaly, cataracts, convulsions	1 month	unknown	48	7 years, 9 months	Has dysphasia.
CP	lethargy, jaundice, vomiting, cataracts, convulsions	1½ years	strict	59	6 years	Refused milk since 1½ years.
BR	jaundice, hepatomegaly, edema, cataracts	8 weeks	strict	95	3 years, 8 months	Sister of CP.
GD	jaundice, hepatomegaly	1 month	strict	97	3 years	
WS	vomiting, diarrhea, jaundice, hepatomegaly, ocular hemorrhage	1 month	strict	100	1 year, 4 months	Perception of light only.

tection of galactose in the urine is only indicative of the disease, and does not constitute proof. Because galactosemia is an abnormality which is present at birth, and persists for the lifetime of the individual, the test for galactose in the urine in infancy is important. If treatment for control of the disease is not begun early in infancy, the chance of avoiding the mental and physical deterioration is lost.

Galactosemia is a very rare disease. The hereditary nature of the defect allows some prediction of infants in whom it may be expected to occur, so that if it is known that both parents are carriers or that another child in the family is galactosemic, the disease can be expected in any offspring. On the average, one of four will be galactosemic, but there is no way to predict which of the four it will be. All offspring should be tested for galactose excretion early in infancy. The lack of any large amount of information on who is a carrier of necessity limits sharply the predictability of cases in the population at large. Intolerance of milk in a young infant is usually a feature of galactosemia, and should thus suggest the use of proper diagnostic tests.

Treatment and prognosis. Many of the features of galactosemia can be controlled by elimination of galactose from the diet. This means the avoidance of milk in infancy, and the replacement of it by a milk substitute. Several of these are now commercially available. One which has been much used is made from soybeans.

The earlier in life that a galactose-free diet can be begun, the greater seems to be the chance of avoiding the mental defect. The data shown in Table 1, which have been taken from the paper of Slack et al. (355), indicate the results of the use of such diets at Northwestern University. When galactose is removed from the diet the physical signs, aside from cataract, disappear. The liver and spleen return to normal size, and the gastrointestinal disturbance disappears. Growth is resumed.

The development of idiocy can be avoided if the treatment with a galactose-free diet is started early in life, and is rigorously followed for several years. The number of treated cases is, however, so small at the present time that this point is not firmly established. Some investigators feel that although the idiocy can be avoided the intelligence quotients of treated patients may be lower than might be anticipated if they had not had the disease. Furthermore, there is the problem of knowing how strictly the prescribed diet was followed. The results obtained by various investigators with forty-six patients as summarized by Slack et al. (355) are shown in Table 2.

TABLE 2. *Effect of lactose-free diet upon intelligence in forty-six cases of galactosemia*

	Intelligence		
	Normal	Moderate Retar-dation	Severe Retar-dation
Adequate dietary control:			
Males	9	3	2
Females	6	1	0
Total	15	4	2
Inadequate dietary control:			
Males	5	5	7
Females	2	5	1
Total	7	10	8

One puzzling and disappointing feature of the treatment is that the development of cataracts is not completely prevented. In fact, it is only slightly reduced. In the fourteen cases studied by Slack et al. (355) for a period of years, eight developed cataracts or visual difficulties despite the use of the galactose-free diet. One may question whether the diet actually was galactose-free, because it is known that the phospholipids of soybeans, which frequently are used as the milk substitute, contain considerable galactose (356). Although the percentage is less than in milk, it is still not inconsiderable. It may be that if a diet rigorously free of galactose could be developed and adhered to for several years during early infancy the cataracts could be avoided. This might also avoid the slight mental handicap which some investigators feel remains with the galactosemic patients.

Relation of galactosemia to the general hypothesis of the biochemical basis of psychoses. In Chapter 11, it was pointed out that one mental disease (phenylketonuria) is known to arise from a specific biochemical defect which is inborn. The mental defect is severe (one might say devastating), and yet the patients show no characteristic anatomical lesions. It is true that they tend to be less pigmented than many human beings, but they have no greater tendency in this regard than do many normal persons. The lesion in phenylketonuria is a biochemical one—the lack of an enzyme, the phenylalanine hydroxylase.

This cannot be seen under a microscope with the ordinary techniques of histology. It can be seen only by specific biochemical techniques.

With galactosemia one has another devastating mental disease which is marked by the lack of a single enzyme. In contrast to the situation with phenylketonuria, however, there are marked physical signs in addition to the mental defect. Consequently, in classical psychiatric terminology galactosemia would be called an organic psychosis in a class with senile dementia or the paresis of syphilis, whereas phenylketonuria would be called a functional psychosis supposed by some to arise from psychological rather than physical defects. The fact that phenylketonuria is noticed in early childhood rather than in adult life would be the only mitigating circumstance, which might thus temper the diagnosis of psychological causes for the mental failure. Even so, some phenylketonurics have been committed to mental institutions with the diagnosis of childhood schizophrenia.

Galactosemia is thus a less clear example than is phenylketonuria of the concept that mental diseases arise from biochemical abnormalities. The occurrence of striking physical signs aside from the mental defect in galactosemia lessens its force in the contest between Freudian and biochemical explanations of mental diseases.

chapter 13

Some other inborn errors of metabolism which cause mental defects

In Chapters 11 and 12 we examined two diseases which are inherited and which result in idiocy. The cause of the mental failure in either phenylketonuria or galactosemia was the lack of a specific enzyme. The inability to form the particular enzyme was inherited as a recessive trait. The enzyme was lacking at birth, and the mental failure became apparent at a very early age. In phenylketonuria the mental failure was the only clinical sign found in all of the patients. The biochemical lesions could be detected in all if suitable chemical tests were performed to find them. In galactosemia on the other hand, clinical signs of physical disorders were quite prominent, and were usually noticeable before the mental failure became dominant.

In the present chapter a few more inborn errors of metabolism will be described briefly. These all lead to mental insufficiency, but in addition most of them are characterized by marked physical changes which can be recognized readily either by gross examination or by histological methods which require only standard techniques. They thus lack the peculiar relevance to the so-called functional mental diseases which phenylketonuria has. Because of the prominent physical abnormalities in most of the diseases of this chapter, the mental failure which accompanies all would cause them to be catalogued by classical psychiatrists as organic psychoses and hence apart from the real mainstream of psychiatric study. Actually, however, the occurrence of mental failures in these inborn diseases shows clearly that biochemical changes can be related to such failures. The concomitant development of changes of the anatomy may be only coincidental.

Most of the diseases to be mentioned in this chapter are noticed in early infancy, and lead to idiocy. However, one (Hartnup's disease) although probably present at birth (as all inborn errors are) does not express itself for several years.[a] This one consequently is characterized not by infantile idiocy, but rather by slowly deteriorating mental abilities during late childhood. It might thus be regarded as a less fulminating disease. The suggestion has already been made, in Chapters 11 and 12, that the development of idiocy early in infancy rather than a slower mental deterioration later in life may be the result of the stage of maturation at which the metabolic difficulty begins to operate.

All of the inborn errors of metabolism which can result in neurological and psychiatric changes will not be listed in this book. Only a few examples will be given to illustrate the point that biochemical changes can cause mental failures, and that these changes can be determined by inheritance. A much more complete description of the symptomatology of these and related diseases can be found in Stanbury et al. (357) and in Slack et al. (355).

Some lipids derived from sphingosine. Because most of the diseases to be mentioned in this chapter represent abnormalities of lipids derived from sphingosine let us consider the chemical structures of some of these compounds. The simplest is ceramide which has the structure shown in Figure 1. It is given in the figure as being formed from palmitic acid united to the amino group of sphingosine. However, various fatty acids such as cerebronic, lignoceric or stearic usually take the place of palmitic acid in brain lipids.

When choline phosphate is linked to ceramide as a phosphate ester of the primary alcoholic group of the sphingosine, the lipid so formed is sphingomyelin, also shown in Figure 1. If galactose (or a simple galactose derivative) is united to the ceramide as shown in Figure 1 of Chapter 12, the lipids so pictured are the cerebrosides. These can differ in the fatty acid component, and in the carbohydrate portion. If the carbohydrate is galactose-6-sulfate the lipid is cerebron sulfate. Additional sugar residues can be found attached to the galactose to form other cerebrosides. The sugar portion can be more complex. If it includes sialic acid (N-acetylneuraminic acid) as one of the sugar residues the lipids are called gangliosides.

[a] Another inherited neurological and mental disease which does not show itself until late in life is Huntington's chorea. This disease will not be mentioned further in this chapter because nothing is known about the biochemical defect associated with it. Its interest for the present discussion is that although it is inherited it does not become manifest until middle age. It is consequently not essential that inherited mental diseases should appear in infancy.

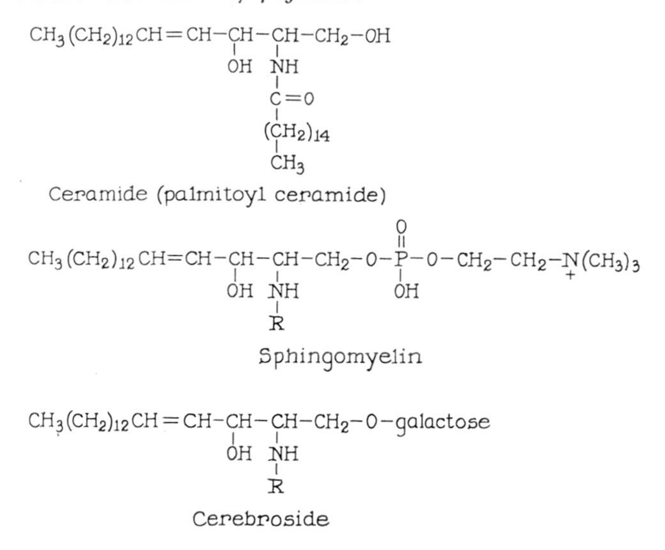

FIG. 1. *Type structures of sphingolipids of the brain.*

It is still not certain how many gangliosides are found in tissues. Various investigators have separated at least two kinds, and some have claimed at least three kinds. The chemical fractionation of these materials is not yet developed to a stage where compounds of certain purity can be obtained. Probably most of the ganglioside preparations are no more than mixtures of closely related chemical compounds.

All of these sphingolipids have been isolated from the central nervous system. In normal animals this is the tissue in which they are present in greatest concentration. However, they do not occur exclusively there, but can be found in the stroma of red blood cells or in lipids extracted from heart, stomach, or other organs. There is a belief which is slowly gaining experimental support that these sphingolipids constitute part of cell membranes. Thus, the microsome fraction of disrupted brain cells has been found to contain the gangliosides (251). When cells are disrupted and the fragments are separated the membranes are found in the microsome fraction. The gangliosides were first discovered because they were present in increased amounts in the ganglion cells of patients with Tay-Sachs disease and Niemann-Pick disease.

As mentioned in Chapter 12, the sphingolipids are made biochemically from ceramide and pyrimidine nucleotides of the type of uridine diphosphate galactose. In some of the syntheses the uridine nucleotide is not the active one, but rather the corresponding cytidine nucleotide is the active participant. Thus, sphingomyelin has been shown to be synthesized enzymatically by reaction of cytidine diphosphate choline and ceramide (358). The products are sphingomyelin and cytidine diphosphate. In like fashion the evidence suggests that cerebrosides can be made from ceramide and UDPGal or other suitable nucleotide-sugar derivatives.

Klenk (359) has suggested that the gangliosides may be intermediates from which other sphingolipids may arise by elimination of some of the sugar residues. Whether this actually is the main pathway remains to be explored. However, in the diseases now to be mentioned some inherited abnormality in the synthesis of various sphingolipids is such a prominent feature that they have been called examples of the lipidoses.

Tay-Sachs disease or infantile amaurotic familial idiocy. This is a disease of infants characterized by blindness, idiocy and the accumulation of lipids thought to be principally gangliosides in the ganglion cells of the central nervous system. A cherry red spot is always observable in the retinae in the macular areas, and was the sign which first led Tay to distinguish the disease. Tay-Sachs disease usually becomes evident during the first year of life and is characterized by the ocular changes, changes in behavior in the direction of excitability, spasticity, and convulsions. There may be occasional bursts of explosive laughter. The infant frequently loses the ability to recognize its mother. The disease usually terminates in a state of decerebrate rigidity and respiratory infection.

In Tay-Sachs disease an accumulation of gangliosides is found in the central nervous system and in the ganglia of peripheral nerves. It might thus be thought of as a dysfunction of ganglioside formation or transformation. If Klenk's hypothesis (359) of sphingolipid biosynthesis is correct, the disease might represent a failure to transform gangliosides into other lipids. However, the precise enzymic lack is unknown.

Tay-Sachs disease seems to be inherited as a single recessive trait. Most of the cases studied have been in Jewish families although occurrence in non-Jews is known. In Slome's investigation of sixty-nine cases of sibships approximately 25 per cent were affected by the disease (360). This is the frequency expected for the appearance of homozygous recessive traits.

Niemann-Pick disease. This is a disease which develops early in infancy, and is marked by considerable enlargement of the liver and spleen and by dullness of intellect which may end in idiocy. The cherry red spot which can be seen in the retinae of all patients with Tay-Sachs disease is also found in about half of those with Niemann-Pick disease. The characteristic histological finding is the appearance of large cells with foamy cytoplasm in the reticuloendothelial system. These cells can be stained with certain lipid stains. They contain large accumulations of sphingomyelin. Affected infants usually do not live for more than 6 years.

Niemann-Pick disease seems to be a condition in which excessive amounts of sphingomyelin accumulate in the reticuloendothelial system and in the central and peripheral nervous systems. Sphingomyelin is, however, not the only sphingolipid which accumulates. Gangliosides also may be present in large amount. It is possible that this disease is nothing more than Tay-Sachs disease which has affected the retinculoendothelial system in addition to the nerves. The close relationship to Gaucher's disease likewise has been mentioned by Slack et al. (355) who state that Niemann-Pick disease may be a more diffusely spread Gaucher's disease. The enzymic difficulty has not been localized beyond the point of finding the accumulation of sphingomyelin in some of the tissues.

Gaucher's disease. This is a disease of early infancy in which the clinical findings are rather similar to those of Niemann-Pick disease. At about 4 months of age the patients show markedly enlarged liver and spleen, defects of vision, although it is said not to progress to blindness, and dullness of mind which can be seen to grow worse. Rigidity of the body or opisthotonos may occur as the disease progresses. The outcome is almost always fatal in the early years of life. Histologically the reticuloendothelial system is always found to contain large pale cells, called Gaucher cells. These have a foamy appearance when stained.

The nervous system and the reticuloendothelial system contain accumulations of sphingolipids, principally cerebrosides. Increased amounts of at least three kinds of cerebrosides have been noted. These differ in the sugar residues attached to the ceramide portion.

Gargoylism. This is a disease of infants which is marked by enlargement of the liver and spleen to a degree which causes most noticeable protuberance of the abdomen. Other abnormalities of form are so prominent that the patients may resemble the grotesque figures of gargoyles. The eyes are wide apart and the ears set low. Mental retardation is marked and progressive. Some patients survive early childhood and finally end up in mental institutions. The condition is associated with accumulations of sphingolipids in the brain and elsewhere.

Possible relationships of these lipidoses. It seems possible that the various conditions mentioned above are not separate and distinct diseases. Rather, they may be the varied manifestations of a defect in sphingolipid metabolism modified in various individuals. The present trend seems to be to subdivide these conditions even more and, thus, for example, to distinguish three diseases in what has been called Gaucher's disease. The contention that a Gaucher cell can be distinguished histologically from a Niemann-Pick cell does not necessarily mean that the two diseases are not intimately related. The primary biochemical lesion may even be the same. Secondary enzymic differences might account for the histological differences observed in the lipidoses described above. It must be evident to many observers that the diseases have many points in common. However, one must not forget that they could equally well be considered as distinctly different entities which happen to affect the metabolism of sphingolipids. Whichever view is right does not change the important fact for the present discussion. This fact is that disturbances of metabolism of sphingolipids can be found associated with profound mental deterioration, and with physical defects of several kinds.

Possible relationship to serotonin and other neurohormones. The lipidoses mentioned above involve the accumulation in the brain and elsewhere of lipids which have been found to have activity as the serotonin receptor in the *in vitro* assays for this receptor (353). It has not yet been shown that these lipids actually do function in living cells as parts of the serotonin receptor, and until they have been shown to do this one must proceed with caution. Nevertheless, gangliosides have been demonstrated to sensitize one tissue (clam heart) to serotonin (354). This sort of activity would be expected of a part of the receptor. Presumably, if a tissue were somewhat deficient in receptor, the addition of that receptor to it might make it become more susceptible to the hormone. It might become responsive to smaller concentrations of serotonin. The net result of increasing the amount of serotonin receptor in a tissue might thus be the same as an increase in serotonin for a normal tissue.

Whether or not such an hypothesis has any bearing on the idiocy which is seen in the above lipidoses remains to be seen. However, the psychiatric manifestations of the lipidoses just described are what might be expected from excess serotonin or norepinephrine on the basis of what has been described in Chapter 6. Excess cerebral serotonin can give rise to excitement. Could it be that an increase in sphingolipids is functionally about the same as an excess of serotonin or of hormones related to it?

This idea could be tested easily by those who have access to patients suffering from these lipidoses. As explained in Chapter 12, for galactosemia, these patients should be hypersensitive to serotonin or epinephrine or acetylcholine or other neurohormones. It might be possible by a set of suitable physiological tests to discover that, let us say, Gaucher patients are hypersensitive to serotonin and Niemann-Pick patients are hypersensitive to epinephrine. It might thus be possible easily to sort out the precise hormone for each disease as well as to gain direct evidence about the validity of the basic idea mentioned above.

It is not necessary that every cause of mental deficiency must be related to serotonin. It is not even necessary that these diseases be related to epinephrine and the other hormones of the nervous system. In succeeding chapters one can see that there are many other biochemical aspects to be considered. Nevertheless, if a unifying concept could be found to apply to a variety of mental diseases our understanding of them would be increased considerably.

Hartnup's disease. The inborn errors of metabolism just described have been concerned with sphingolipids, and have brought about mental failure in early infancy. Let us now consider an hereditary disease of another kind. In this one the disease makes its appearance after infancy and leads to a slowly developing mental deterioration, but apparently not to complete idiocy. This is Hartnup's disease, first recognized by Baron et al. in 1956 (361). Only a very few cases have been described up to the present time so that it is entirely possible that many features of the disease are still unknown.

The disease has many of the physical signs of pellagra, but unlike pellagra it was not cured by administration of nicotinic acid. The affected, red tongue commonly found in pellagra was not observed, but the typical pellagrous rash which appeared on the face and hands, especially after exposure to sunlight, was prominent. An ataxia which altered the gait to a high-stepping one and caused tremors of the hands and involuntary movements of the tongue was present. Slowly progressing mental deficiency was found. In a family of eight children, four of whom exhibited the physical signs of the disease, the intelligence quotients declined regularly with age. The oldest at the age of 19 years had an IQ of 61, and the youngest, aged 6 years, 101. This regular decline in IQ was followed in one patient during a period of several years.

Biochemical examinations of the urine of patients showed that an abnormally large amount of amino acids was being excreted. Furthermore, derivatives of tryptophan were being excreted excessively. Indican and indoleacetic acid were particularly abundant in the urine. As much as 200 mg indoleacetic acid was being eliminated in a day. By contrast, another degradation product of tryptophan by way of another pathway, viz., kynurenine, was present in the urine in markedly subnormal amounts.

These findings suggested that a defect in the metabolism of tryptophan was present in the disease. It is known that tryptophan is the precursor from which nicotinic acid is made in the body. Kynurenine lies along this pathway of conversion. Because kynurenine was being excreted in subnormal amounts, and because of the pellagra-like physical signs of the disease, it seemed possible that the patients were deficient in this pathway from tryptophan to nicotinic acid.[b] The indican which was present in the urine presumably arose from bacterial action on tryptophan in the intestinal tract, because feeding of an antibiotic drug eliminated it, and cessation of the antibiotic drug caused it to reappear. The indoleacetic acid arose from tryptophan by a separate pathway from the one leading to nicotinic acid. This pathway seemed to be greatly augmented in the disease. No measurements were made of excretion of 5-hydroxyindoleacetic acid because the work was done before the relationship of serotonin to mental diseases was discovered. It would be of much interest to know whether this pathway of tryptophan metabolism, which leads by way of 5-hydroxytryptophan to serotonin and thence to 5-hydroxyindoleacetic acid, was affected in the disease.

The mental deterioration may have had no relationship to serotonin, but might be attributable to the defect of nicotinic acid metabolism which was indicated (but not proved) by the pellagra-like manifestations. In Chapter 15, the mental changes and neurological signs associated with a deficiency of nicotinic acid will be discussed. The ataxia of Hartnup's disease is of interest because of the ability of

[b] Nevertheless, dietary administration of nicotinic acid did not cure the disease. Consequently, if the defect was concerned with nicotinic acid biosynthesis it must have been of a complicated kind. Otherwise dietary nicotinic acid should have overcome it.

antimetabolites of nicotinic acid to induce such ataxia in animals through the induction of a specific lesion in the hippocampus.

The hereditary aspects of Hartnup's disease appeared from the fact that four of eight children of a family from which the first patient came were affected with it.

chapter 14

Thyroxine and the steroid hormones

Serotonin is not the only hormone concerned with mental diseases. Even if the epinephrines, acetylcholine, and histamine are excluded as being related to the serotonin story, there are other hormones which, when present in excess or when lacking, can be the cause of mental diseases. Thyroxine and the steroid hormones of the adrenal glands are examples of such. These will be mentioned briefly in this chapter. A comprehensive description would be redundant because the essential facts in the case are widely known, and there are available many reviews documenting the details. The mental disturbances associated with these hormones are summarized here in this book to emphasize the variety of biochemical defects which can result in mental failures and to indicate that the present author does not believe that all psychoses must be related directly to serotonin.

Many patients afflicted with a lack of thyroxine or of cortisone show mental changes. They may also show (and usually do show) frank physical changes as well. Thus in cretinism or myxedema (which represent thyroxine deficiencies) the expression of the face is altered in a characteristic way, and the basal metabolic rate is subnormal and other changes which are demonstrable by chemical tests can be found. However, the line between frank deficiency and normality is not clear. Adult patients for whom the only presenting symptom has been psychiatric abnormality have been found to respond to thyroxine administration (362). The condition of periodic catatonia in which again the main discernible difficulty is psychiatric likewise has been shown to respond to thyroxine (363 and 364). The mental disease related to thyroxine is thus not always heralded by physical signs.

Biosynthesis and uses of thyroxine. Thyroxine is made in the thyroid gland by a series of enzymic reactions. Iodide ions taken in the

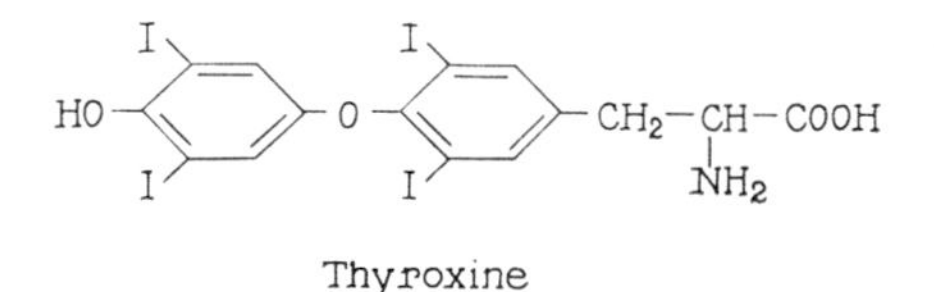

FIG. 1. *An active hormone of the thyroid gland.*

food and drink are trapped by this gland and oxidized to iodine which is used to iodinate tyrosine. Two molecules of the 3,5-diiodotyrosine which results may be condensed with the loss of the side chain of one of them to give thyroxine, the structure of which is shown in Figure 1. One iodine atom may be taken away from thyroxine to yield triiodothyronine. Both of these compounds occur in the gland and are active as the hormone. They are incorporated into a protein of the thyroid gland called iodothyroglobulin.

The precise biochemical reaction by means of which thyroxine and triiodothyronine exert their physiological effects is unknown, despite much intensive study. It has been known for a long time that the hormone regulates the metabolic rate of an animal—the rate at which fuel is burned and energy mobilized. What is not known is precisely how this comes about. It can be shown that thyroxine uncouples oxidative phosphorylation as several other phenolic substances (such as dinitrophenol) do, but the concentrations required seem to be out of the range of the physiologically active dose of the hormone. There are other difficulties as well with this as an explanation of the hormonal action. Much recent work has been directed to the idea that the hormone changes the permeability to water of the membrane surrounding mitochondria (365). In any event, what is known is that thyroxine increases the metabolic rate of animals, but the precise chemical reaction by which this is done is not understood.

Cretinism. Cretinism is a disease of children caused by a lack of thyroxine. This lack is usually the result of a deficiency of iodine in the food and water. Since thyroxine is an iodine derivative, this element must be ingested if the hormone is to be made. In addition to cretinism which arises from dietary lack of iodine, there are thyroxine deficiencies which are the result of inborn errors of metabolism not related to dietary iodine. In such deficiencies, one of the enzymes concerned in thyroxine synthesis is lacking as the result of gene mutation.

Cretins are mentally dull or moronic children with coarse hair and dry skin. If the disease has arisen from lack of iodine, the addition of iodide to the food or water will bring about recovery provided that the deficiency has not been of such long duration that it has resulted in irreversible developmental changes. If the disease has arisen from an inborn lack of one of the enzymes concerned with thyroxine synthesis, iodide is ineffective, and the hormone itself must be given.

Myxedema. This is a disease of adults suffering from a deficiency of thyroxine just as cretinism is the condition in children. The skin is dry and the hair coarse. A puffy edema of the features of the face gives a characteristic appearance to many of these patients. They are dull mentally, and usually tired, but the mental deterioration is usually not as great as in the cretin. Treatment with thyroxine can lead to marked improvement, and a return to normal behavior and appearance in myxedemic persons.

Periodic catatonia. Kraepelin (366) in 1913 first defined a group within his classification of schizophrenia which he described as periodic catatonia. These patients suffered regularly recurring bouts of catatonic stupor in which they would lie curled up and resistant to external stimuli. Each bout lasted anywhere from a few days to many weeks. The disease usually made its appearance during adult life. It has been studied extensively by Gjessing (363 and 364) and by several others (367). In the periods between stupors the patients may show almost normal behavior, although as Lindsay (367) has pointed out they may in these periods exhibit irrational speech and other signs of schizophrenia.

Most of the patients with periodic catatonia can be protected against the stupors by daily administration of thyroxine (368). Gjessing was led to this discovery because of his finding that in one category of patients there was nitrogen retention at the onset of the stupors. The known effects of thyroxine on nitrogen retention suggested the treatment with this hormone. The patients are not myxedemic and consequently do not show the classical signs of thyroxine deficiency. Nevertheless, the occurrence of the stupors can be prevented in many of the patients by the prolonged administration of thyroxine.

In untreated patients the periods of activity between the catatonic episodes are characterized by dullness and apathy although it may be possible for them to carry out routine work. As the period of catatonia approaches the patients exhibit restlessness and apparently some sort of anxiety that something is happening inside. Lindsay (367) has spoken of this as the panic stage of the cycle. In this phase, signs of sympathetic nervous activity may be prominent. Thus there may be changes in blood pressure and increases in body temperature along with the tenseness and other behavioral effects. The catatonic stupor finally intervenes.

The control of the catatonia by administration of thyroxine may be merely the effect of a general increase in the rate of metabolic reactions which superimposes adequate control mechanisms on an underlying mental insufficiency. Thus Lindsay (367) has speculated that the catatonia may arise from a storing up in the hypothalamus of impulses which ordinarily would be dissipated either with no harmful effects or with milder expressions of schizophrenia. Whether this be true or not, the ability to suppress the major manifestation—that is, catatonia—by administration of the hormone thyroxine demonstrates clearly the relationship of this hormone to a mental disease which might otherwise be called a functional psychosis and which might be in the older philosophy of mental diseases attributed to psychological rather than biochemical causation.

Hyperthyroidism. In sharp contrast to the tired, dull, catatonic or moronic condition which arises from lack of thyroxine is the agitation and overactivity of hyperthyroidism. Patients who form too much thyroxine, or who fail to destroy it rapidly enough, and who thus suffer from an excess of the hormone, belong in this group. The wild behavior of such individuals is common enough to give rise to the term "hyperthyroidal behavior" which is understood by all. Such patients are frequently treated successfully by surgical removal of the thyroid gland, or by chemical inhibition of thyroxine biosynthesis by administration of thiouracil or one of its congeners. These drugs are believed to act by trapping iodine before it can be incorporated into the hormone in the gland.

Relation of steroid hormones to affect and behavior. The steroid hormones, especially those of the adrenal glands, can influence markedly the mental state of an individual. This can be seen to some extent from the psychiatric state of people suffering from an overproduction of adrenal hormones (Cushing's syndrome), but more especially from that of some individuals who have received large amounts of these hormones as medication. Patients with Cushing's syndrome frequently are slightly abnormal mentally, although they can be distinguished readily from those affected with the so-called functional psychoses (schizophrenia or manic depressive psychosis, for example).

The administration of adrenal cortical hormones such as cortisone, which has been carried out in attempts to control cancerous growths, arthritis, and other physical abnormalities, can lead to psychiatric changes. Delusions and hallucinations and other manifestations of excitement are found if relatively large doses are employed. References to the literature of this subject can be found in the review of Hoagland and Freeman (369) and in (370).

The fact that steroid hormones can exert a pronounced action on the nervous system is exemplified further by the anesthetic effects of some of them. This was first described by Selye (371 and 372) for estrogenic and progestational hormones. Subsequent chemical modification of pregnanediol led to the development of a synthetic derivative, viz., pregnane-3,20-dione-21-ol hemisuccinate (373 and 374), which has found clinical application as an anesthetic of practical usefulness. Such findings show clearly that the steroid hormones and their derivatives can exert very marked neurological actions.

Several efforts have been made to determine whether functional psychoses such as schizophrenia are characterized by abnormalities in the metabolism of adrenal cortical hormones. These have been summarized by Hoagland and Freeman (369). They conclude from the results of their own extensive study of schizophrenic patients, and from the results of others, that there may be some change from normal in the urinary excretion of 17-ketosteroids. Pincus and Elmadjian (375) reported that although schizophrenic patients tended to excrete more than normal amounts of 17-ketosteroids, the application of a heat stress which brought about increased excretion in normal persons did not do so as markedly in the schizophrenics, so that under this stress the urinary excretion of the patients was less than normal. When aldosterone excretion was measured some schizophrenic persons *in the agitated phase* had higher than normal values without recourse to the heat stress. Chronic patients, however, tended not to show this elevation, and some excreted no aldosterone.

The findings of all investigators have not been in agreement with regard to the steroid hormone excretions of mental patients, so that no clearly established biochemical abnormality is visible. Hoagland and Freeman express the view that there is some abnormality in the metabolism of adrenal cortical hormones in schizophrenia, but that it probably is a secondary feature of the disease rather than a primary cause. It is entirely possible that a class of schizophrenic patients exists which does not include all. This class may be typified by some metabolic disturbance in the formation of the steroidal adrenal hormones. One is reminded of the phenylketonuric children who have been judged to be childhood schizophrenics but who in fact suffer from a lack of a single enzyme which metabolizes phenylalanine. These phenylketonurics represent only a small fraction of people with psychoses, but they do constitute a separate disease group with an abnormal excretion of phenylpyruvic acid. It may be so with respect to psychoses arising from steroid dysgenesis. Nevertheless it is important to note that this has not been proved. All that is available is some suggestive evidence of a controversial nature.

Despite the suggestive evidence mentioned in the preceding paragraph the fact remains that no success has attended attempts to treat schizophrenia with steroid hormones (369). This shows rather directly that schizophrenia is not a simple deficiency of one of those steroids which have been so tested. One cannot leave this subject, however, with any finality. The mental disturbances which can be induced with steroid hormones are very real. There have been some suggestive findings made in schizophrenic patients which tend to point to some disturbance of one if not more of these hormones. It would not be too surprising if future experiments should demonstrate that these substances may be involved in the production of the disease, but the relationship if it exists must be more subtle than that imagined in the first attempts to show such a relationship.

Antagonism between lysergic acid diethylamide (LSD) and steroid hormones. Some of the behavioral disturbances caused by LSD in rats can be prevented by administration of certain steroid hormones (285). The test of behavior used in these studies was the rope-climbing assay already described in Chapter 6. Rats were trained to climb a rope to get food. When they were given LSD the time required for them to accomplish this feat was markedly increased. Although treatment of the rats with any one of the steroids shown in Table 1 did not affect the time required for the animals to climb the rope, when the steroid was given, and then LSD was administered, the effect of the LSD was reduced; that is, the rats approached the behavior of normal animals. The steroid had inhibited the action of LSD on this test of behavior. All steroid hormones were not able to counteract LSD. The estrogens were without significant effect. As can be seen from the data in Table 1, many others were effective to a greater or lesser extent. These data have been taken from the paper of Bergen et al. (285).

In human beings it has also been possible to overcome some of

TABLE 1. *Prevention by various steroids of the effect of LSD on the rope-climbing test of rats (Each rat was injected daily with 1 mg of the steroid for 3 days. LSD (40 μg per rat) was then injected and the time required to climb the rope to receive the food reward was measured 15 minutes later. The results are expressed as per cent of the time required by control animals treated with LSD alone.)*

Steroid	Number of Rats	Decrease in Climbing Time, per cent
None	5	0
Estradiol	10	8
11-Desoxycortisol	5	16
Cortisone	10	26
Corticosterone	5	25
Desoxycorticosterone	5	38
Testosterone	15	52
Progesterone	10	58
Cortisol	15	61
Dehydroisoandrosterone	5	70

the psychic effects of LSD. Thus when normal persons were treated with prednisone (Δ^1-dehydrocortisone) and then given LSD the anxiety was prevented, although all of the psychotomimetic effects were not (284). Other steroid hormones have not yet been tested in human beings as antagonists to LSD, but it is possible that the ones found most active in the rat test may also be more effective than prednisone in human beings.

It is possible to relate these effects of steroid hormones on the LSD-psychosis to the serotonin hypothesis, primarily by way of the serotonin receptor. However, the data to support the ideas are scanty so that it is unprofitable to belabor this point. In addition the main purpose of this chapter has been to show some of the effects of other hormones than serotonin on mental processes. What the experiments with LSD and steroids demonstrate is that a "model" psychosis can be influenced by hormones of the adrenal glands.

chapter 15

Neurologic and psychiatric involvements of nicotinic acid

The examples given in Chapter 14 showed that hormones other than serotonin may exert a profound effect on mental processes. Abnormal amounts of thyroxine or of cortisone can lead to pronounced mental changes. There is a possibility of interrelationships between these hormones and serotonin, but this remains conjectural. What is certain is that the effects of the hormones on normal mental processes can be demonstrated directly and unequivocally. In the present chapter a vitamin (nicotinic acid or nicotinamide) will be considered. When it is not present in sufficient amounts, or when not functioning normally, the result can be mental disease with or without accompanying neurologic abnormalities.

Nicotinamide and its derivative nicotinic acid (niacin) were shown to be vitamins by Elvehjem, Madden, Strong, and Woolley who, in 1937, isolated nicotinamide from liver and demonstrated that it cured black tongue in dogs (376). Black tongue had been known to be the canine analog of pellagra in human beings, so that when the curative effects of nicotinamide were discovered the cure of pellagra followed logically. The chemical structures of nicotinamide and of nicotinic acid are shown in Figure 1. Either substance possesses the vitamin activity because they are interconvertible in the body.

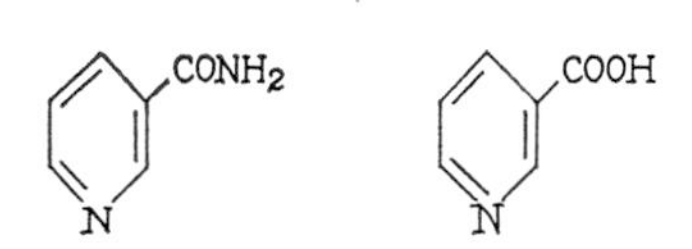

FIG. 1. *The antipellagra vitamin.*

Pellagra is a disease of man distinguishable by characteristic physical signs and frequently by mental abnormalities. Before nicotinic acid was discovered it was endemic in those parts of the world where corn was the predominant cereal eaten and where economic depression minimized the consumption of meat and other proteinaceous foods. Such regions as northern Italy (where it was first described by Magendi), southern France, and southern United States presented thousands of cases annually. The most noticeable sign of the disease is the lesion of the tongue, and the rash on those parts of the skin exposed to sunlight or to excessive friction from clothing. The tongue becomes glossy, swollen, and red. Indentations of the edges where the teeth press against it may be prominent. A rash usually develops on the face, hands, forearms, and knees. Exposure to sunlight particularly seems to call forth this rash. Other physical signs such as intestinal disturbances are common in pellagra but are less distinctive than the glossitis and the rash.

The mental abnormality of pellagra is not found in all of the cases, but it is frequently present. Like many other mental disorders it is difficult to describe precisely. Depression or agitation may be present. Occasionally paranoid symptoms predominate in which the usual delusions of persecution are prominent, but they are not the frequent manifestations. The patients act queerly. Their behavior may be so queer that they are committed to mental hospitals where some of them end up in the classification of "agitated." Administration of nicotinic acid or nicotinamide will restore these patients to normal behavior, usually with dramatic rapidity. The physical signs of pellagra can also be caused to regress and disappear by feeding the vitamin.

The cure of the mental defect of pellagra by nicotinic acid assumes considerable historical importance because it was one of the first demonstrations that a chemical cause could be ascribed to an obscure mental disease. Before 1937 it was well known that cretinism or myxedema could be treated successfully with thyroxine or just plain iodine. It was also known that paresis of syphilis could be arrested by elimination of the infection with high fever or with arsenical drugs. These diseases, however, had been set apart in most medical thinking as special cases representative of organic disorders with a component of mental involvement. When it became possible, as it did in 1937, to treat patients in mental hospitals in the southern United States with nicotinic acid, and to find that a few of them became well (that is, the ones who owed their mental defect to unrecognized pellagra), a powerful argument was presented to some minds that other mental diseases of obscure causation might have a biochemical basis. The numbers who were so persuaded however were very small, probably because most inmates of mental hospitals were not pellagrins and consequently were not helped by nicotinic acid. Also, the Freudian view of mental disease was sweeping the intellectual world to the partial exclusion of other ideas about causation.

Biochemical reactions of nicotinamide. Nicotinamide is converted to two coenzymes in the body, viz., diphosphopyridine nucleotide (DPN) and triphosphopyridine nucleotide (TPN). The structures of these coenzymes are shown in Figure 2. To form DPN, nicotinamide is first converted to its ribotide. This then reacts with adenosine triphosphate under the catalysis of the Kornberg enzyme (377) to yield inorganic pyrophosphate and DPN.

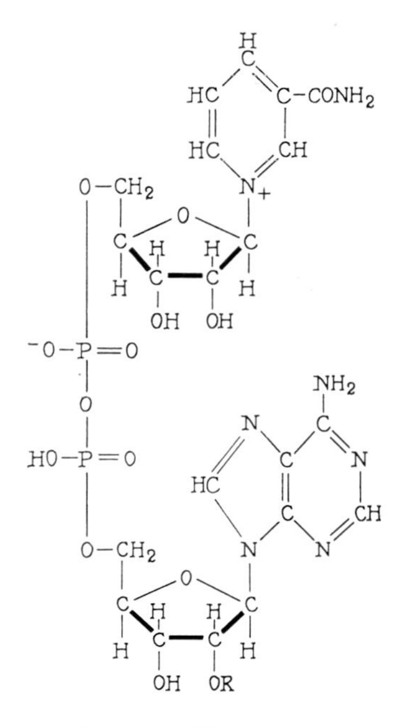

FIG. 2. *Structures of nicotinamide-containing coenzymes.*

DPN and TPN are the coenzymes for a large number of enzymes which bring about oxidations and reductions in the body. They are the coenzymes for dehydrogenases and also for many of the hydroxylases of animal tissues. In some of these reactions either coenzyme can function, but in others DPN is specifically required and in still others only TPN is effective. For most of the hydroxylases studied up to the present time, TPN is specifically needed. DPN and TPN can serve as coenzymes for the dehydrogenases because the pyridine ring in either coenzyme can undergo reversible reduction and oxidation. Hydrogen can be accepted at the 4-position of the pyridine ring with consequent reduction of the pyridinium nitrogen atom to a trivalent state. The hydrogen can then be donated to another molecule and the DPN or TPN thus regenerated. Reactions of this sort catalyzed by DPN or TPN in combination with a specific apoenzyme are found in many steps of the metabolic schemes by means of which glucose is converted to carbon dioxide and water. They are also found in the mechanisms for metabolism of amino acids, and of fats and in many other kinds of metabolic transformations.

In earlier chapters many of these reactions have been discussed, as for example, the transformation of UDPG to UDPGal by means of the epimerase which depends on DPN. This was discussed in connection with galactosemia in Chapter 12. The oxidation of tryptophan to 5-hydroxytryptophan and of dopamine to norepinephrine are examples of hydroxylations and are reactions dependent on TPN specifically. One can thus find many biochemical reactions of great importance to the nervous system which depend on these nicotinamide-containing coenzymes. They range from the combustion of glucose, on which the brain (not to mention other tissues) relies for its source of energy, to the formation of hormones such as serotonin and epinephrine which can be shown to influence the functions of nerves. Interference with the formation or functioning of these coenzymes might be expected to cause disruptions of various kinds in the performance of the brain. The surprising thing is that the changes which are so produced are not greater.

One reason why dietary nicotinic acid deficiency and the use of antimetabolites of nicotinic acid do not cause greater havoc than they do is probably that the concentrations of DPN and TPN do not decrease markedly during the deficiency. Although the content of these coenzymes may fall markedly in blood or some other special tissue, any major decrease in brain or muscle or other vital organ is incompatible with life. When animals die of nicotinic acid deficiency they still contain in these tissues a considerable amount of the coenzymes.

DPNase. The brain contains an unusually large amount of an enzyme which attacks DPN and TPN and cleaves from them the nicotinamide portion. This enzyme is called DPNase or diphosphopyridine nucleotidase. The remaining portion of the DPN molecule, consisting of ribose-phosphate-adenylic acid is the other product along with a hydrogen ion. If a suitable acceptor for this portion of the molecule is provided, other biochemically important compounds can be synthesized by action of DPNase. Thus, if the acceptor is 4-amino-5-carboxamidoimidazole, a new dinucleotide is formed into which the imidazole derivative is incorporated as shown in Figure 3 (378).

Certain other imidazole derivatives, notably histamine, likewise can act as good acceptors (379) and can yield a histamine-containing dinucleotide analogous to the one shown in Figure 3. This histamine-containing dinucleotide is probably one of the intermediates in the biological inactivation of histamine in higher animals. It is known that some of injected histamine is excreted in the urine as the riboside

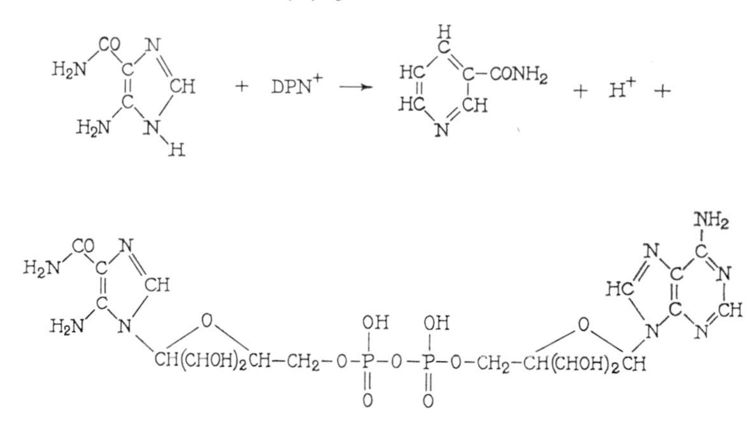

FIG. 3. *Formation of an imidazole-containing dinucleotide from DPN by means of DPNase.*

of imidazoleacetic acid (380). This riboside probably originates from hydrolysis and oxidative deamination of the dinucleotide.

The production of a hydrogen ion in the DPNase reaction may be of importance in the processes which occur at cell membranes by means of which electrical potentials are generated or changed and metallic ions are moved (381). The DPNase reaction is exceedingly fast, and might thus provide the necessary speed required in the actions of nerves. Furthermore, the hydrogen ion is one which diffuses very rapidly. If it were to be used to displace sodium or potassium, the speed of its production by DPNase would be advantageous for nerve action. It may well be that DPNase in brain is used for purposes of this sort as well as for bringing to an abrupt stop (by conjugation) the actions of compounds such as histamine, or even DPN. The fact that brain is so richly supplied with this enzyme must not be forgotten. Another good source of it is the reticuloendothelial system.

These reactions catalyzed by DPNase are oxidation-reductions in which the pyridinium nitrogen atom is reduced to a trivalent state and the linkage of ribose and nicotinamide is disrupted. They are thus different from the dehydrogenase reactions or hydroxylations which are oxido-reductions but in which no bond of the coenzyme is broken. In the latter reactions, only hydrogen is transferred and portions of the DPN molecule are not built into new molecules. In the DPNase reactions, a hydrogen is eliminated as a hydrogen ion instead of as a hydrogen atom, and a portion of the DPN molecule is used to form a new compound. These DPNase reactions are not reversible, probably because of the elimination of a hydrogen ion with the reduction of the quaternary nitrogen atom (378 and 381).

A second kind of reaction has also been found to be catalyzed by DPNase. These are the transfer reactions (381 and 382). They are not oxidation-reductions, and no hydrogen ion is liberated by them. They are reversible. The same DPNase enzyme can catalyze both kinds of reaction. What makes the difference is the type of acceptor molecule; that is, whether it is a tertiary base (transfer reaction) or something else (oxido-reduction). Thus, if the acceptor is pyridine or nicotinic acid or some other pyridine derivative, nicotinamide is released from the DPN and its place is taken by the acceptor molecule just as in the case of the oxido-reduction shown in Figure 3, but no hydrogen ion is eliminated. In this way, analogs of DPN are formed with the nicotinamide replaced by the extraneous pyridine base. The new DPN analog is still a quaternary salt. The products of a transfer reaction are thus nicotinamide plus an analog of DPN. In the oxidation-reduction reactions of DPNase the acceptor is a primary or secondary nitrogen atom (as in the imidazole derivatives) or an hydroxyl group as when the acceptor is just plain water.

Various analogs of DPN have been synthesized enzymatically by use of the DPNase transfer reaction (383). They contain nicotinic acid, or pyridine, or 3-acetylpyridine, or isonicotinic acid hydrazide in place of nicotinamide. When these are tested for activity in place of DPN in the dehydrogenase reactions for which DPN is the coenzyme, some are found to act as antimetabolites of DPN, and thus block its biochemical action. Others can take the place of DPN, but not as efficiently as DPN itself. One can even find that a given analog can act like DPN for one dehydrogenase, and as antagonist to it in a second dehydrogenase. In other words, one finds the spectrum of antimetabolite action with these analogs just as was described in Chapters 3, 4, and 6 for antimetabolites of serotonin and other hormones. The analogs can act like the essential metabolite or as antagonists to it depending on the receptors (apoenzymes).

Biosynthesis of nicotinic acid. Nicotinic acid is made in many living things from tryptophan. The indole ring of tryptophan is ruptured between carbon atoms 2 and 3 by action of an oxidase to yield formylkynurenine. This is the same kind of indole cleavage as was described in Chapter 4 for the destruction of serotonin and of indoleacetic acid. The formylkynurenine is then hydrolyzed to kynurenine and formic acid. The kynurenine is then oxidized (through the aid of a TPN-

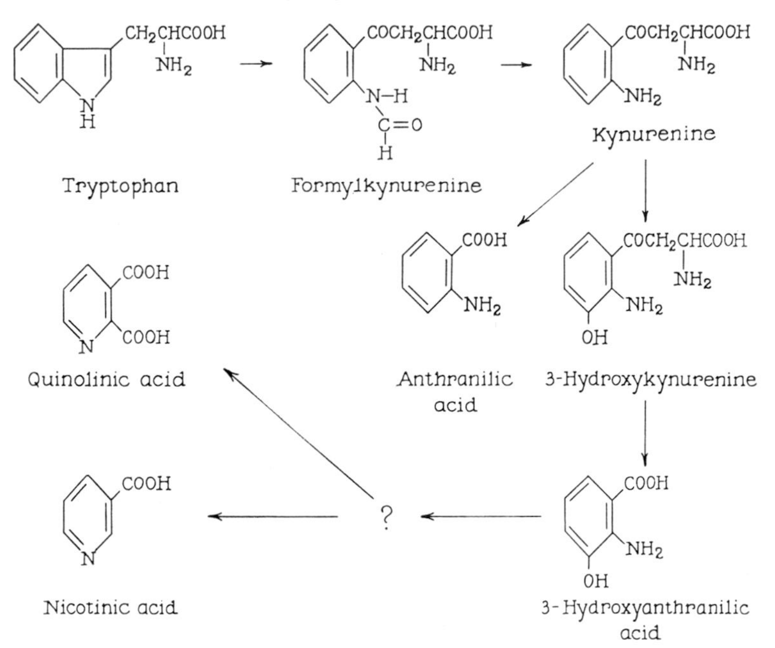

FIG. 4. *Some steps in the biosynthesis of nicotinic acid from tryptophan.*

containing enzyme) to 3-hydroxykynurenine, which is then further hydrolyzed to 3-hydroxyanthranilic acid and alanine. The 3-hydroxyanthranilic acid undergoes reactions not yet fully understood but which involve reclosure to quinolinic acid and nicotinic acid. Some of these steps are sketched in Figure 4.

Although nicotinic acid is a dietary requirement or vitamin for man and many other animals, this does not mean that it cannot be synthesized by these organisms. They can make it provided that they have suffiicent starting materials. The mechanism of synthesis is that just described. The question is whether they can synthesize enough nicotinic acid to meet their needs. The deciding factor seems to be the dietary supply of tryptophan, and of course, the species of animal. If enough tryptophan is eaten, enough nicotinic acid will be synthesized, and there will be no dietary need for this vitamin. Tryptophan will cure or prevent pellagra in man and black tongue in dogs. One of the reasons why the eating of corn has long been known to be associated with the induction of pellagra is that corn has only minimal amounts of tryptophan. When the protein supply in a ration is low, and of poor quality (lacking in tryptophan, for example), pellagra is more likely to occur unless adequate amounts of nicotinic acid are eaten. Similarly, pellagra is not seen when diets rich in proteins well supplied with tryptophan are used, even though their nicotinic acid content may be low (384).

The various biochemical transformations of tryptophan. Tryptophan is the starting point of a variety of biochemical transformations, and thus acts as precursor of many compounds. Some of these are important in reactions concerned with mental processes directly, and others serve as guides to indicate to the biochemist what may be happening to tryptophan derivatives in certain mental diseases. A few of the biochemical reactions of tryptophan can be listed as follows.

a. Synthesis of protein. Most proteins contain tryptophan, and are built from it along with other amino acids.

b. Synthesis of nicotinic acid and the coenzymes derived from it. These reactions have just been described in the foregoing sections. Kynurenine, which is an intermediate in this process, is found in small amounts in normal urine. Marked change in the amount excreted, as in Hartnup's disease (see Chapter 13), gives a suggestion that this pathway of tryptophan metabolism is not functioning normally.

c. Synthesis of serotonin. This hydroxylation and decarboxylation of tryptophan was described in Chapter 4.

d. Synthesis of tryptamine and indoleacetic acid. Decarboxylation of tryptophan yields tryptamine, which can then be attacked by monoamine oxidase and subsequently by other oxidases to give finally indoleacetic acid. Tryptamine is not normally found in the tissues of mammals but it can be caused to appear by administration of an inhibitor of monoamine oxidase such as Marsilid (iproniazid) (385). It has long been known that perfusion of the liver with solutions of tryptamine gives rise to the formation of large amounts of indoleacetic acid. Normal urine contains indoleacetic acid which presumably has arisen from tryptophan by way of tryptamine. Some of this conversion may occasionally be ascribable to bacterial action in the intestinal tract; but it is also clear that animal tissues per se can bring about the change. The urinary excretion of indoleacetic acid is thus an index of some value in assessing this pathway of tryptophan metabolism just as the urinary excretion of 5-hydroxyindoleacetic acid is a guide to the operation of the serotonin pathway.

e. Synthesis of indican, indole and skatole. Bacterial action in the intestinal tract can lead to the formation of indole and skatole (3-methylindole) from tryptophan. The indole may be oxidized to indoxyl and excreted as indoxylsulfate or indican. All of these products may be present in the urine. Because they are not normally formed by animal tissues from tryptophan, their presence in large amounts in urine may indicate only faulty functioning of the intestines, either the failure to absorb dietary tryptophan or merely the result of constipation.

Mammals do not synthesize tryptophan. Their entire supply comes from their food. The tryptophan thus provided is limited in amount, and it must be allocated to all of the uses described above, and probably more. What it is that controls this allocation is not known. Possibly one of the controlling factors is the relative abundance of tryptophan, provided that the enzymes concerned with each pathway are present and functioning normally. If the serotonin pathway is expanded, as it is in carcinoid tumors of the intestines, as much as half of the dietary supply of tryptophan can be shunted into that pathway, whereas normally only about 1 per cent passes in that direction. If the nicotinic acid pathway is closed, as it possibly may be in Hartnup's disease, more tryptophan is available for the other pathways. If the serotonin pathway is partially closed, as it is in phenylketonuria, more tryptophan is available for the other pathways, and this may be the reason why excretion of indoleacetic acid is increased in that disease. Available supply of tryptophan is not the only controlling factor which decides which pathways are favored. It may be only a minor factor. The other parts of the control mechanism are not understood.

Antimetabolites of nicotinic acid which cause neurologic and psychiatric changes associated with hippocampal lesions. Two different kinds of antimetabolites of nicotinic acid are known which cause a specific lesion in the hippocampus of animals, but no other discernible lesion. These are 3-acetylpyridine and 6-aminonicotinamide. Their structures are shown in Figure 5. The lesion is believed to be the cause of a permanent ataxia which is seen in dogs and other animals after ingestion of either antimetabolite (386, 387, and 388).

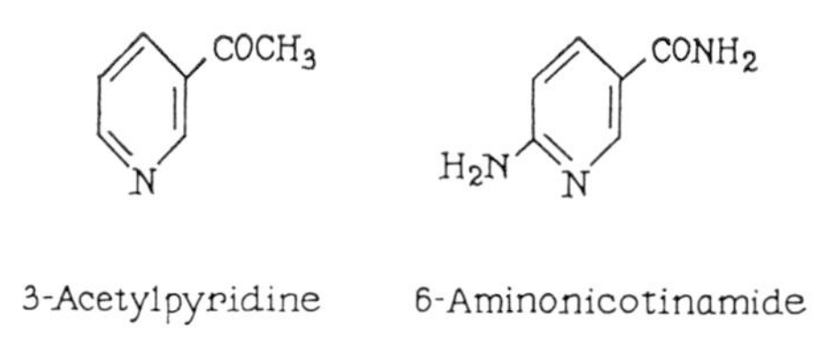

FIG. 5. *Two antimetabolites of nicotinamide which selectively damage the hippocampus.*

A few human patients who were treated with 6-aminonicotinamide in an effort to control cancers experienced psychotic episodes (387).

3-Acetylpyridine was one of the first antimetabolites to be discovered. It was found in 1938 (389) to be poisonous to nicotinic acid-deficient dogs, but not to well-nourished dogs. Some time later when the antimetabolite phenomenon had unfolded to view, 3-acetylpyridine was reinvestigated (390). It was found to induce failure of growth and lesions of the tongue in mice. Especially did it cause a characteristic behavioral change (390). After receiving this compound the mice would stand up on their hind legs in the attitude of a trained dog begging for food. All of the changes induced by it in mice could be prevented if nicotinic acid was given in sufficiently large amount before administration of the drug. Once the effects of the drug had been produced they could not be cured with any amount of the vitamin. The probable reason for this became apparent several years later when Kaplan and his associates showed that DPNase acted on DPN and 3-acetylpyridine to give rise, by an exchange reaction, to nicotinamide and the acetylpyridine analog of DPN (383). The drug was thus incorporated into an antimetabolite of DPN inside the cells of the brain. Feeding of nicotinic acid was of no help once this had taken place. Even DPN from other tissues was ineffective in causing reversal probably because this nucleotide, as is well known, does not pass freely in and out of cells.

The ataxia and behavioral changes caused by 3-acetylpyridine had thus been observed, but it remained for Coggeshall and MacLean (386) to study the ataxia more carefully, and to trace it to a lesion in the hippocampus of the brain. In dogs the ataxia which follows the administration of 3-acetylpyridine is permanent. So also is the histologically visible lesion in the hippocampus.

While these facts were being discovered, other investigators were attempting to make antimetabolites of nicotinic acid which might be useful in the treatment of cancers. One of these compounds seemed particularly promising because it would arrest certain transplanted cancers of laboratory animals. This was 6-aminonicotinamide. It was studied in dogs, and when no marked toxic manifestations were found, it was tested on a few human patients with cancers (387). The humans experienced psychiatric disturbances and ataxia. Restudy of dogs which had received the drug revealed that they too had ataxia. Histological examination of their brains showed the similar kind of lesion in the hippocampus which Coggeshall and MacLean had described in dogs treated with 3-acetylpyridine (387,

388). DPNase will incorporate 6-aminonicotinamide to give an analog of DPN just as in the case of 3-acetylpyridine (391).

The selective action of these two antimetabolites in being able to single out and damage the hippocampus specifically is an important clue. It probably means that nicotinic acid, its amide, or more likely DPN or TPN are of great importance in the functioning of this structure of the brain. It also shows that psychiatric disturbances can arise from selective change in the hippocampus.

Summary. Deficiency of nicotinic acid leads to neurologic difficulties (e.g., ataxia) and to mental disturbances. This is true whether the deficiency is produced by dietary lack of the vitamin or is the result of administration of an antimetabolite of it. The changes caused by the antimetabolites 3-acetylpyridine or 6-aminonicotinamide can be permanent and can be traced to histological lesions in the hippocampus. Many biochemical reactions are known which depend on nicotinic acid in the form of its coenzymes DPN and TPN. These reactions are concerned not only with the fuel supply of the brain, but also with the formation of several chemical substances known from other evidence to be of importance in mental processes, or to be present in abnormal amounts in human beings suffering from certain mental diseases.

The precise reason why a lack of nicotinic acid causes psychiatric disturbance is not known, but its relationship to these known substances and reactions gives valuable clues for the design of experiments which may lead to an understanding. Probably it is not the slowing in general of all the processes catalyzed by nicotinamide-containing coenzymes which is the cause of the mental and neurologic failures. It may be the lack of only one which is crucial. It is important to discover that one, for it may show something of the causes of other mental disorders.

chapter 16

Chemotherapy

Two general methods of attempting to discover chemical substances for the control of mental diseases are available. One is to test chemicals more or less at random or on the basis of a favorable chance clue, and hope that a useful drug will turn up. The second general method is to start with the idea that the disease is the result of an abnormality of cerebral serotonin or norepinephrine or other hormone as outlined in preceding chapters, and to construct drugs which will overcome the defect in metabolism, or which will alter the amount of the hormone in the brain. Regardless of which strategy is followed, the final testing for effectiveness must be done on human beings suffering from a mental disease. However, before this is done, considerable experimentation with laboratory animals is carried out, especially to safeguard the human subjects but also to learn about the actions of the drugs.

The first of these general methods is the classical way of finding useful drugs for all kinds of medicinal purposes. It relies on a chance observation to provide the first member of the series. Once this one has been found better ones may be made by modifications in its chemical structure. The second general method does not rely on chance to provide the first member of the series. In this method the first member is predicted from the knowledge about the relationship of the hormone to the mental disorder. Most of the drugs in use today were found by the empirical or first general method, both because it has been used for a longer time, and because most people working in chemotherapy believe it is the best way to proceed. Reserpine, chlorpromazine, and imipramine were discovered in this way. The second general method is much more recent, having been first mentioned less than 10 years ago (78). One purpose of this book is to explain this second general method of chemotherapy. A few of the drugs now being introduced into the practice of psychiatry were discovered wholly or partly as a result of its influence. The present author believes that a relatively small expenditure of energy on exploration of this second method may yield practical therapeutic agents if the investigators understand fully and apply the facts set forth in preceding chapters.

Chemotherapy of the inborn mental defects. Let us leave out of consideration the chemotherapy of the idiocies which arise from the inborn errors of metabolism. In these (for example, phenylketonuria, galactosemia, etc.) the mental defect probably arises from an error in normal development. The defect, once established, appears to be built into the individual, and probably cannot be changed after the first few years of life. The idiocy can be avoided if the proper dietary restrictions are followed in infancy, as was described in Chapters 11 and 12, but once the mental disease is established firmly (that is, for several years) the dietary treatment fails to remedy it. In a very real sense this specific dietary restriction is chemical prophylaxis which effectively prevents the development of the irreversible mental failure. However, once the mental failure has been completely established, prophylaxis is too late.

Although the phenylalanine-low diet does not help an adult phenylketonuric patient whose disease was not corrected early in life, there is still some possibility of chemotherapy. For example, chemical steps might be taken to increase serotonin in the brain. This might be done with 5-hydroxytryptophan, or by other means. The chances of success, however, are small because the difficulty appears to be some irreversible change brought about early in life by a serotonin deficiency rather than the mental effects of the deficiency per se. Also, the fact that one would be starting with an adult with practically no education and without normal experience of life would, if nothing else did, make the prospect seem difficult. The hope for chemotherapy in these conditions of infancy lies in specific prophylaxis rather than in treatment after the disease is firmly established.

This state of affairs may also have a bearing on the treatment of mental diseases of adults such as schizophrenia. The chemotherapy may need to be begun early in the disease if it is to succeed. The deterioration which slowly sets in and produces the so-called "burned out" schizophrenic dementia may be as irreversible as the idiocy of an adult phenylketonuric patient seems to be.

Chemotherapy of functional psychoses. If we turn now to efforts to control the so-called functional psychoses (schizophrenia, manic depressive psychosis, etc.) by means of drugs we find first that the choice is influenced largely by the kind of symptom being exhibited and much less by the name of the disease. This seems wise because as we have seen in earlier chapters, there is no assurance that a single disease is classified under a single name. Schizophrenia may include many distinct diseases so that it might be a mistake to attempt to find a drug for the treatment of all schizophrenic persons. Let us therefore recall what the symptoms are of these functional psychoses.

As a first approximation we may say that these symptoms are either of depression or of agitation.[a] By agitation is meant the mania or hysteria or wild behavior. It includes the anxiety which can build up to monstrous proportions in some patients, and the hallucinations and fantastic flights of ideas and delusions. These are the symptoms often associated in the popular mind with mental disease, but they are only a part of the picture. Perhaps the largest feature of these mental diseases is depression. This phase is often forgotten, but it is probably true that schizophrenia begins with depression. The agitated phase may be a psychological reaction in which the patient strains to escape from his depressed moods. There are many hypotheses on this subject [b] and much debate about a matter which can probably never be proved. Despite this, however, it is plain that both depression and agitation are aspects of many mental diseases. Frequently both extremes can be found to alternate in the same patient until he finally withdraws into catatonia or slowly sinks into some other compromise with society.

At the present time then, most chemotherapeutic efforts are directed against symptoms. One tries to control agitation or one attempts to relieve depression. The drugs employed are different for the two extremes, although a few enthusiastic investigators still attempt to control depressions with tranquilizers in the belief that depression is just another form of excitement. To base the choice of drug on symptomatology alone may well prove to be a mistake, but at the present time the knowledge of causation is so lacking that there is no better basis for choice.

It must be emphasized that there is no adequate chemotherapeutic

[a] This statement may seem a gross oversimplification especially to those who have subscribed to any one of a number of psychological hypotheses to explain the symptomatology of mental disease. There are even some who consider that depression is one form of excitement. Nevertheless, this simplification has its merits.

[b] A conservative statement of these hypotheses can be found in Strecker's book (227). More elaborate treatments can be found in the works of Freud, Jung, and their disciples.

treatment for the functional psychoses. Some symptoms can be lessened in some patients but the disease as a whole cannot be abolished.

Existing drugs for control of agitation. These may be called the tranquilizing drugs. The principal ones in use today are chlorpromazine, certain phenothiazines related to chlorpromazine, reserpine, and meprobamate. The purpose of the following remarks is not to be encyclopedic, but rather to give a short summary of existing knowledge. Similarly it is not intended to list all of the drugs which have been or are being now tested in patients with mental diseases in which agitation or mania is prominent. Chlorpromazine has proved to be the most effective, and is used today in mental hospitals on a very large scale, sometimes with beneficial results. Reserpine has also been widely used, but is slowly losing favor. Meprobamate (Miltown) is very widely used, frequently without medical supervision. For many years barbituric acid derivatives have been employed to induce sleep, and consequently calm, in cases of acute agitation. They have also been used to induce sleep for very long periods in depressed patients. When the patients are eventually allowed to waken, some may be improved in mental status, but the results in all patients have not been very promising. Nevertheless, an acute hysteria can be controlled with barbiturates, although the long-term result may be quite disappointing.

All these tranquilizing drugs were discovered by chance. That is to say, the first member of each series was so found. Succeeding members, as for example, the various phenothiazines, were produced in the classical fashion by making and testing all sorts of related structures. These tranquilizers, therefore, illustrate well the operation of the empirical method of discovery.

A. ***Chlorpromazine*** has the chemical structure shown in Figure 11 of Chapter 6. Its complete chemical name is N-(3-dimethylaminopropyl)-3-chlorophenothiazine. It was discovered during a routine search for more potent antagonists of histamine. A prior phenothiazine antihistamine drug, viz., Phenergan, or N-(2-dimethylamino-1-propyl)phenothiazine, was the starting point of this search. In the classical fashion, various structural alterations were made in Phenergan, and these derivatives were tested pharmacologically. Chlorpromazine was at first thought not to have any antihistamine activity, but subsequently it was shown to have some.

Chlorpromazine was not used originally in psychiatry. During the course of pharmacological testing of it (in the antihistamine work), it was found to reduce the body temperatures of mammals markedly.[c] It was then introduced into medical practice for the control of vomiting of pregnancy, a use to which it is still put on a wide scale. Quite by chance its tranquilizing action was noticed in the course of these other applications, and it was put to use in the calming of agitated mental patients.

Chlorpromazine, also called Thorazine or Largactil, and many other names, seems to be the most favored drug today for the control of agitated mental patients. The opinion of many careful observers of such patients is that it makes them more manageable but does not cure the underlying mental disease. Thus, it is possible to detect the underlying schizophrenic personality of many patients who have been made manageable by this drug. Many of these patients have been able to leave the hospital and to find a place in the world which probably would not have been the case without the drug. In all fairness, however, it must be said that many patients given chlorpromazine have not been able to leave the hospital and return to the world.

Chlorpromazine has some serious undesirable effects. Like so many other chlorine-containing substances it may cause liver damage with resultant jaundice in some people. In some it may cause (after long usage) tremors resembling those seen in Parkinson's disease (paralysis agitans).

Following the introduction of chlorpromazine into psychiatry other phenothiazine drugs were developed and tested in the hope that one might be found which was more effective than the parent compound, and might lack its shortcomings. A considerable number of these congeners are now being tested clinically. Some of them do seem to have advantages over chlorpromazine, but it will take much clinical testing before the best member of the series can be identified with certainty. The adequate evaluation of a drug is a very slow process, and this is especially the case in mental disorders in which the criteria of a beneficial response in the patients are quite vague. It may be relatively easy to tell when a patient is less assaultive, but it is not easy to tell when his mental condition has improved.

B. *Reserpine*, which has the chemical structure shown in Figure 6 of Chapter 3 was discovered in the classical fashion as a result of the chance observation made in India many centuries ago. The ingestion

[c] This property of reducing body temperature is exhibited by many antimetabolites of serotonin which are of such a structure that they reach the brain. The demonstration that chlorpromazine, although not an antimetabolite of serotonin, does strongly interfere with the action of this hormone on smooth muscles (see Chapter 6), thus fits well with its ability to lower body temperature.

of the roots of the plant *Rauwolfia serpentina* was noticed to lead to a change in mood which is now called tranquilization. The principal active substance in the plant responsible for the tranquilization is the alkaloid reserpine. It is also called Serpasil and many other names. Reserpine was first introduced into Western medicine for the control of hypertension. The tranquilizing action was noticed during the course of a study of its effects in that disease.

Reserpine brings about tranquilization of men and higher animals. Thus, a monkey, which ordinarily is an agitated, combative animal, is rendered docile and calm by administration of this drug. Agitated mental patients undergo similar changes, and are rendered more manageable. However, the use of reserpine in the cases of the agitation of mental disease is declining. Chlorpromazine is gaining in popularity over it not only because the type of tranquilization caused by chlorpromazine seems more desirable, but also because of undesirable actions of reserpine. A considerable number of people eventually develop marked depression after extended use of it. Some develop Parkinsonism.[d]

C. ***Meprobamate,*** or Miltown, has the structure shown in Figure 1. Like the preceding drugs, it was discovered largely by chance (392). A series of structurally related drugs was being tested for ability to cause relaxation of muscles in living animals. Meprobamate was one of the series and it attracted attention because of its marked sedative effects in addition to its muscle relaxant powers. It was accordingly tested in human patients to relieve tension. Its effects on mood and behavior are less marked, and of somewhat different kind, than those caused by chlorpromazine or by reserpine. However, undesirable toxic actions of meprobamate have been much less severe, and it is partly for this reason that it is so much used. Many details of its actions have been described both in human beings and laboratory animals in a symposium (393). In general, meprobamate is used in efforts to relieve tension and anxiety and rather less for the relief of extreme agitation.

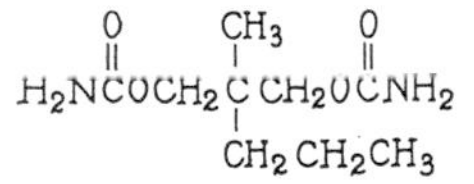

$$H_2N\overset{O}{\overset{\|}{C}}OCH_2\underset{CH_2CH_2CH_3}{\underset{|}{\overset{CH_3}{\overset{|}{C}}}}CH_2O\overset{O}{\overset{\|}{C}}NH_2$$

Meprobamate

FIG. 1.

[d] The fact that Parkinsonism may develop in human beings after prolonged use of either chlorpromazine or reserpine is of much interest because it suggests a relationship of this disease to serotonin and related neurohormones. Either drug brings about a failure in functioning of serotonin and the catechol amines although as we have seen in Chapters 6, 7, and 8, the mechanism of interference by the two drugs is different.

Existing drugs for the reduction of depression. There are a variety of drugs being used at the present time in an effort to combat depressions. These are sometimes called "psychic energizers." Three different kinds will be mentioned: amphetamine, imipramine, and inhibitors of monoamine oxidase such as Marsilid, nialamide, and other hydrazine derivatives. Some of these were discovered solely by chance but for most of them some elements of biochemical reasoning played a role in their development. Amphetamine was discovered partly by chance and partly by design since it was produced as a relative of the epinephrines and resembles them in some pharmacological properties. Marsilid was first introduced into medicine for the control of tuberculosis. Its effect on mood was a chance observation during the trials with tuberculous patients. The elevation of mood which it caused fitted so well into the serotonin hypothesis of mental disease which was put forward at about the same time, that further development of inhibitors of monoamine oxidase has a logical basis. Marsilid inhibits monoamine oxidase, and thereby increases the serotonin and norepinephrine contents of brain and other tissues. This stimulated a search for other inhibitors of this enzyme which might likewise cause accumulations of these hormones and elevation of mood. In this way nialamide and other hydrazines which inhibit monoamine oxidase were developed. Imipramine arose from structural alterations of chlorpromazine, with the idea of improving on that tranquilizer. Instead of a tranquilizer, however, an antidepressant drug was found.

A. ***Amphetamine,*** shown in Figure 1 of Chapter 8, may be regarded as dopamine or norepinephrine from which hydroxyl groups have been omitted, and which has been made into a derivative with its side chain modified in such a way as to escape the action of monoamine oxidase. The methyl group attached to the carbon atom which bears the amino group renders the molecule stable to this enzyme. One might say that both of these structural changes have been the ones which would convert norepinephrine into a substance which should penetrate readily from the periphery into the nervous system. We have seen in Chapter 6 that these are the kinds of structural change needed to allow serotonin or the epinephrines to pass the blood-brain barrier. Actually, amphetamine was made and studied before these ideas arose about the blood-brain barrier, but in retrospect they contribute to an understanding of its pharmacological properties. Amphetamine actually inhibits monoamine oxidase, and was one of the first inhibitors of this enzyme to be found. It has many of the activities of epinephrine and norepinephrine on smooth muscles and on nerves. Probably because of its penetrability its actions on nerves may be more prominent than is the case with the hormones themselves. Amphetamine may thus be regarded as a modified epinephrine which retains some of the hormonal activities, and which has acquired new ones because of its resistance to enzymic destruction and ability to pass into the nervous system.

Amphetamine was among the first synthetic chemicals to be used to combat depression. It will successfully overcome simple depressions in some people (259). However, it can lead to excitement, agitation, and sleeplessness, and patients usually develop a tolerance to it so that the dose must be raised as time goes on. Furthermore, its prolonged use can cause paranoid delusions and other signs of mental disease as was mentioned in Chapter 8. These properties detract from its clinical usefulness, and although it is still used, it is not a satisfactory drug for the control of depression. Because it inhibits monoamine oxidase as well as exerting some of the actions of the epinephrines it is not easy to judge the exact reason for its effects. The net result of either action would be to provide excess epinephrines, but it might also increase other hormonal amines such as serotonin. In experimental animals it has been found to do so (294).

B. *Marsilid* or iproniazid has been described in Chapter 6 and its chemical structure was shown in Figure 12 of that chapter. The relief of mild depressions and the elevation of mood which it causes are well established. Simple depressions in many patients can be relieved by it (258). The psychotic depressions such as the ones found in schizophrenia, either do not respond to it favorably, or are actually made worse.

Despite these favorable findings, Marsilid has almost passed out of clinical use. In some patients it causes severe damage of the liver which may even be fatal. Like other inhibitors of monoamine oxidase, Marsilid often gives rise to orthostatic hypotension which may be accompanied by fainting spells.

Many drugs which inhibit monoamine oxidase and thereby increase the content of serotonin, the epinephrines, and other amines in the tissues are being tested for ability to control depressions. As mentioned above, this is being done because it was recognized that the action of Marsilid on the mind was due largely to its ability to inhibit the enzyme and cause increases in these hormones. Because Marsilid is a hydrazine derivative, many other such derivatives have been tested. A comprehensive description of many of the findings has been published as a symposium (258). The hope of these studies is to find a more active drug which will lack the undesirable toxic actions of Marsilid. Although nialamide (a Marsilid congener) and JB-516,

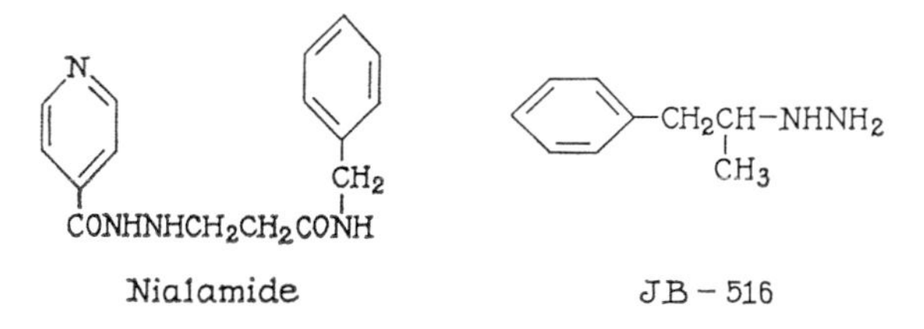

FIG. 2. *Structures of some inhibitors of monoamine oxidase which have given favorable clinical results in some depressed patients.*

the structures of which are given in Figure 2, have shown promise, it is yet too early to say whether they will be of lasting help in the treatment of non-psychotic depressions.

C. ***Imipramine*** (Tofranil) differs from the preceding antidepressant drugs in that it does not inhibit monamine oxidase. Its psychiatric effects can thus not be ascribed to an increase in serotonin and the catechol amines brought about in this fashion. The reasons for its effect on mood are not yet understood. This drug has not been used long enough to allow adequate evaluation of its usefulness, but the findings up to the present show clearly that it can relieve some depressions (259). Preliminary evidence suggests that it may prove to be a most valuable drug.

The structures of imipramine and of chlorpromazine are shown in Figure 3. The relationship is clear. The S atom of chlorpromazine has been replaced by two C atoms in imipramine. Although chlorpromazine brings about tranquilization and changes in mood in the direction of depression, imipramine causes, in the main, an opposite effect. It stimulates. The exchange of a sulfur atom for two carbon

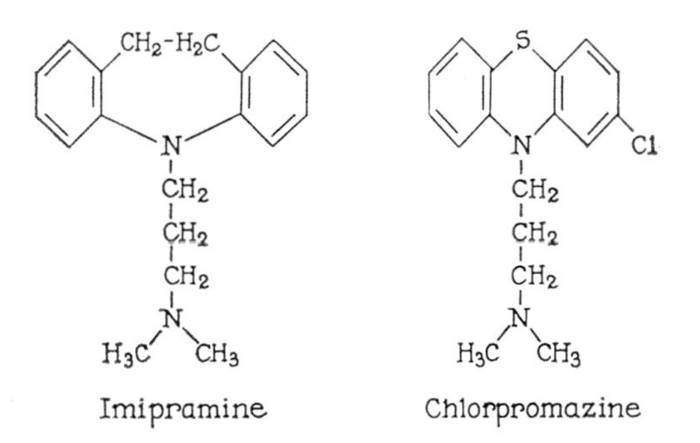

FIG. 3. *Relation in structure of imipramine and chlorpromazine.*

atoms in a ring system is a well-known method for converting essential metabolites into antimetabolites. For example, this is the change involved in passing from thiamine to pyrithiamine (see chapter 3). The opposite kinds of action of chlorpromazine and imipramine on the mind take on new interest in light of this fact and might even suggest that an essential metabolite related in structure to both of these drugs is yet to be found in the brain.

Imipramine does have some sort of pharmacological relationship to serotonin, but whether this is of any importance to explain its action on mood is unknown. Thus either chlorpromazine or imipramine can antagonize the action of serotonin in bringing about increased permeability of blood capillaries in the rat's paw (394). Of the two drugs, chlorpromazine is the more potent in this particular test.

Effectiveness of existing drugs. Neither the tranquilizers for the control of agitation nor the drugs for the treatment of depression are able to cure most cases of mental disease. Tranquilizers such as chlorpromazine can help a patient through a period of mania or hysteria. Sometimes a patient suffering from the agitation or the anxiety of schizophrenia can be calmed with one of these drugs, and can slowly find an adjustment to society great enough that he can live in the community adequately. Many schizophrenic persons, however, end up in mental hospitals for long periods despite the use of these substances. In the mental hospitals these drugs, especially chlorpromazine, make possible much less assaultive and agitated behavior. The patients are thus easier to control, but they remain mentally defective.

The drugs for treatment of depression seem able to benefit many cases of depression, but seem usually to fail in the severe psychotic depressions. They may even make worse such a severe depression.

An appraisal of the effectiveness of existing drugs thus indicates that a large area of mental disease remains in which chemotherapy is of limited value, or of no value at all. Nevertheless, the existing drugs are of considerable benefit to many patients, particularly those in whom the mental defect is not too far advanced. Rees (259) has recently compared the effectiveness of antidepressant drugs with electric shock therapy. His conclusion was that the shock therapy was superior in results to the use of these agents. However, the frequent failure of electric shock therapy for depressions is well known.

Relationship of the serotonin hypothesis to the designing of new drugs. The serotonin hypothesis of mental diseases allows prediction of the chemical structures of drugs which may prove useful in the chemotherapy of these diseases. The rationale is as follows. Suppose that the agitation of schizophrenia and of manic depressive psychosis arises from an excess of cerebral serotonin and related changes in norepinephrine and the other hormones. Suppose that the depressions of these diseases are connected with a deficiency of serotonin. It might be possible to relieve the agitation by use of a specific drug designed to counteract the excess serotonin. It might be possible to combat the depression with a drug designed to increase cerebral serotonin specifically.

Several biochemical reactions are known, each of which plays a role in the control of the serotonin content of the brain. There are thus several ways open to manipulation. At least three means are available: (*a*) the production of serotonin can be increased or decreased; (*b*) the rate of destruction can be changed; (*c*) the utilization can be changed by affecting the receptors. This is what an antimetabolite does. One might even suppress the synthesis of the serotonin receptors. The result of a deficiency of receptors so induced would be similar to that of a lack of the hormone. The aim should be to produce therapeutic agents designed to change the functioning serotonin in any one of the three ways mentioned above.

The biological results to be achieved by changes in each of these three factors will not be the same, but they may be similar. Thus, suppose that the biosynthesis of serotonin were to be inhibited by administration of an inhibitor of the decarboxylase. Such inhibitors are known, as, for example, phenylpyruvic or phenyllactic acids. The inhibition of this enzyme brings about a reduction in the amount of serotonin, but is this the same effect to be expected from the use of an antimetabolite of serotonin? The answer is, probably not. The antimetabolite blocks the receptor and thereby creates a specific deficiency in the functioning of the hormone. Because the inhibition of the decarboxylase results not only in a failure to produce serotonin but also in a failure to produce dopamine (and consequently the epinephrines), the result of the inhibition is complex. It reduces not only serotonin but norepinephrine, epinephrine and dopamine. The net effect on the brain may, thus, not be the same as is achieved by specific blocking of the serotonin receptor with an antimetabolite which does not interfere with the activities of the epinephrines.

Consider also the increase in serotonin content of the brain brought about by a drug which inhibits monoamine oxidase. Inhibition of this enzyme brings about a simultaneous increase in the epinephrines. The effects on the brain of such a drug may, therefore, not be identical with those achieved by increases in serotonin only, which can be brought about by administration of 5-hydroxytryptophan. One can see similarities in the behavioral changes in animals subjected to these two different ways of increasing brain serotonin. They both result in excitement. Nevertheless, one sees also differences in the behavioral changes produced.

Because there is this interlocking of events, one has available a variety of avenues of approach to the chemotherapeutic problem. Up to the present time only two of these have been explored at all. These are the increase in brain serotonin which can be brought about specifically by 5-hydroxytryptophan, and less specifically by an inhibitor of monoamine oxidase. Of these, the latter, less specific way, has been the only one to receive anything like intensive study. One may object that the use of monoamine oxidase inhibitors has given drugs which will combat simple depressions, but which fail in the depressions of schizophrenia. Consequently one might argue that increases in brain serotonin do not control these psychoses. All that they do is influence a mild disorder of the mind. For this reason it is regrettable that so little has been done with the more specific method (the 5-hydroxytryptophan method) for the increase in brain serotonin. It is entirely possible that the increases in compounds other than serotonin which follow the administration of monoamine oxidase inhibitors influence the response of patients with psychotic depressions. There is also the problem of established mental habit in psychoses which will be discussed in a later section of this chapter.

Another way for combatting depressions is to design compounds so that they will have a serotonin-like action on the brain, but unlike serotonin itself will be able to penetrate into the brain from the periphery. This would be a kind of replacement therapy familiar in other hormonal deficiencies of the periphery. Such serotonin-like compounds could be administered orally and would be expected to overcome depression. The kinds of structural change which allow serotonin relatives to pass freely from the blood into the brain have been discussed in Chapter 6, and will be mentioned again below. However, the problem of penetration into the brain is not the only one which must receive attention in the design of chemotherapeutic agents with serotonin-like activity. The hormone performs its physiological function by acting and then by being destroyed in the field of action.

Therapeutic agents designed to exert serotonin-like action must also be designed so that they can be removed readily at the proper time by the enzymes provided for this purpose in the body. This presents some difficulty in design because the feature which allows penetration in a compound like bufotenine is also a feature which interferes with the rapid removal by means of monoamine oxidase. Perhaps one way to avoid this difficulty is to use derivatives with serotonin-like action which are not subject to attack by monoamine oxidase but which can be readily removed by other means, as, for example, by enzymes which attack the indole ring.

Turning now from drugs to increase serotonin and thus to combat depression to those for combatting agitation, we see that if one supposes that agitation in its various forms is connected with excess cerebral serotonin, this excess could be combatted in two ways: (*a*) the rate of destruction of the hormone could be increased; or (*b*) the receptors could be blocked with an antimetabolite. If the antimetabolite method is to be tried, much attention must be given to the formation of an analog which acts only as an antagonist. If it can also act like serotonin with some cerebral receptors, as lysergic acid diethylamide or harmine or medmain can (see Chapter 6), then the drug may well induce rather than prevent the mental difficulties. The designing of a drug to avoid serotonin-like action is thus of importance.

Assays have been developed which can indicate whether a given serotonin analog shows serotonin-like actions (133). The clam heart assay is particularly good to give indication of such action, whereas that involving the rat uterus or rat stomach is not. The blood pressure response in dogs, and the contractions of isolated oligodendroglia of the brain are also useful tests for detection of serotonin-like action. The oligodendroglial test is particularly good for indicating a serotonin-like action on tissues of the central nervous system. The data of Table 1 show how small changes in the structure of a single antimetabolite of serotonin can alter its serotonin-like activity as well as its antimetabolite potency. The compounds shown in this table were designed so that they would be excluded from the brain but they can be made to penetrate into that organ by methylation of the primary amino groups. The data of this table were taken from the paper of Woolley (133).

The design of any drug for the control of any mental disorder must take into account the problem of getting the drug from the periphery into the brain, and of proper distribution in the various parts of the brain. This is the case whether one is dealing with an antimetabolite, or with an inhibitor of amine oxidase, or of the decarboxylase, or of one of the other enzymes which inactivate serotonin. It is also true of any serotonin-like compound which might be administered with the idea of combatting a deficiency by replacement therapy. The chemicals must be designed so that they can reach the susceptible tis-

TABLE 1. *Serotonin-like and antiserotonin activities of some 1-benzyl-2-methyl tryptamines*

Compound Number	Additional Substituents	Antiserotonin Activity: Rat Uterus,* μg per ml	Antiserotonin Activity: Mouse Assay,† μg per mouse	Serotonin-Like Activity,‡ per cent
	5-Methoxy (or BAS)	0.2	250	3.0
	5-Hydroxy (or BAS-phenol)	—	50	0.3 §
(I)	1′:10′-Decamethylenebis-(5-oxy)	0.5	—	
(II)	5-(β-Aminoethoxy)	0.1	100	0.1 §
(III)	N-*Iso*Indoline-5-(β-amino-ethoxy)	0.5	75	0.05 ‖
(IV)	5-Oxyacethydrazide	0.05	10	less than 0.04 ¶
(V)	5-Benzyloxy	0.4	—	0.2–1.0 **
(VI)	5-(*p*-Methoxybenzyloxy)	0.02	5	1.0

* Expressed as the amount required to cause half-maximal inhibition of a contraction elicited by an amount of serotonin just sufficient to cause maximal contraction. All values were in direct comparison with the standard analog (BAS) as explained in the text.

† Amount required to protect half of the mice against diarrhea induced by 1 mg 5-hydroxytryptophan per mouse.

‡ Expressed as percentage of the activity of serotonin creatinine sulphate in causing increased amplitude of beat of clam hearts. Thus, 1 per cent means that 100μg of analog caused the same response as 1 μg of serotonin creatinine sulphate.

§ Dose-response curve less steep than for serotonin.

‖ The analog decreased the base beat in two of five hearts (anti-activity?). In one of five no detectable serotonin-like or antiserotonin action.

¶ Detectable serotonin-like activity in only one of five hearts.

** Considerable variation from heart to heart; almost inactive for some.

sues. For analogs of serotonin this means that the primary amino group must be protected against destruction by amine oxidase. One can do this by converting the amino group into a dimethylamino group, but such compounds suffer from the defect that they are sometimes rapidly excreted by the kidneys. The use of more complicated alkyl groups, as, for example, the incorporation of the amino group into a heterocyclic ring system is a more promising approach. Furthermore, the phenolic hydroxyl group of serotonin must be protected in such a way as to escape oxidation and sulfation. One way to do this is to convert it to an ether. Recent studies have shown that the nature of this ether grouping which is introduced can greatly affect both potency and serotonin-like activity (133). Data to illustrate this point are shown in Table 1.

A variety of ways are known for changing the structure of serotonin or other hormones in such a way that an antimetabolite antagonistic to the hormone can be realized. These include alterations in the ring system and changes in the substituents attached to the ring. In the case of serotonin, changes in the ring have proved to be less effective than changes in the substituents. The general rules which have been developed for making antimetabolites are discussed in some detail in the monograph on antimetabolites (1). This monograph also tells about some of the structural features which can be introduced into a molecule to render it capable of being anchored more or less irreversibly to certain tissues. Such ability to be retained in tissues is an important property of many useful therapeutic agents. Consequently, designers of such agents for use in psychiatric difficulties also pay attention to this property.

Plan of attack. Chemotherapeutic efforts based on the serotonin hypothesis might profitably be directed at the following approaches.

a. Antimetabolites of serotonin with no serotonin-like action should be made. They should be capable of entering readily all parts of the brain from the blood stream. Successful antimetabolites of this kind would be expected to reduce agitation, including hallucinations and delusions, hysteria and flights of ideas. They might well prove to induce depression, and might require rigid control of dosage to avoid this.

b. Inhibitors of the 5-hydroxytryptophan decarboxylase should be sought which will penetrate from the blood into the brain. These inhibitors would be expected to decrease production of serotonin and catechol amines in the brain, and might control agitation. Phenylpyruvic acid and phenyllactic acid are already known, and other suitable antimetabolites of either 5-hydroxytryptophan or of dopa might be expected to do this. Such an antimetabolite, viz., α-methyldopa (α-methyl-3,4-dihydroxyphenylalanine) has recently been described (395). In dogs this compound brought about some sedation and reduced the serotonin content of the brain. It has been used in human beings suffering from hypertension, but its action in agitated mental patients has not yet been described. Its potency is not as great as might be desired, so that more active compounds are needed. Perhaps the α-methyl-5-hydroxytryptophan might be more potent but the cost of its production would be very high.

The decarboxylase can be inhibited in other ways than by use of an analog of its substrates. The enzyme contains pyridoxal phosphate as coenzyme. If an antimetabolite of this coenzyme could be found which had a much greater affinity for this particular decarboxylase than for other pyridoxal-containing enzymes it might prove satisfactory for reduction of serotonin content of the brain. Any specific inhibitor for this decarboxylase might prove to be useful for reduction of serotonin content of tissues. It need not be an antimetabolite of anything. Nevertheless, because pyridoxal phosphate is the coenzyme of a large number of enzymes both in the brain and in the periphery, it will be necessary to find inhibitors which will more or less specifically retard the action of this decarboxylase only, if the necessary selective action is to be achieved.

c. Inhibitors of monoamine oxidase should be sought which will increase cerebral serotonin. This aspect of chemotherapy is now well under way. Not only have various substituted hydrazines been found such as Marsilid and JB-516, but analogs of serotonin are also being tested. One of these, viz., indole-3-isopropylamine or α-methyltryptamine, has shown considerable promise in clinical trials. This compound is not a hydrazine and thus avoids the toxicity which many hydrazines show. It is entirely conceivable that an inhibitor of monoamine oxidase akin to this one might inhibit the enzyme principally when it is acting on serotonin, and less when it is acting on the epinephrines. One might thus achieve a specific increase in serotonin without concomitant increases in the other amines, and thus be able to shed much light on the role of serotonin per se in depressions.

d. The serotonin receptors might be modified by means other than an antimetabolite of the hormone so that they would no longer react with serotonin. The net result would be to induce a deficiency of serotonin. Existing information suggests that chlorpromazine acts partly in this way. A knowledge of the chemical structures of these receptors (which is just now being found) might make possible the design of much better agents of this kind.

e. The reactions leading to the formation of serotonin can be controlled before the stage of the decarboxylase. Thus, the hydroxylase which converts tryptophan to 5-hydroxytryptophan might be inhibited. The results of such an inhibition would be similar to those of inhibition of the decarboxylase. In like fashion serotonin content of tissues might be raised not only by inhibition of monoamine oxidase, but also by stimulation of the hydroxylases or inhibition of the oxidases which attack the indole ring, as described in Chapter 4.

f. To those who understand the biochemical origins and fate of serotonin, other points will be evident in the reaction sequences at which controlling drugs might be directed. Similarly those who explore and understand the interplay of acetylcholine, the epinephrines and serotonin will be able to devise drugs which affect the mind. They may be able to realize therapeutically useful agents. Thus, in general, antimetabolites of acetylcholine or norepinephrine-like substances might be expected to dispel depressions in accordance with the principles discussed in Chapter 9.

In following these plans of attack, one must remember that they are based partly on the idea that depression arises from deficiency and excitement from excess of serotonin. We have seen earlier that this is a first approximation to the truth but is not established firmly. Because of this, one must keep in mind the alternative possibility and must not be too surprised if a pure antimetabolite (one without any serotonin-like action) were to cause excitement or a serotonin-like analog were to induce depression. These possibilities will be readily detected in the course of the biological testing.

Designing selective action. Any drug designed to induce an effect on cerebral serotonin (or on cerebral acetylcholine or norepinephrine for that matter) should be constructed with the idea of having it show maximal selective action. It should exert the largest possible effect in the brain and the least possible in the periphery. Even in the brain it might be desirable for it to select certain regions (e.g., the hypothalamus or the hippocampus or the pineal body) and act on those in preference to certain others. Thus, if one wished to produce a drug with serotonin-like actions aimed at controlling depressions it would be necessary to remember that such a drug would probably also cause serotonin-like responses in the smooth muscles of blood vessels, intestines, heart, and other peripheral organs. Many of these responses might be undesirable. Consequently, it is necessary to design the drug so that these peripheral effects are reduced or eliminated. Similarly, if one wished to form an antagonist of serotonin for the control of agitation it would be advantageous to have it affect, more or less selectively, the cerebral receptors in preference to those in the periphery. It is not beyond the range of possibility to build into a molecule some of these features. There is already some knowledge of how to proceed.

Any drug for the control of cerebral processes must be administered orally or subcutaneously but at least through the periphery. It must pass through the periphery to reach the brain. One must, therefore, attempt to prevent or eliminate its pharmacological effects on the peripheral organs. In the case of antiserotonins designed to combat peripheral excesses of the hormone, the problem is simpler. It is only necessary to confine the drug to the periphery and to exclude it from the central nervous system. This has actually been done. The antiserotonin 1-benzyl-2-methyl-5-methoxytryptamine or BAS (109) which is useful in the treatment of hypertension as described in Chapter 6 was designed so that it affected the brain very little but did act in the periphery. Another example is the antimetabolites of acetylcholine which because of their quaternary N atom or for other reasons are confined to the periphery. To have a drug excluded from the central nervous system and yet to act in the periphery is thus possible. It is more difficult to design one to act on the central nervous system and not on the periphery because it must pass through the periphery to reach the brain.

Two general strategies can be applied to this problem. Let us illustrate them with drugs which have a serotonin-like effect, but let us bear in mind that similar principles are applicable to other kinds of drugs. The first strategy is to attempt to make the drug so that it will have little if any affinity for peripheral receptors but will have good affinity for cerebral receptors. The inadequacies in the present experimental procedures for measurement of affinities for the cerebral receptors have been largely responsible for the lack of information about compounds which show such selective affinity. Nevertheless, there is reason to believe that lysergic acid diethylamide may have greater affinity for some cerebral receptors than for some peripheral ones. Quantities which affect thought and behavior in men and animals are insufficient to affect the serotonin responses in peripheral tissues such as blood vessels or intestines. It should be possible eventually to measure such differences in affinity for cerebral and peripheral receptors and to learn to design serotonin-like compounds more reactive with the cerebral ones.

Another way to see that such selective action may be possible is to remember that in peripheral tissues examples of such selective action are already known. Thus, as described in Chapters 3 and 4, medmain has serotonin-like action on the uterus but not on the muscles of blood vessels, and tryptamine has greater serotonin-like action on blood vessels than it does on stomach.

The second strategy for bringing about selectively a serotonin-like action in the brain is to protect the peripheral receptors with an antimetabolite of serotonin which does not enter the brain and then to increase the hormone everywhere. If serotonin in all tissues is increased (by administration of 5-hydroxytryptophan, for example) the excess in the peripheral tissues is prevented from acting by the antimetabolite there. The excess in the brain, however, is free to exert its biological effect. In this way a selective increase in the functioning hormone in the brain can be accomplished. This method (77) was discussed in Chapter 6 and data to illustrate the selective action were given in Table 5 of that chapter. Obviously, one can use drugs other than hydroxytryptophan with serotonin-like actions capable of penetrating into the brain and may be able by suitable choice of antimetabolite and serotonin-like compound to design a combination which may have clinical usefulness.

The periphery and the central nervous system are not as isolated from each other as one might be led to believe from the foregoing discussion. It is useful to separate them for clarity of thinking but it must not be forgotten that the brain is receiving all kinds of sensory stimuli from the periphery and is sending out constantly all sorts of stimuli to it. To illustrate how much of the activities of mind can be influenced by effects of drugs in the periphery, the following unpublished experiment is quoted. The speed with which mice learn to find their way unerringly through a simple maze can be measured and expressed as the percentage of correct turns which the animals make after any stated period of learning. Thus, when they were allowed 5 minutes to learn the correct way they made the correct turn in 90 per cent of the attempts. When they were allowed only 1 minute to learn, they made the correct turn in 75 per cent. When they were allowed no learning time, they made the correct turn 50 per cent of the time because, if the choice depended on chance alone, they made the correct turn in half the attempts and the incorrect one in the other half. Suppose that the learning time is restricted to one minute and that the mice are treated in various ways to change the serotonin contents of their brains and that their ability to learn their lesson is then measured as described. When 5-hydroxytryptophan (10 mg per kg body weight) was injected intraperitoneally the serotonin content of all tissues was increased. The learning ability was not changed as can be seen from the data in Table 2. When BAS (10 mg per kg) was given intraperitoneally to another group of mice their learning

TABLE 2. *Learning abilities of mice as influenced by changes in functional serotonin in the brain and in the body as a whole*

BAS, mg per kg	5-Hydroxy-tryptophan, mg per kg	Learning Score *
0	0	75
10	0	76
0	10	75
10	10	51

* The learning score was the average of a group of mice. Each group contained twelve to forty-two individuals.

ability was also not changed. However, when BAS and then 5-hydroxytryptophan were both given and the functioning serotonin was increased only in the brain, the learning ability was greatly reduced. Such experiments indicate that events relative to serotonin in the periphery can influence the mental powers of animals and may suggest that although specific increases of the hormone in the brain are one aim of chemotherapeutic experiments, the path in this direction is not to be considered free of effects in the periphery.

Irrespective of the interplay between the peripheral organs and the central nervous system, it is useful to give attention to the problems of selectivity of action of the drugs one designs. Without selectivity the drug may so alter the whole economy of the individual that it may be unusable for the treatment of mental disorders.

Methods of testing. The only adequate test of a chemotherapeutic agent for the control of mental disease is to use the drug in human patients suffering from the disease and to find that it controls it. No amount of laboratory experimentation, no matter how ingenious, can substitute for the clinical demonstration. This is not to say that trials in laboratory animals are not useful. They can often give valuable information about effects of a drug on various aspects of behavior, and they are absolutely indispensable to show whether or not the drug is so toxic that it cannot be used in clinical trial. However, the effects of a chemical substance on behavior of laboratory animals are not always certain guides as to what will be the effects in human beings. Species differ in responses to chemical agents possibly because of the relative importance of a given biochemical reaction in the organization of the control mechanisms in the whole animal. Many tests with laboratory animals have been devised which are believed to measure such psychological factors as anxiety or pleasure. These are sometimes used to evaluate drugs in the belief that the stress factor, which contributes to the development of human psychoses is composed primarily of anxiety or of the lack of pleasure. Psychology, despite its hypotheses of the relationship of anxiety and tensions and memories of childhood to the induction of mental diseases, is not yet able to predict whether the reduction of an anxiety by a drug will invariably make a schizophrenic patient better. It is not even possible to show without question that a drug has reduced or abolished anxiety. We are consequently left with the only true test, viz., the trial on patients suffering from the disease.

The evaluation of the results of a clinical trial is very difficult. In the first place, one cannot be sure that each one of a group of patients diagnosed as having schizophrenia actually has the same disease. Patient A may be suffering from an excess of cerebral serotonin, whereas patient B may have too little acetylcholine or norepinephrine. Both may exhibit a similar type of abnormal behavior. The best that can be done in the designing of a clinical trial is to select a group of patients in which the symptomatology is similar, and to select a group large enough to increase the probability of inclusion of several individuals with the same disease.

Because the difference between normal and abnormal is so difficult to define and to measure, the decision as to whether a given individual has improved under administration of a drug is open to much question. It is not easy to tell whether a schizophrenic patient has grown better or worse or has not changed. The increased interest taken by the nursing staff, or even by the experimenter may be communicated to the patient, and may influence his behavior aside from any effect of the drug which is being tested.

One way to reduce these psychological influences on the patient as well as the experimenter, is to use the so-called double blind procedure. Only some of the patients receive the drug. The others are given seemingly identical pills or injections which contain no drug. No one knows which is placebo and which is drug except a clerk, who does not participate in the administration or the evaluation of the responses. The materials being used are identified only by code numbers, and the code is not revealed until the clinical evaluation has been made. Most clinical testing now being carried out is not conducted under these conditions. In fact, rarely is a double blind study done. Usually everyone, including the patients, knows when a drug is being tested.

The importance of habits of thinking must not be overlooked in the testing of drugs on mental patients. A person develops certain mental habits just as he does other kinds of habits. These may take much time and training to change. A drug may correct the biochemical defect which has given rise to a mental disorder, but it may take time and considerable education to bring the patient back to normal. This is a point not always or even often appreciated by those who carry out clinical trials with drugs. Perhaps the desire to see immediate responses, as when a raving maniac is tranquilized with chlorpromazine, pushes into the background the knowledge that much of the mental insufficiency is still there. By concentration on achievement of these rapid responses another important aspect of the problem may be pushed aside. How important this aspect of established habit is is not known. It may be that there are drugs to be found which will eradicate schizophrenia as rapidly as nicotinic acid eradicates the mental defect of a pellagrin, but it may also be that all that can be hoped for is the suppression of the gross behavioral abnormalities. The restoration of the contact with reality may then slowly bring about normality.

Testing methods in laboratory animals. Because clinical testing is slow, very expensive, uncertain in interpretation and restricted by the ever present need of not doing harm to the patient, preliminary information is obtained from experiments in laboratory animals. The kinds of testing fall into three main groups: (*a*) direct alteration of behavior; (*b*) antagonism of a behavioral change brought about by a psychotomimetic drug; and (*c*) use of responses based on a psychological hypothesis about the causation of psychoses and neuroses. In addition to these behavioral assays just mentioned there are many tests which do not undertake to assess behavior at all. Thus, inhibitors of monoamine oxidase are tested first on the enzyme itself outside the living animal to determine whether or not they are good inhibitors. Antimetabolites of serotonin are tested first on isolated smooth muscles for ability to antagonize serotonin-induced contractions, and for ability to act like serotonin in causing contractions. The most active compounds are next taken through the behavioral tests in living animals.

A. *Direct alteration of behavior.* Several of the tests used to determine the effects of a chemical substance on the behavior of an animal have already been described in this book. The walking backwards with attendant signs of anxiety seen in mice injected with lysergic acid diethylamide (LSD), the changes induced in fighting fish by LSD, the changes in rope climbing abilities of rats given LSD, the abnormal behavior of dogs given harmine, the tranquilization of monkeys given reserpine or chlorpromazine, and several other tests have been described. Some investigators have used such simple procedures as measurement of the amount of movement of an animal before and after administration of a compound. Although this can be done by a robot, and consequently requires little attention, it seems questionable whether such tests can tell much of value for the purpose at hand. They are said to give a measure of agitation (and conversely of sedation). Often much can be learned, however, by careful observation of the effects of a drug on the manifold kinds of behavior of an animal if some imagination is also used to relate the changes seen to the responses of the same animal under a variety of natural stresses. Too much mechanization of the tests can be misleading even though it may give a long series of numbers which can be tabulated in a publication.

For studies of tranquilizing drugs the use of excitable wild animals caged in the laboratory may be helpful. A monkey or a wolverine can be calmed down to a docile state rather dramatically by some of these compounds. Librium and reserpine were found at least in part by the use of such tests.

The variety of tests which may be devised is very great. The validity of the information which each yields for the purpose of evaluation of drugs for use in mental disturbances of man is uncertain. They do give useful information, which if not taken too seriously, can be valuable.

B. *Alteration of drug-induced behavioral changes.* In this type of test a behavioral change is induced in an animal by the use of a psychotomimetic drug which is known to call forth in man some of the signs of a mental disease. Various chemical substances are then tested for ability to overcome this behavioral change. Some of these tests have already been described, such as the one in which the rope climbing ability of a rat is impaired by administration of LSD, and this effect is then overcome by adrenal steroid hormones (285). Another is the reversal of the walking backwards of LSD-treated mice when serotonin and carbamylcholine are injected intracerebrally (210). Another example is a test in which animals are first tranquilized with reserpine and then this tranquilization is overcome and agitated behavior produced by administration of an inhibitor of monoamine oxidase such as Marsilid. Obviously a great number of such tests can be readily imagined and many have been used.

Tests of this sort have been used more for exploration of the biochemical bases of psychoses (or at least of behavior) than for efforts directed at chemotherapy of mental diseases. The reason for this is obvious.

C. *Alteration of conditioned responses involving a psychological theory of mental disease.* The idea in this third class of test is to induce in an animal a state of mind which psychological hypothesis says may be the cause of human mental diseases. One then measures the effects of various chemical substances on this state of mind. One judges the state of mind of the animal by certain kinds of conditioned behavior. Many of these tests are based on the psychological hypothesis that anxiety in sufficient amount can cause mental failure, and that it may be a principal reason for the common human mental diseases. Some rely on measurement of the ability of an animal to learn a lesson for which the reward is food or pleasure.

In some of the early tests of this kind, animals (dogs or sheep) were driven into neurosis and finally into psychosis by being conditioned to respond to two different signals, and then to have the difference in the signals gradually reduced until they experienced increasing difficulty in telling them apart. This was the Pavlovian method of producing experimental psychoses. One could then determine the effectiveness of a drug in prevention of the development of the psychosis, or could attempt to cure it. The practical shortcoming of this test was the difficulty of producing the psychoses. Much time was required, and all animals did not develop a psychosis.

During the past ten years a different technique has attracted widespread attention. This is the so-called operant conditioning or Skinner box technique (396, 397, and 398). An animal is trained to press a lever or to do some other task for which it receives a reward to inspire it to learn the task properly. Thus it must learn that it must press a lever fifty times and it will be presented with the reward, or it must learn that it must wait for 5 minutes and then press the lever once to get the reward. If it does not wait for 5 minutes, it does not get the reward. When the animal has been so conditioned or trained some new influence is introduced to distract from the learned lesson. Thus a noise may be sounded as a signal that a painful electric shock is about to be applied to the feet. This additional conditioning soon produces an emotional reaction when the signal is sounded. The various aspects of the conditioning can be changed by administration of drugs such as tranquilizers or excitants of the central nervous system.

One of the advantages of the operant conditioning technique is that it makes possible the separation of several of the factors which enter into ability to learn and into emotional responses. It thus becomes possible to measure individual changes in the psychology of the animal rather than to make a judgment of any change produced merely from the total behavior of the animal.

Many variations of the design of the apparatus are used, and also in the interpretation of what is being measured. Very often the animal is not trained by means of a reward; instead, it is trained to perform the task in order to avoid some disagreeable sensation. This is known as avoidance conditioning. For example, a rat may be placed in a box in which the floor consists of metal wires. These can be electrified at intervals and simultaneously a buzzer is sounded. The box contains a pole or a shelf which is not electrified. The rat soon learns that it can avoid the painful sensation by jumping onto the pole or shelf when the buzzer sounds. It is thus conditioned to jump at the sound of the buzzer. By use of two different kinds of signals, the rat can also be conditioned to know that the first signal will cause no painful stimulus but that the second one will unless it jumps to safety. The interval between signals and especially the interval after the second signal is supposed to be a period of anxiety to the rat. Various kinds of drugs are tested with such an apparatus and technique to determine whether they will lengthen the time period before the jump (399 and 400). With variations of this technique some sort of measure is made of the effect of a drug in bringing about reduction of anxiety. It is plain that one must believe the psychological hypothesis about the relationship of the action of the rat to its anxiety and the relationship of anxiety to schizophrenia before one can use the answers from such tests in selecting suitable therapeutic agents for human use. Despite these uncertainties, however, such tests frequently give clues about promising drugs.

The place of chemotherapy. There are several indications that an era of chemotherapy of mental diseases is upon us. More and more people both in and out of mental hospitals are being treated with tranquilizing drugs and "psychic energizers" for the control of agitation or depression or the relief of tension. It does not matter whether or not the existing drugs are effective in the treatment of schizophrenia and manic depressive psychosis and involutionary melancholia. They are effective enough against undesirable mental aberrations that there are going to be more of these chemical agents.[e] The non-psychotic population may turn more and more to some of these compounds for relief or escape from the manifold and increasing pressures of society. Are we then eventually going to see a country or a world in which most of the people will be avoiding mental collapse by taking some drug, or who are being maintained after a mental collapse by such materials? The tranquilizing drug "soma" imagined by Aldous Huxley in "Brave New World" may materialize as the new "opiate of the mass" of humanity. It is equally conceivable that sensible use will be made of the inevitable discoveries. The present author believes that a sensible use might be something of the following kind. If the serotonin hypothesis of mental diseases is valid, or approximately so, there are many reasons to believe that really effective drugs will soon come forth from it for the control of some of the major mental diseases.

Many of the inborn errors of metabolism which lead to idiocy early in life will probably be controlled as phenylketonuria and galactosemia are now being controlled. The metabolic error will be identified and the deficiency made good either by dietary control or by the use of some specific drug to prevent the harmful effects of the products which accumulate as a result of the metabolic error. Chemical procedures of these kinds would seem to be the only available way to control these disorders. It would seem totally unrealistic to suppose that by detection of all the carriers, and prevention of their mating with each other, the diseases could be eliminated at the source by eugenic means.

If we turn now from these diseases (in which mental failure is inevitable unless something chemical is done) to schizophrenia and manic depressive psychosis we see that although there may be a predisposing genetic basis in the latter, the disorders arise in adult life in the less resistant individuals partly as a result of environmental factors such as emotional stress. It may be possible to increase their resistance by drug therapy but it may be possible also to change so-

[e] It is futile to think that they can be controlled by legislative enactments. The experience with opium and hashish and ethyl alcohol shows clearly that legislation cannot withstand the demand once the information has been broadcast about the existence of drugs which change the mind in some sought-after way. It is true that drugs such as those just mentioned, which are made from plant sources, are more readily obtainable than the complicated synthetic chemicals which are now being discovered. Nevertheless, the syntheses will be done regardless of their complexity and almost despite legislative edicts if the mental effect produced is one in great demand.

ciety enough to reduce the stress. The sensible thing to do would seem to be to reduce the stress so that the risk to all is diminished, and to save the chemotherapy for those accidents in which a few individuals do actually develop the mental diseases. This would seem much more sensible than any plan to aim only at treating the cases as they come in, and to do nothing about the contributing environmental causes.

The situation is analogous to that with respect to infectious diseases. Take the case of typhoid fever or cholera. There are now adequate chemotherapeutic ways of treating either of these diseases. One could argue that the only thing to do is to treat the cases as they come in with the effective drugs. Everyone knows, however, that the way to deal with these diseases is to clean up the environment, specifically the food and water supplies. Occasionally one encounters cases despite the cleaning up of the environment. For these cases the chemotherapeutic agents are on hand. There are in addition means of immunizing people against many infectious diseases so that if their exposure to risk of infection is to be unusually high they can take specific steps to protect themselves. Examples of this kind could be multiplied to include most of the infectious diseases. It would seem to be a wise precedent to follow with respect to mental disorders as well.

Some may ask if there is any known way of cleaning up the environment with respect to mental diseases. Most certainly much is known about this. It is just that although it is known it is not widely known, and not widely practiced. The teachings of religion and philosophy tell much that has been learned about the subject in the past several thousand years of trial and error and keen observation. If society chooses to disregard some of these precepts because it thinks that they are outmoded, the result can be similar to what might happen if society decided that chlorination and filtration of the water supply are old-fashioned and of no account.

The sociological adjustment which is desirable requires no political action. In fact, participation in political activity (going to meetings, organizing committees, engendering hate for the opposing view, etc., etc.) may for many individuals be a contributing factor in what seems to be wrong. However, this book is not intended as a treatise on sociology. Some of the fundamentals about what is wrong can be found in non-technical language in Ellis' book, *How to Live with a Neurotic* (401). Society has become so organized and so complicated that a vast amount of nervous energy is expended in order to comply with the numerous dictates of fashion and usage and to succeed economically and socially. The load is too great for an increasing number of people. This is especially true when one reflects on the fact that many of the things which people strive for with great expenditure of energy, as, for example, "keeping up with the Joneses," are of questionable value aside from the establishment of a spurious prestige. The simple and direct dealing with situations as they arise has given way to all sorts of cultivations of subtle innuendos and subterfuges, not to mention the organized fashioning of various kinds of hate. All of these put strains on the emotions and an increasing number of people fail to withstand the pressures. There are plenty of maxims which tell us how to deal with these pressures. They can be found in all sorts of classical non-scientific literature. For example, they tell us to pay no attention, or at least as little as possible, to the vanities which would have us constantly worrying about an infinity of trivia. They also give us such practical advice as to deal with problems as they arise. Every sensible person knows about many of these things. It is sad that although we know them we find it increasingly difficult to practice them. It should be possible to make it easier for most people to practice more of them.

In speaking of the pressures in the environment, and especially in speaking of the increase in these pressures as societies grow older, one should not give the impression that mental disease is found only in civilized societies. It is well known that schizophrenia can be found in primitive societies also, but it is likewise well known that they are plentifully supplied with taboos and other pressures. The basic cause of the disease seems to be a biochemical defect, possibly a failure in the metabolism of serotonin. For some individuals the defect is severe enough to insure mental failure regardless of the environment. For others it is not so severe, but it can result in mental failure if the environmental pressures are strong enough. Still others seem almost able to withstand anything. It may be that the susceptible individuals should protect themselves (especially under adverse circumstances) by some chemical means to make good their deficiency. However, the wise thing to do would seem to be to attempt to ease the pressures for all and to reserve chemotherapy and chemoprophylaxis for those few who still cannot make the grade.

chapter 17

Philosophical aspects

A little learning *is a dang'rous thing;*
Drink deep, or taste not the Pierian spring.
There shallow draughts intoxicate the brain,
And drinking largely sobers us again.

ALEXANDER POPE, *An Essay on Criticism*

A discovery about the nature of a mental disease inevitably will influence philosophy. These diseases are so intimately related to thinking and emotion and intellect in general that when the nature of the disease is clarified, much is made clear about emotion and intellect. Hypotheses about these have been derived in the past mainly from observations of the effects of changes in the environment. One learns about man by seeing how he reacts to the physical world, how he learns, how various emotions are stirred and how sequestered, how social customs arise, and how habits are formed. Philosophy is an attempt to catalog all of this information and to rationalize it.

Insight into being can be gained by looking through a variety of keyholes. Each keyhole reveals to us a small segment of the truth, but only a fragment, not the whole truth. It should be the business of philosophy to look into as many of these keyholes as possible.

Formal philosophy has been looking through a few selected keyholes in an effort to understand the nature of emotion and intellect. With few exceptions the scientific discoveries about the nature of the physical world have been ignored or left for the next generation to incorporate into the system. In connection with psychology it has explored in much detail the various instinctual drives which play a large role in animal behavior and in human behavior as well. A great store of information has been assembled on the reactions of men (and animals) to all grades of intensity of these drives alone and in combination. This information is the basis of wisdom, and allows prediction of many coming events. It also allows much control of the outside world and of right action in the individual.

Formal philosophy has taken less account of the specific chemical factors in an individual which can govern or modify his reactions to the outside world. This is probably because the physical sciences especially biochemistry and physiology have not been studied by most philosophers. They are thus less vividly aware of the effects on intellect and behavior which can be brought about in an individual by changes in the amount of a sex hormone, or an adrenal hormone or of any one of a number of such essential metabolites.

In earlier chapters of this book we have had frequent occasion to describe the changes in mood, in affect, in learning ability, and in all sorts of behavior, which inevitably follow deficiencies and excesses of certain single essential metabolites. To recall only a few we need think of the dullness, torpor, and general mental insufficiency of people suffering from a lack of thyroxine, the mental disorders of those who have eaten insufficient nicotinic acid, and the excitement of those who produce an excess of thyroxine. In these conditions one can usually find physical signs of the sickness, and one might attribute the mental disturbances to the fact that the individual is demonstrably ill. It is important to remember however, that a specific type of mental disorder often accompanies each kind of these illnesses. This fact shows that the mental change is not just a concomitant of sickness.

The use of psychotomimetic substances in normal individuals brings out rather clearly the relationship of certain emotions to specific substances. Some of these agents bring about their mental effects without markedly affecting the functioning of bodily processes. For example, the visual hallucinations and changes in the contact with reality which follow the ingestion of lysergic acid diethylamide (LSD) are not accompanied by marked physical changes such as increases in blood pressure and respiration. Injection of a small amount of LSD into a cat will cause the animal to spit and arch its back and exhibit the other signs of rage. Electrical stimulation of specific parts of the brain in either animals or man can call forth specific emotions. Thus, stimulation of certain parts of the mid-brain in man can also elicit rage. Stimulation of specific discrete areas in the cortex near the Sylvian fissure can, as Penfield has shown (402), bring back memories of musical selections or of childhood emotional episodes long since forgotten. Insatiable thirst can be induced at will in goats by electrical stimulation of certain areas of the hypothalamus, and ravenous appetite can be produced by stimulation to, or damage of, another section of the hypothalamus.

It is thus abundantly clear that specific chemical or electrical stimulation can call forth well-defined mental and psychic responses and instinctual drives without noticeably altering the main economy of the individual. Because these mental changes can be thus linked to chemical changes it seems reasonable to suppose that a physical basis or matrix for emotions exists in the brain and that it is mediated by specific chemical reactions. The purpose of the author in writing this book has been to point out some of these reactions and their psychic connections.

If we then admit the chemical control of some emotions and appetites must we conclude that it is the only control? Are we being driven into a position of defining the mind or the soul as a set of chemical reactions? This would seem to be a very extreme position, and one not justifiable on the basis of present evidence. We must take care to remember that we have been looking through a chemical keyhole, and that we see only one fragment of the whole. Life and living have a physical aspect and a chemical aspect and a morphological aspect, and a network of other aspects which we know of now only under the descriptive terms of habit, imagination, thinking, and the like.

These many aspects are interdependent. The anatomy of the brain would not be possible without the chemical substances from which it is made, nor without the enzymic processes by means of which these substances are formed. The biochemical reactions which constitute activity of the brain are carried out and kept in order by a physical compartmentalization. The electrical potentials which are an intimate feature of nerve transmission are generated by biochemical reactions. In turn some of these reactions are activated by the ionic changes within and without the cell which are influenced by electrical potentials. We now see that some of the psychic phenomena are influenced by certain biochemical reactions too. It would not be too surprising to find that the mind expresses its will by reliance on biochemical reactions, anatomical structures, and electrical potentials, and that memory and imagination need these also.

The Freudian hypothesis of the origin of mental diseases of the functional kind (that is, those lacking demonstrable anatomical causes) laid stress on the baleful influences of memory (of childhood experiences and even of prenatal experiences), instinctual drives (especially sex) and anxiety. The anxiety was supposed to arise from an interaction of the first two with training and social customs. These factors seem now to be descriptions of some of the environmental pressures by which an individual is beset rather than the origin of the mental diseases. If genic makeup (inheritance) has given him adequate biochemical equipment (enough of each enzyme, etc.) he will be able to withstand most or all of these pressures. If his biochemical equipment is lacking in one or two respects, a particularly stressful situation may push him into a mental breakdown by calling for, let us say, excessive amounts of cerebral serotonin. This pattern of increased production once set up may continue and lead to secondary biochemical changes (let us say an induced increase of the decarboxylase and hydroxylase) which may persist. Such an individual would be diagnosed as, let us say, a deteriorated schizophrenic. Finally, inheritance may have endowed the individual with none of some particular enzyme, as in the phenylketonuric person who lacks the phenylalanine hydroxylase system. Such an individual falls prey early in life to mental deterioration without the intervention of unusual environmental stresses.

Viewed in this way, the biochemical basis of the various mental diseases is of utmost importance. The biochemical shortcomings are the principal factor in the causation. Prevention may well take the form of keeping down the environmental pressures, as discussed in the last section of Chapter 16, but once faced with the disease a biochemical solution by the use of suitable drugs seems necessary.

Some investigators of functional psychoses have taken the point of view that even though one may find characteristic biochemical changes in patients with a given mental disease this does not mean that the cause of the disease is to be associated with this change. They contend that the biochemical change is the result of the psychosis, and not its cause. Thus, the deficiency of serotonin in phenylketonuric idiots would be ascribed to a defect in the intellect which arose from the primary idiocy and was accompanied by a reduction in serotonin production. Similarly, any abnormality of serotonin in the brains of schizophrenics would be ascribed likewise to secondary causes. The shortcoming of this position would seem to be the fact that many of the mental changes which characterize the disease can be called forth at will in normal persons by chemical agents which more or less specifically bring about changes in the serotonin activity in the brain. Likewise, the elimination of the biochemical defect in phenylketonuric infants by suitable dietary control also eliminates the mental failure.

It really seems that the biochemical aspects of various features of the mind have become clear enough that formal philosophy must take official recognition of them if it wishes to portray a comprehensive and true picture of man and the world. Formal philosophers cannot continue to remain aloof from the laboratory. If they do, the full nature of consciousness may escape them.

Bibliography

1. Woolley, D. W., *A Study of Antimetabolites,* John Wiley and Sons, New York, 1952.
2. Tréfouël, J., Nitti, F., and Bovet, D., *C. R. Soc. Biol.,* **120,** 756 (1935).
3. Domagk, G., *Deut. med. Wochschr.,* **61,** 250 (1935).
4. Woods, D. D., *Brit. J. Exptl. Pathol.,* **21,** 74 (1940).
5. Nimmo-Smith, R. H., Lascelles, J., and Woods, D. D., *Brit. J. Exptl. Pathol.,* **29,** 264 (1948).
6. Woolley, D. W., and White, A. G. C., *J. Biol. Chem.,* **149,** 285 (1943).
7. Woolley, D. W., *J. Biol. Chem.,* **191,** 43 (1951).
8. Hirs, C. H. W., Moore, S., and Stein, W. H., *J. Biol. Chem.,* **235,** 633 (1960).
9. Shaw, E., and Woolley, D. W., *Science,* **124,** 121 (1956).
10. Franchi, R. I. B., and Matthews, R. E. F., *Biochim. et Biophys. Acta,* **34,** 570 (1959).
11. Jeener, R., *Biochim. et Biophys. Acta,* **23,** 351 (1957).
12. Ephrati-Elizur, E., and Zamenhof, S., *Nature,* **184,** 472 (1959).
13. Szybalski, W., Opara-Kubinska, Z., Lorkiewicz, Z., Ephrati-Elizur, E., and Zamenhof, S., *Nature,* **188,** 743 (1960).
14. Litman, R. M., and Pardee, A. B., *Biochim. et Biophys. Acta,* **42,** 117 (1960).
15. Richmond, M. H., *Biochem. J.,* **77,** 121 (1960).
16. Vaughan, M., and Steinberg, D., *Biochim. et Biophys. Acta,* **40,** 230 (1960).
17. Ehrenpreis, S., *Biochim. et Biophys. Acta,* **44,** 561 (1960).
18. Ehrenpreis, S., Private communication.
19. Woolley, D. W., *Proc. Natl. Acad. Sci. U. S.,* **44,** 197 (1958).
20. Woolley, D. W., *Proc. Natl. Acad. Sci. U. S.,* **44,** 1202 (1958).
21. Woolley, D. W., and Campbell, N. K., *Biochim. et Biophys. Acta,* **40,** 543 (1960).
22. Woolley, D. W., *Science,* **128,** 1277 (1958).
23. Daniel, L. J., and Norris, L. C., *Proc. Soc. Exptl. Biol. Med.,* **72,** 165 (1949).
24. Soodak, M., and Cerecedo, L. R., *J. Am. Chem. Soc.,* **66,** 1988 (1944).
25. Frohman, C. E., and Day, H. G., *J. Biol. Chem.,* **180,** 93 (1949).
26. De Caro, L., Rindi, G., Perri, V., and Ferrari, G., *Experientia,* **12,** 300 (1956).
27. Pletscher, A., Shore, P. A., and Brodie, B. B., *Science,* **122,** 374 (1955).

28. Woolley, D. W., and Edelman, P. M., *Science,* **127,** 281 (1958).
29. Shaw, E., and Woolley, D. W., *J. Pharmacol. Exptl. Therap.,* **111,** 43 (1954).
30. Strominger, J. L., Threnn, R. H., and Scott, S. S., *J. Am. Chem. Soc.,* **81,** 3803 (1959).
31. Strominger, J. L., Ito, E., and Threnn, R. H., *J. Am. Chem. Soc.,* **82,** 998 (1960).
32. Woolley, D. W., *J. Biol. Chem.,* **185,** 293 (1950).
33. McIlwain, H., *Biochem. J.,* **37,** 265 (1943).
34. Woolley, D. W., Schaffner, G., and Braun, A. C., *J. Biol. Chem.,* **215,** 485 (1955).
35. Shaw, E., and Woolley, D. W., *J. Biol. Chem.,* **203,** 979 (1953).
36. Costa, E., *Proc. Soc. Exptl. Biol. Med.,* **91,** 39 (1956).
37. Woolley, D. W., *Science,* **100,** 579 (1944).
38. Woolley, D. W., *J. Biol. Chem.,* **164,** 11 (1946).
39. Woolley, D. W., *in* "The Strategy of Chemotherapy," *Symposium Soc. Gen. Microbiol.,* **8,** 139 (1958).
40. Rapport, M. M., Green, A. A., and Page, I. H., *Science,* **108,** 329 (1948); *J. Biol. Chem.,* **176,** 1243 (1948).
41. Rapport, M. M., *J. Biol. Chem.,* **180,** 961 (1949).
42. Hamlin, K. E., and Fischer, F. E., *J. Am. Chem. Soc.,* **73,** 5007 (1951).
43. Erspamer, V., *Naunym-Schmiedeberg's Arch. exptl. Pathol. u. Pharmakol.,* **196,** 366 (1940).
44. Erspamer, V., and Asero, B., *Nature,* **169,** 800 (1952).
45. Sirek, A., *Nature,* **179,** 376 (1957).
46. Udenfriend, S., Weissbach, H., and Clark, C. T., *J. Biol. Chem.,* **215,** 337 (1955).
47. Speeter, M. E., and Anthony, W. C., *J. Am. Chem. Soc.,* **76,** 6208 (1954).
48. Udenfriend, S., Weissbach, H., and Clark, C. T., *J. Biol. Chem.,* **215,** 337 (1955).
49. Vane, J. R., *Brit. J. Pharmacol.,* **12,** 344 (1957).
50. Erspamer, V., *Nature,* **170,** 281 (1952).
51. Erspamer, V. *Ricerca sci.,* **22,** 694 (1952).
52. Gaddum, J. H., and Hameed, K. A., *Brit, J. Pharmacol.,* **9,** 240 (1954).
53. Erspamer, V., and Ghiretti, F., *J. Physiol.,* **115,** 470 (1951).
54. Welsh, J. H., *Nature,* **173,** 955 (1954).
55. Puente-Duany, G. A., Riemer, W. E., and Miale, J. B., *Proc. Soc. Exptl. Biol. Med.,* **98,** 499 (1958).
56. Bruce, D. W., *Nature,* **188,** 147 (1960).
57. Udenfriend, S., Lovenberg, W., and Sjoerdsma, A., *Arch. Biochem. Biophys.,* **85,** 487 (1959).
58. Erspamer, V., and Vialli, M., *Nature,* **167,** 1033 (1951).
59. Erspamer, V., *Naturwissenschaften,* **40,** 318 (1953).
60. Giarman, N. J., and Freedman, D. X., *Nature,* **186,** 480 (1960).
61. Woolley, D. W., and Campbell, N. K., *Ann. N. Y. Acad. Sci.,* **96,** 108 (1962).
62. Florey, E., and Florey, E., *Naturwissenschaften,* **40,** 413 (1953).
63. Twarog, B. M., and Page, I. H., *Am. J. Physiol.,* **175,** 157 (1953).
64. Amin, A. H., Crawford, T. B. B., and Gaddum, J. H., *Intern. Physiol. Congr., 19th,* Montreal, 1953, *Abstr. Commun.,* 1953, p. 165.
65. Amin, A. H., Crawford, T. B. B., and Gaddum, J. H., *J. Physiol.,* **126,** 596 (1954).

66. Wieland, T., and Motzel, W., *Ann. Chem.*, **581,** 10 (1953).
67. Fish, M. S., Johnson, N. M., and Horning, E. C., *J. Am. Chem. Soc.*, **77,** 5892 (1955).
68. Bumpus, F. M., and Page, I. H., *J. Biol. Chem.*, **212,** 111 (1955).
69. Rodnight, R., *Biochem. J.*, **64,** 621 (1956).
70. Lerner, A. B., Case, J. D., Takahashi, Y., Lee, T. H., and Mori, W., *J. Am. Chem. Soc.*, **80,** 2587 (1958).
71. Lerner, A. B., Case, J. D., and Heinzelman, R. V., *J. Am. Chem. Soc.*, **81,** 6084 (1959).
72. Lerner, A. B., Case, J. D., Mori, W., and Wright, M. R., *Nature,* **183,** 1821 (1959).
73. Udenfriend, S., Clark, C. T., and Titus, E., *J. Am. Chem. Soc.,* **75,** 501 (1953).
74. Udenfriend, S., Lovenberg, W. M., and Weissbach, H., *Federation Proc.*, **19,** 7 (1960).
75. Udenfriend, S., Titus, E., Weissbach, H., and Peterson, R. E., *J. Biol. Chem.*, **219,** 335 (1956).
76. Bogdanski, D. F., Weissbach, H., and Udenfriend, S., *J. Pharmacol. Exptl. Therap.*, **122,** 182 (1958).
77. Woolley, D. W., Van Winkle, E., and Shaw, E., *Proc. Natl. Acad. Sci.,* **43,** 128 (1957).
78. Woolley, D. W., and Shaw, E., *Proc. Natl. Acad. Sci.,* **40,** 228 (1954).
79. Born, G. V. R., Ingram, G. I. C., and Stacey, R. S., *Brit. J. Pharmacol.,* **13,** 62 (1958).
80. Blaschko, H., *Experientia,* **13,** 9 (1957).
81. Blaschko, H., Hagen, P., Hagen, J. M., and Schumann, H. J., *Arch. intern. pharmacodynamie,* **110,** 128 (1957).
82. Weissbach, H., Redfield, B. G., and Titus, E., *Nature,* **185,** 99 (1960).
83. Erspamer, V., *Experientia,* **10,** 471 (1954).
84. Sjoerdsma, A., Smith, T. E., Stevenson, T. D., and Udenfriend, S., *Proc. Soc. Exptl. Biol. Med.,* **89,** 36 (1955).
85. Udenfriend, S., Titus, E., and Weissbach, H., *J. Biol. Chem.,* **216,** 499 (1955).
86. Blaschko, H., and Hellmann, K., *J. Physiol.,* **122,** 419 (1953).
87. Weissbach, H., Redfield, B. G., and Udenfriend, S., *J. Biol. Chem.,* **229,** 953 (1957).
88. Kopin, I. J., Pare, C. M. B., Axelrod, J., and Weissbach, H., *Biochim. et Biophys. Acta.,* **40,** 377 (1960).
89. Woolley, D. W., and Shaw, E., *J. Pharmacol. Exptl. Therap.,* **108,** 87 (1953).
90. Page, I. H., *J. Pharmacol. Exptl. Therap.,* **105,** 58 (1952).
91. Hollander, W., Michelson, A. L., and Wilkins, R. W., *Circulation,* **16,** 246 (1957).
92. Page, I. H., and McCubbin, J. W., *Circulation Research,* **1,** 354 (1953).
93. Erspamer, V., and Ottolenghi, A., *Arch. intern. pharmacodynamie,* **93,** 177 (1953).
94. Page, I. H., *Physiol. Revs.,* **38,** 277 (1958).
95. Woolley, D. W., *Proc. Soc. Exptl. Biol. Med.,* **98,** 367 (1958).
96. Marrazzi, A. S., and Hart, E. R., *Science,* **121,** 365 (1955).
97. Marrazzi, A. S., *Ann. N. Y. Acad. Sci.,* **92,** 990 (1961).
98. Evarts, E. V., *Ann. N. Y. Acad. Sci.,* **66,** 479 (1957).
99. McCubbin, J. W., Green, J. H., Salmoiraghi, G. C., and Page, I. H., *J. Pharmacol. Exptl. Therap.,* **116,** 191 (1956).

100. Schneider, J. A., and Yonkman, F. F., *Am. J. Physiol.,* **174,** 127 (1953).
101. Heymans, C., *Pharmacol. Revs.,* **7,** 119 (1955).
102. Cossio, P., *Ann. N. Y. Acad. Sci.,* **80,** 1009 (1959).
103. Master, A. M., and Donoso, E., *Ann. N. Y. Acad. Sci.,* **80,** 1020 (1959).
104. Chadwick, B. T., and Wilkinson, J. H., *Biochem. J.,* **76,** 102 (1960).
105. Eriksen, N., Martin, G. M., and Benditt, E. P., *J. Biol. Chem.,* **235,** 1662 (1960).
106. Lumsden, C. E., and Pomerat, C. M., *Exptl. Cell Research,* **2,** 103 (1951).
107. Benitez, H. H., Murray, M. R., and Woolley, D. W., *Proc. 2nd Intern. Congr. of Neuropathol.,* London, 1955, *Excerpta Med.,* Amsterdam, 1957; *Anat. Record,* **121,** 446 (1955).
108. Gross, R., and Staufenberg, E., *Thrombosis et Diathesis Haemorrhagica,* **2,** 125 (1958).
109. Woolley, D. W., and Shaw, E. N., *Science,* **124,** 34 (1956).
110. Herxheimer, H., *J. Physiol.,* **128,** 435 (1955).
111. Garven, J. D., *J. Pharm. and Pharmacol.,* **8,** 256 (1956).
112. Woolley, D. W., and Shaw, E., *Brit. Med. J.,* **2,** 122 (1954).
113. Woolley, D. W., *Assoc. Research Nervous Mental Disease,* Res. Pub., **36,** 381 (1958).
114. Costa, E., and Aprison, M. H., *Am. J. Physiol.,* **192,** 95 (1958).
115. Lembeck, F., *Nature,* **172,** 910 (1953).
116. Sjoerdsma, A., *New Engl. J. Med.,* **261,** 181 (1959).
117. Thorson, A., Biörck, G., Björkman, G., and Waldenström, J., *Am. Heart J.,* **47,** 795 (1954).
118. Gessner, P. K., McIsaac, W. M., and Page, I. H., *Nature,* **190,** 179 (1961).
119. Woolley, D. W., and Shaw, E., *J. Am. Chem. Soc.,* **74,** 2948 (1952).
120. Davson, H., and Danielli, J. F., *Permeability of Natural Membranes,* 2nd ed., Cambridge University Press, Cambridge, 1952.
121 Shanes, A. M., and Bianchi, C. P., *J. Gen. Physiol.,* **43,** 481 (1960).
122. Szent-Györgyi, A., *Chemical Physiology of Contraction in Body and Heart Muscle,* Academic Press, New York, 1953.
123. Heilbrunn, L. V., and Wiercinski, F. J., *J. Cellular Comp. Physiol.,* **29,** 15 (1947).
124. Erspamer, V., *Rendi. sci. farm.,* **1,** 1 (1954).
125. Mansour, T. E., Sutherland, E. W., Rall, T. W., and Buedin, E., *J. Biol. Chem.,* **235,** 466 (1960).
126. Rall, T. W., and Sutherland, E. W., *J. Biol. Chem.,* **232,** 1065 (1958).
127. Woolley, D. W., and Shaw, E., *J. Biol. Chem.,* **203,** 69 (1953).
128. Woolley, D. W., and Shaw, E., *J. Am. Chem. Soc.,* **74,** 4220 (1952).
129. Shaw, E., and Woolley, D. W., *J. Am. Chem. Soc.,* **79,** 3561 (1957).
130. Shaw, E., and Woolley, D. W., *Proc. Soc. for Exptl. Biol. Med.,* **93,** 217 (1956).
131. Shaw, E. N., and Woolley, D. W., *J. Pharmacol. Exptl. Therap.,* **116,** 164 (1956).
132. Shaw, E., and Woolley, D. W., *Proc. Soc. Exptl. Biol. Med.,* **96,** 439 (1957).
133. Woolley, D. W., *Biochem. Pharmacol.,* **3,** 51 (1959).
134. Woolley, D. W., and Shaw, E., *J. Pharmacol. Exptl. Therap.,* **121,** 13 (1957).
135. Gaddum, J. H., *J. Physiol.,* **119,** 363 (1953).
136. Woolley, D. W., *Nature,* **180,** 630 (1957).
137. Pickles, V. R., and Sutcliffe, J. F., *Biochim. et Biophys. Acta,* **17,** 244 (1955).

138. Sato, C. S., Byerrum, R. U., Albersheim, P., and Bonner, J., *J. Biol. Chem.*, **233**, 128 (1958).
139. Ross, D. M., *Experientia*, **13**, 192 (1957).
140. Mathias, A. P., Ross, D. M., and Schachter, M., *Nature*, **180**, 658 (1957).
141. Woolley, D. W., *Proc. Natl. Acad. Sci. U. S.*, **41**, 338 (1955).
142. Cerletti, A., and Rothlin, E., *Nature*, **176**, 785 (1955).
143. Elliott, T. R., *J. Physiol.*, **31**, 20 P (1904).
144. Loewi, O., *Arch. ges. Physiol. (Pflüger's)*, **189**, 239 (1921).
145. Loewi, O., *Naturwissenschaften*, **14**, 994 (1926).
146. Nachmansohn, D., *Harvey Lectures*, **49**, 57 (1953–1954).
147. Eccles, J. C., *The Physiology of Nerve Cells*, Johns Hopkins Press, Baltimore, 1957.
148. Whittaker, V. P., *Biochem. Pharmacol.*, **5**, 392 (1961).
149. Hestrin, S., *J. Biol. Chem.*, **180**, 249 (1949).
150. Woolley, D. W., *Federation Proc.*, **18**, 461 (1959).
151. Hunt, R., *J. Pharmacol. Exptl. Therap.*, **6**, 477 (1915).
152. Hosein, E. A., and Proulx, P., *Nature*, **187**, 321 (1960).
153. Bülbring, E., and Burn, J. H., *Brit. J. Pharmacol.*, **4**, 245 (1949).
154. Gaddum, J. H., and Holzbauer, M., *Vitamins and Hormones*, **15**, 151 (1957).
155. Euler, U. S. von, *Acta Physiol. Scand.*, **16**, 63 (1948).
156. Euler, U. S. von, and Gaddum, J. H., *J. Physiol.*, **73**, 54 (1931).
157. West, G. B., *Quart. Rev. Biol.*, **30**, 116 (1955).
158. Blaschko, H., Hagen, P., and Welch, A. D., *J. Physiol.*, **129**, 27 (1955).
159. Gurin, S., and Delluva, A. M., *J. Biol. Chem.*, **170**, 545 (1947).
160. Udenfriend, S., and Wyngaarden, J. B., *Biochim. et Biophys. Acta*, **20**, 48 (1956).
161. Leeper, L. C., and Udenfriend, S., *Federation Proc.*, **15**, 298 (1956).
162. Blaschko, H., *Biochim. et Biophys. Acta*, **4**, 130 (1950).
163. Schmiterlow, C. G., *Brit. J. Pharmacol.*, **6**, 127 (1951).
164. Clark, W. G., Akawie, R. I., Pogrund, R. S., and Geissman, T. A., *J. Pharmacol. Exptl. Therap.*, **101**, 6 (1951).
165. Clark, W. G., and Drell, W., *Federation Proc.*, **13**, 343 (1954).
166. Richter, D., *J. Physiol.*, **98**, 361 (1940).
167. Shaw, K. N. F., McMillan, A., and Armstrong, M. D., *J. Biol. Chem.*, **226**, 255 (1957).
168. Euler, U. S. von, and Floding, I., *Acta Physiol. Scand.*, **33**, Suppl. 118, 45 (1955).
169. Weil-Malherbe, H., and Bone, A. D., *Biochem. J.*, **51**, 311 (1952).
170. Whitehorn, J. C., *J. Biol. Chem.*, **108**, 633 (1935).
171. Shaw, F. H., *Biochem. J.*, **32**, 19 (1938).
172. Haynes, R. C., Jr., Sutherland, E. W., and Rall, T. W., *Recent Progress in Hormone Research*, **16**, 121 (1960).
173. Haynes, R. C., Jr., *J. Biol. Chem.*, **233**, 1220 (1958).
174. Weil-Malherbe, H., Axelrod, J., and Tomchick, R., *Science*, **129**, 1226 (1959).
175. Holtz, P., and Credner, K., *Naunyn-Schmiedeberg's Arch. Exptl. Pathol. u. Pharmakol.*, **200**, 356 (1942).
176. Goodall, McC., *Acta Physiol. Scand.*, **24**, *Suppl.* **85** (1951).
177. Shepherd, D. M., and West, G. B., *J. Physiol.*, **120**, 15 (1953).
178. Schümann, H. J., *Naunyn-Schmiedeberg's Arch. Exptl. Pathol. u. Pharmakol.*, **227**, 566 (1956).

179. Van Meter, J. C., and Oleson, J. J., *Proc. Soc. Exptl. Biol. Med.*, **71**, 163 (1949).
180. Gaddum, J. H., *Brit. Med. J.*, **1**, 867 (1948).
181. Woolley, D. W., *Advances in Enzymol.*, **6**, 129 (1946).
182. Feldberg, W., *J. Pharm. and Pharmacol.*, **6**, 281 (1954).
183. Karjala, S. A., *J. Am. Chem. Soc.*, **77**, 504 (1955).
184. Alivisatos, S. G. A., Ungar, F., Lukacs, L., and La Mantia, L., *J. Biol. Chem.*, **235**, 1742 (1960).
185. Edman, K. A. P., and Schild, H. O., *Nature*, **190**, 351 (1961).
186. Elliott, D. F., Horton, E. W., and Lewis, G. P., *Biochem, J.*, **78**, 60 (1961).
187. Boissonnas, R. A., Guttmann, S., and Jaquenoud, P.-A., *Helv. Chim. Acta*, **43**, 1349 (1960).
188. Rocha e Silva, M., *Acta Physiol. Latinoam.*, **2**, 238 (1952).
189. Hamberg, U., *Biochim. et Biophys. Acta*, **34**, 135 (1959).
190. Rocha e Silva, M., Beraldo, W. T., and Andrade, S. O., *Abstr. Communs. 1st Intern. Congr. Biochem.*, 119 (1949).
191. Prado, J. L., Monier, R., Prado, E. S., and Fromageot, C., *Biochim. et Biophys. Acta*, **22**, 87 (1956).
192. Chapman, L. F., and Wolff, H. G., *A.M.A. Arch. Internal Med.*, **103**, 86 (1959).
193. Bumpus, F. M., Schwarz, H., and Page, I. H., *Circulation*, **17**, 664 (1958).
194. Schwarz, H., Bumpus, F. M., and Page, I. H., *J. Am. Chem. Soc.*, **79**, 5697 (1957).
195. Plentl, A. A., and Page, I. H., *J. Biol. Chem.*, **147**, 135 (1943).
196. Edman, K. A. P., and Schild, H. O., *Nature*, **190**, 351 (1961).
197. du Vigneaud, V., *Harvey Lectures*, **50**, 1 (1956).
198. Sawyer, W. H., Munsick, R. A., and Van Dyke, H. B., *Nature*, **184**, 1464 (1959).
199. Schally, A. V., Saffran, M., and Zimmermann, B., *Biochem. J.*, **70**, 97 (1958).
200. Guillemin, R., Schally, A., Andersen, R., Lipscomb, H., and Long, J., *Compt. rend.*, **250**, 4462 (1960).
201. Fong, C. T. O., Schwartz, I. L., Popenoe, E. A., Silver, L., and Schoessler, M. A., *J. Am. Chem. Soc.*, **81**, 2592 (1959).
202. Schwartz, I. L., Rasmussen, H., Schoessler, M. A., Silver, L., and Fong, C. T. O., *Proc. Natl. Acad. Sciences U. S.*, **46**, 1288 (1960).
203. Rasmussen, H., Schwartz, I. L., Schoessler, M. A., and Hochster, G., *Proc. Natl. Acad. Sciences*, **46**, 1278 (1960).
204. Gaddum, J. H., *Ann. N. Y. Acad. Sci.*, **66**, 643 (1957).
205. Rothlin, E., *Ann. N. Y. Acad. Sci.*, **66**, 668 (1957).
206. Huxley, A. L., *The Doors of Perception*, Harper, New York, 1954.
207. Stoll, W. A., *Schweiz. Arch. Neurol. Psychiat.*, **60**, 279 (1947).
208. Stoll, A., and Hofmann, A., *Helv. Chim. Acta*, **26**, 944 (1943).
209. Stoll, A., and Hofmann, A., *Helv. Chim. Acta*, **38**, 421 (1955).
210. Woolley, D. W., *Proc. Natl. Acad. Sci. U. S.*, **41**, 338 (1955).
211. Gaddum, J. H., and Vogt, M., *Brit. J. Pharmacol.*, **11**, 175 (1956).
212. Abramson, H. A., and Evans, L. T., *Science*, **120**, 990 (1954).
213. Keller, D. L., and Umbreit, W. W., *Science*, **124**, 723 (1956).
214. Barger, G., *Ergot and Ergotism*, Gurney and Jackson, London, 1931.
215. Page, I. H., Personal communication.
216. Naranjo Vargas, P., *Rev. confederación med. panam.*, **6**, 1 (1959).

217. Bartlett, M. F., Dickel, D. F., and Taylor, W. I., *J. Am. Chem. Soc.*, **80,** 126 (1958).
218. Schneider, J. A., and Sigg, E. B., *Psychopharmacology,* edited by Pennes, H. H., Hoeber-Harper, N. Y., 1958.
219. Fabing, H. D., and Hawkins, J. R., *Science,* **123,** 886 (1956).
220. Turner, W. J., and Merlis, S., *Arch. Neurol. and Psychiat.*, **81,** 121 (1959).
221. Evarts, E. V., *Ann. N. Y. Acad. Sci.*, **66,** 479 (1957).
222. Hofmann, A., Heim, R., Brack, A., Kobel, H., Frey, A., Ott, H., Petrzilka, T., and Troxler, F., *Helv. Chim. Acta,* **42,** 1557 (1959).
223. Wasson, R. G., *Trans. N. Y. Acad. Sci.*, **21,** 325 (1959).
224. Woolley, D. W., and Shaw, E. N., *Ann. N. Y. Acad. Sci.*, **66,** 649 (1957).
225. Woolley, D. W., and Shaw, E., *J. Pharmacol. and Exptl. Therap.*, **108,** 87 (1953).
226. Bleuler, M., *Deut. Med. Wochschr.*, **81,** 1078 (1956).
227. Strecker, E. A., *Fundamentals of Psychiatry,* 4th Ed., Lippincott, Philadelphia, 1947.
228. Davis, W. A., Personal communication.
229. Moser, M., Syner, J., Malitz, S., and Mattingly, T. W., *J. Am. Med. Assoc.*, **152,** 1329 (1953).
230. Taylor, R. D., Page, I. H., and Corcoran, A. C., *Arch. Int. Med.*, **88,** 1 (1951).
231. Szára, S., *Experientia,* **12,** 441 (1956).
232. Marrazzi, A. S., and Hart, E. R., *Science,* **121,** 365 (1955).
233. Welsh, J. H., and McCoy, A. C., *Science,* **125,** 348 (1957).
234. Mansour, T. E., *Brit. J. Pharmacol.*, **12,** 406 (1957).
235. Gaddum, J. H., *Ann. N. Y. Acad. Sci.*, **66,** 643 (1957).
236. Ginzel, K. H., and Mayer-Gross, W., *Nature,* **178,** 210 (1956).
237. Woolley, D. W., and Shaw, E. N., Unpublished data.
238. Woolley, D. W., and Campbell, N. K., *Science,* **136,** in press.
239. Hollander, W., Michelson, A. L., and Wilkins, R. W., *Circulation,* **16,** 256 (1957).
240. Wilkins, R. W., *New Engl. J. Med.*, **255,** 115 (1956).
241. Yonkman, F. F. et al., *Ann. N. Y. Acad. Sci.*, **61,** 1 (1955).
242. Pletscher, A., Shore, P. A., and Brodie, B. B., *J. Pharmacol. Exptl. Therap.*, **116,** 84 (1956).
243. Shore, P. A., Pletscher, A., Tomich, E. G., Carlsson, A., Kuntzman, R., and Brodie, B. B., *Ann. N. Y. Acad. Sci.*, **66,** 609 (1957).
244. Hughes, F. B., Shore, P. A., and Brodie, B. B., *Experientia,* **14,** 178 (1958).
245. Schneider, J. A., and Rinehart, R. K., *Arch. intern. pharmacodynamie,* **105,** 253 (1956).
246. Holzbauer, M., and Vogt, M., *J. Neurochem.*, **1,** 8 (1956).
247. Cole, J. W., and Bertino, G. G., *Proc. Soc. Exptl. Biol. Med.*, **93,** 100 (1956).
248. Benditt, E. P., and Rowley, D. A., *Science,* **123,** 24 (1956).
249. Karreman, G., Isenberg, I., and Szent-Györgyi, A., *Science,* **130,** 1191 (1959).
250. Harris, A. F., Saifer, A., and Volk, B. W., *Proc. Soc. Exptl. Biol. Med.*, **104,** 542 (1960).
251. Wolfe, L. S., *Biochem. J.*, **79,** 348 (1961).
252. Dombro, R. S., Bradham, L. S., Campbell, N. K., and Woolley, D. W., *Biochim. et Biophys. Acta,* **54,** 516 (1961).
253. Marshall, P. B., *Brit J. Pharmacol.* **10,** 270 (1955).

254. Hoffer, A., Osmond, H., Callbeck, M. J., and Kahan, I., *J. Clin. Exptl. Psychopathol.*, **18,** 131 (1957).
255. Woolley, D. W., *Science*, **128,** 1277 (1958).
256. Woolley, D. W., in Rinkel, M., and Denber, H. C. B., eds., *Chemical Concepts of Psychoses*, McDowell, Obolensky, New York, 1958.
257. Therman, P. O., and Woolley, D. W., Unpublished data.
258. Woolley, D. W. et al., *Ann. N. Y. Acad. Sci.*, **80,** 551 (1959).
259. Rees, L., *Nature*, **186,** 114 (1960).
260. Loomer, H. P., Saunders, J. C., and Kline, N. S., *Psychiatric Research Rep. Wash.*, No. 8, 129 (1957).
261. Barsky, J., Berman, E. R., and Zeller, E. A., *Intern. Physiol. Congr.*, 19th, Montreal, 1953, *Abstr. Commun.*, 1953, p. 191.
262. McCormick, D. B., and Snell, E. E., *Proc. Natl. Acad. Sci. U. S.*, **45,** 1371 (1959).
263. Speeter, M. E., Personal communication.
264. Zeller, E. A., *J. Clin. Exptl. Psychopathol.*, **19,** *Suppl.* **1,** 106 (1958).
265. Bulle, P. H., and Konchegul, L., *Quart. Rev. Psychiat. Neurol.*, **18,** 287 (1957).
266. Banerjee, S., and Agarwal, P. S., *Proc. Soc. Exptl. Biol. Med.*, **97,** 657 (1958).
267. Akcasu, A., Akcasu, M., and Tumay, S. B., *Nature*, **187,** 324 (1960).
268. Ashcroft, G. W., and Sharman, D. F., *Nature*, **186,** 1050 (1960).
269. Leyton, G. B., *Brit. Med. J.*, **2,** 1136 (1958).
270. Rodnight, R., and Aves, E. K., *J. Mental Sci.*, **104,** 1149 (1958).
271. Sprince, H., *Ann. N. Y. Acad. Sci.*, **96,** 399 (1962).
272. Bertaccini, G., *J. Neurochem.*, **4,** 217 (1959).
273. Green, J. P., Paasonen, M. K., and Giarman, N. J., *Proc. Soc. Exptl. Biol. Med.*, **94,** 428 (1957).
274. Gal, E. M., and Drewes, P. A., *Nature*, **189,** 234 (1961).
275. Saunders, J. C., and Chipkiewicz, H., *J. Clin. Exptl. Psychopathol. and Quart. Rev. of Psychiat. Neurol.*, **20,** 7 (1959).
276. Angel, C., Leach, B. E., Martens, S., Cohen, M., and Heath, R. G., *A.M.A. Arch. Neurol. Psychiat.*, **78,** 500 (1957).
277. Horwitt, M. K., Meyer, B. J., Meyer, A. C., Harvey, C. C., and Haffron, D., *A.M.A. Arch. Neurol. Psychiat.*, **78,** 275 (1957).
278. Akerfeldt, S., *Science*, **125,** 117 (1957).
279. Blaschko, H., and Levine, W. G., *Brit. J. Pharmacol.*, **15,** 625 (1960).
280. Elvidge, A. R., and Reed, G. E., *Arch. Neurol. Psychiat.*, **40,** 227 (1938).
281. Hollister, L. E., *Ann. N. Y. Acad. Sci.*, in press.
282. Hampton, W. H., *Bull. N. Y. Acad. Med.*, **37,** 167 (1961).
283. Montanari, C., and Tonini, G., *Riv. Sper. Fren. e Med. Leg.*, **79,** 465 (1955).
284. Abramson, H. A., and Sklarofsky, B., *A.M.A. Arch. Gen. Psychiat.*, **2,** 89 (1960).
285. Bergen, J. R., Krus, D., and Pincus, G., *Proc. Soc. Exptl. Biol. Med.*, **105,** 254 (1960).
286. Woolley, D. W., and Shaw, E., *Science*, **119,** 587 (1954).
287. Fingl, E., and Gaddum, J. H., *Federation Proc.*, **12,** 320 (1953).
288. Woolley, D. W., and Shaw, E., *Federation Proc.*, **12,** 293 (1953).
289. Gaddum, J. H., *J. Physiol.*, **121,** 15 P (1953).
290. Gaddum, J. H., *in Ciba Foundation Symposium on Hypertension*, Little, Brown and Company, Boston, 1954.

291. Sicuteri, F., *Med. Exptl.,* **2,** 36 (1960).
292. Melville, K. I., *Arch. intern. pharmacodynamie,* **115,** 278 (1958).
293. Magoun, H. W., *The Waking Brain,* Charles C Thomas, Springfield, 1958.
294. McLean, J. R., and McCartney, M., *Proc. Soc. Exptl. Biol. Med.,* **107,** 77 (1961).
295. Carlsson, A., Lindqvist, M., and Magnusson, T., *Nature,* **180,** 1200 (1957).
296. Brodie, B. B., Finger, K. F., Orlans, F. B., Quinn, G. P., and Sulser, F., *J. Pharmacol. Exptl. Therap.,* **129,** 250 (1960).
297. Thompson, R. H. S., Tickner, A., and Webster, G. R., *Brit. J. Pharmacol.,* **10,** 61 (1955).
298. Sprince, H., and Lichtenstein, I., *A.M.A. Arch. Gen. Psychiat.,* **2,** 385 (1960).
299. Abood, L. G., Ostfeld, A. M., and Biel, J., *Proc. Soc. Exptl. Biol. Med.,* **97,** 483 (1958).
300. Abood, L. G., Ostfeld, A. M., and Biel, J. H., *Mol. Mental Health, Papers Sci. Congrs.,* Brain Research Foundation; New York and Chicago, 69 (1958) (Pub. 1959).
301. Hoffer, A., Osmond, H., and Smythies, J., *J. Mental Sci.,* **100,** 29 (1954).
302. Hoffer, A., in Rinkel, M., and Denber, H. C. B., eds., *Chemical Concepts of Psychosis,* McDowell, Obolensky, New York, 1958.
303. Woolley, D. W., *Proc. Natl. Acad. Sci. U. S.,* **46,** 923 (1960).
304. Erspamer, V., *Ricerca sci.,* **22,** 1568 (1952).
305. Gláz, E. T., Gyermek, L., and Nógrádi, T., *Arch. intern. pharmacodynamie,* **108,** 420 (1956).
306. Gordon, P., Haddy, F. J., and Lipton, M. A., *Science,* **128,** 531 (1958).
307. Gordon, P., Haddy, F., and Lipton, M., *Federation Proc.,* **18,** 397 (1959).
308. Erspamer, V., *Ricerca sci.,* **22,** 2148 (1952).
309. Huebner, C. F., Donoghue, E., Wenk, P., Sury, E., and Nelson, J. A., *J. Am. Chem. Soc.,* **82,** 2077 (1960).
310. Abood, L. G., Rinaldi, F., and Eagleton, V., *Nature,* **191,** 201 (1961).
311. Selye, H., *Stress of Life,* McGraw-Hill Book Company, New York, 1956.
312. Srb, A. M., and Owen, R. D., *General Genetics,* W. H. Freeman, San Francisco, 1952.
313. Armstrong, M. D., and Robinson, K. S., *Arch. Biochem. Biophys.,* **52,** 287 (1954).
314. Pare, C. M. B., Sandler, M., and Stacey, R. S., *Arch. Disease Childhood,* **34,** 422 (1959).
315. Fellman, J. H., *Proc. Soc. Exptl. Biol. Med.,* **93,** 413 (1956).
316. Davidson, A. N., and Sandler, M., *Nature,* **181,** 186 (1958).
317. Pare, C. M. B., Sandler, M., and Stacey, R. S., *Lancet,* **1,** 551 (1957).
318. Berendes, H., Anderson, J. A., Ziegler, M. R., and Ruttenberg, D., *A.M.A. J. Disease Childhood,* **96,** 430 (1958).
319. Baldridge, R. C., Borofsky, L., Baird, H., III, Reichle, F., and Bullock, D., *Proc. Soc. Exptl. Biol. Med.,* **100,** 529 (1959).
320. Sandler, M., and Close, H. G., *Lancet,* **2,** 316 (1959).
321. Sandler, M., Davies, A., and Rimington, C., *Lancet,* **2,** 318 (1959).
322. Huang, I., Tannenbaum, S., Blume, L., and Hsia, D. Y., *Proc. Soc. Exptl. Biol. Med.,* **106,** 533 (1961).
323. Weil-Malherbe, H., *J. Mental Sci.,* **101,** 733 (1955).
324. Cannon, W. B., Newton, H. F., Bright, E. M., Menkin, V., and Moore, R. M., *Am. J. Physiol.,* **89,** 84 (1929).

325. Fölling, A., *Z. physiol. Chem. Hoppe-Seyler's,* **227,** 169 (1934).
326. Jervis, G. A., *Assoc. Research Nervous Mental Disease, Res. Pub.,* **33,** 259 (1954).
327. Jervis, G. A., *Diseases of Nervous System,* **18,** Monograph Suppl., 93 (1957).
328. Tischler, B., Gibson, W. C., McGeer, E. G., and Nuttall, J., *Am. J. Mental Deficiency,* **65,** 726 (1961).
329. Udenfriend, S., and Cooper, J. R., *J. Biol. Chem.,* **194,** 503 (1952).
330. Jervis, G. A., *Proc. Soc. Exptl. Biol. Med.,* **82,** 514 (1953).
331. Fölling, A., and Class, K., *Z. physiol. Chem. Hoppe-Seyler's,* **254,** 115 (1938).
332. Jervis, G. A., Block, R. J., Bolling, D., and Kanze, E., *J. Biol. Chem.,* **134,** 105 (1940).
333. Udenfriend, S., *J. Biol. Chem.,* **203,** 961 (1953).
334. Schrappe, O., *Nervenarzt,* **23,** 175 (1952).
335. Wilhelmi, G., and Schindler, W., *Arch. Exptl. Pathol. Pharmakol.,* **236,** 49 (1959).
336. Haverback, B. J., and Bogdanski, D. F., *Proc. Soc. Exptl. Biol. Med.,* **95,** 392 (1957).
337. Auerbach, V. H., Waisman, H. A., and Wyckoff, L. B., Jr., *Nature,* **182,** 871 (1958).
338. Bickel, H., Gerrard, J., and Hickmans, E. M., *Lancet,* **2,** 812 (1953).
339. Armstrong, M. D., Low, N. L., and Bosma, J. F., *Am. J. Clin. Nutrition,* **5,** 543 (1957).
340. Jervis, G. A., *Clin. Chim. Acta,* **5,** 471 (1960).
341. Kalckar, H. M., and Maxwell, E. S., *Physiol. Revs.,* **38,** 77 (1958).
342. Kalckar, H. M., *Advances in Enzymol.,* **20,** 111 (1958).
343. Isselbacher, K. J., *in* Stanbury, J. B., Wyngaarden, J. B., and Fredrickson, D. S., Eds., *The Metabolic Basis of Inherited Disease,* McGraw-Hill Book Company, New York, 1960.
344. Göppert, F., *Berlin klin. Wochschr.,* **54,** 473 (1917).
345. Mason, H. H., and Turner, M. E., *Am. J. Diseases Children,* **50,** 359 (1935).
346. Komrower, G. M., Schwarz, V., Holzel, A., and Goldberg, L., *Arch. Disease Childhood,* **31,** 254, (1956).
347. Schwarz, V., Goldberg, L., Komrower, G. M., and Holzel, A., *Biochem. J.,* **62,** 34 (1956).
348. Watkins, W. M., and Hassid, W. Z., *Science,* **136,** 329 (1962).
349. Kalckar, H. M., and Maxwell, E. S., *Physiol. Revs.,* **38,** 77 (1958).
350. Burton, R. M., Sodd, M. A., and Brady, R. O., *Federation Proc.,* **16,** 161 (1957).
351. Munch-Petersen, A., Kalckar, H. M., and Smith, E. E. B., *Kgl. Danske Videnskab. Selskab Biol. Medd.,* **22,** No. 7, 3 (1955).
352. Kalckar, H. M., Anderson, E. P., and Isselbacher, K. J., *Biochim. et Biophys. Acta,* **20,** 262 (1956).
353. Dombro, R. S., Bradham, L. S., Campbell, N. K., and Woolley, D. W., *Biochim. et Biophys. Acta,* **54,** 516 (1961).
354. Bogoch, S., and Bogoch, E. S., *Nature,* **183,** 53 (1959).
355. Slack, J., Simpson, K., and Hsia, D. Y.-Y., *Pediatric Clinics of North America,* **7,** 627 (1960).
356. Woolley, D. W., *J. Biol. Chem.,* **147,** 581 (1943).
357. Stanbury, J. B., Wyngaarden, J. B., and Fredrickson, D. S., Eds., *The Met-*

abolic Basis of Inherited Disease, McGraw-Hill Book Company, New York, 1960.

358. Sribney, M., and Kennedy, E. P., *J. Biol. Chem.,* **233,** 1315 (1958).
359. Klenk, E., *in* Waelsch, H., ed., *Biochemistry of the Developing Nervous System,* Academic Press, New York, 1955.
360. Slome, D., *J. Genet.,* **27,** 363 (1933).
361. Baron, D. N., Dent, C. E., Harris, H., Hart, E. W., and Jepson, J. B., *Lancet,* **2,** 421 (1956).
362. Rawson, R. W., Koch, H., and Flach, F. F., *in* Hoagland, H., ed., *Hormones, Brain Function, and Behavior,* Academic Press, New York, 1957.
363. Gjessing, R., *Arch. Psychiat. Nervenkrankh.,* **96,** 319 (1932).
364. Gjessing, R., *Arch. Psychiat.,* **191,** 191 (1953).
365. Lehninger, A. L., *J. Biol. Chem.,* **234,** 2187 (1959).
366. Kraepelin, E., *Psychiatrie,* 8th ed., vol. 3, p. 806, J. A. Barth, Leipzig, 1913.
367. Lindsay, J. S. B., *J. Mental Sci.,* **94,** 590 (1948).
368. Gjessing, R., *J. Mental Sci.,* **84,** 608 (1938).
369. Hoagland, H., and Freeman, H., in Braceland, F. J., *The Effects of Pharmacologic Agents on the Nervous System,* Williams and Wilkins Company, Baltimore, 1959; *Assoc. Research Nervous Mental Disease, Res. Pub.,* **37,** 183 (1959).
370. Glaser, G. H., *Psychosomat. Med.,* **15,** 280 (1953).
371. Selye, H., *Proc. Soc. Exptl. Biol. Med.,* **46,** 116 (1941).
372. Selye, H., *Endocrinol.,* **30,** 437 (1942).
373. Laubach, G. D., P'an, S. Y., and Rudel, H. W., *Science,* **122,** 78 (1955).
374. P'an, S. Y., Gardocki, J. F., Hutcheon, D. E., Rudel, H., Kodet, M. J., and Laubach, G. D., *J. Pharmocol. Exptl. Therap.,* **115,** 432 (1955).
375. Pincus, G., and Elmadjian, F., *J. Clin. Endocrinol.,* **6,** 295 (1946).
376. Elvehjem, C. A., Madden, R. J., Strong, F. M., and Woolley, D. W., *J. Am. Chem. Soc.,* **59,** 1767 (1937).
377. Kornberg, A., *J. Biol. Chem.,* **182,** 779 (1950).
378. Alivisatos, S. G. A., and Woolley, D. W., *J. Biol. Chem.,* **221,** 651 (1956).
379. Alivisatos, S. G. A., *Nature,* **181,** 271 (1958).
380. Karjala, S. A., Turnquest, B., 3rd, and Schayer, R. W., *J. Biol. Chem.,* **219,** 9 (1956).
381. Woolley, D. W., *Nature,* **171,** 323 (1953).
382. Zatman, L. J., Kaplan, N. O., Colowick, S. P., and Ciotti, M. M., *J. Biol. Chem.,* **209,** 453 (1954).
383. Kaplan, N. O., Ciotti, M. M., Van Eys, J., and Burton, R. M., *J. Biol. Chem.,* **234,** 134 (1959).
384. Krehl, W. A., Teply, L. J., Sarma, P. S., and Elvehjem, C. A., *Science,* **101,** 489 (1945).
385. Hess, S. M., Redfield, B. G., and Udenfriend, S., *J. Pharmacol. Exptl. Therap.,* **127,** 178 (1959).
386. Coggeshall, R. E., and MacLean, P. D., *Proc. Soc. Exptl. Biol. Med.,* **98,** 687 (1958).
387. Sternberg, S. S., and Philips, F. S., *Bull. N. Y. Acad. Med.,* **35,** 811 (1959).
388. Wolf, A., and Cowen, D., *Bull. N. Y. Acad. Med.,* **35,** 814 (1959).
389. Woolley, D. W., Strong, F. M., Madden, R. J., and Elvehjem, C. A., *J. Biol. Chem.,* **124,** 715 (1938).
390. Woolley, D. W., *J. Biol. Chem.,* **157,** 455 (1945).

391. Dietrich, L. S., Friedland, I. M., and Kaplan, L. A., *J. Biol. Chem.*, **233,** 964 (1958).
392. Berger, F. M., *J. Pharmacol. Exptl. Therap.,* **112,** 413 (1954).
393. Miller, J. G., and Berger, F. M., *Ann. N. Y. Acad. Sci.,* **67,** 671 (1957).
394. Bode, H. H., *Ann. Univ. Saraviensis,* **6,** 119 (1958).
395. Goldberg, L. I., DaCosta, F. M., and Ozaki, M., *Nature,* **188,** 502 (1960).
396. Skinner, B. F., *Am. Psychologist,* **8,** 69 (1953).
397. Ferster, C. B., *Psychol. Bull.,* **50,** 263 (1953).
398. Brady, J. V., *Ann. N. Y. Acad. Sci.,* **66,** 719 (1957).
399. Pfeiffer, C. C., and Jenney, E. H., *Ann. N. Y. Acad Sci.,* **66,** 753 (1957).
400. Cook, L., and Weidley, E., *Ann. N. Y. Acad. Sci.,* **66,** 740 (1957).
401. Ellis, A., *How to Live with a Neurotic,* Crown Publishers, New York, 1957.
402. Penfield, W., *Proc. Natl. Acad. Sci.,* **44,** 51 (1958).
403. McGeer, E. G., McGeer, P. L., and McLennan, H., *J. Neurochem.,* **8,** 36 (1961).
404. Nicolaides, E. D., and DeWald, H. A., *Ann. N. Y. Acad. Sci.,* in press.
405. Webster, M. E., and Pierce, J. V., *Ann. N. Y. Acad. Sci.,* in press.
406. Lewis, G. P., *Ann. N. Y. Acad. Sci.,* in press.
407. Boissonnas, R. A., Franz, J., and Sturmer, E., *Ann. N. Y. Acad. Sci.,* in press.
408. Vogler, K., and Haefely, W., *Ann. N. Y. Acad. Sci.,* in press.
409. Bogdanski, D. F., Weissbach, H., and Udenfriend, S., *J. Neurochem.,* **1,** 272 (1957).
410. Paasonen, M. K., MacLean, P. D., and Giarman, N. J., *J. Neurochem.,* **1,** 326 (1957).

Index of Structural Formulae

Subject Index